# TRAVELING-WAVE
# TUBES

THEORY OF VIBRATING SYSTEMS AND SOUND. *By* IRVING B. CRANDALL.

CONTEMPORARY PHYSICS. *By* KARL K. DARROW. Second Edition.

SPEECH AND HEARING. *By* HARVEY FLETCHER.

PROBABILITY AND ITS ENGINEERING USES. *By* THORNTON C. FRY.

ELEMENTARY DIFFERENTIAL EQUATIONS. *By* THORNTON C. FRY. Second Edition.

TRANSMISSIONS CIRCUITS FOR TELEPHONIC COMMUNICATION. METHODS OF ANALYSIS AND DESIGN. *By* K. S. JOHNSON.

TRANSMISSION NETWORKS AND WAVE FILTERS. *By* T. E. SHEA.

ECONOMIC CONTROL OF QUALITY OF MANUFACTURED PRODUCT. *By* W. A. SHEWHART.

ELECTROMECHANICAL TRANSDUCERS AND WAVE FILTERS. *By* WARREN P. MASON. Second Edition.

RHOMBIC ANTENNA DESIGN. *By* A. E. HARPER.

POISSON'S EXPONENTIAL BINOMIAL LIMIT. *By* E. C. MOLINA.

ELECTROMAGNETIC WAVES. *By* S. A. SCHELKUNOFF.

NETWORK ANALYSIS AND FEEDBACK AMPLIFIER DESIGN. *By* HENDRIK W. BODE.

SERVOMECHANISMS. *By* LEROY A. MACCOLL.

QUARTZ CRYSTALS FOR ELECTRICAL CIRCUITS. *By* R. A. HEISING.

CAPACITORS—THEIR USE IN ELECTRONIC CIRCUITS. *By* M. BROTHERTON.

FOURIER INTEGRALS FOR PRACTICAL APPLICATIONS. *By* GEORGE A. CAMPBELL AND RONALD M. FOSTER.

VISIBLE SPEECH. *By* RALPH K. POTTER, GEORGE A. KOPP, AND HARRIET C. GREEN

APPLIED MATHEMATICS FOR ENGINEERS AND SCIENTISTS. *By* S. A. SCHELKUNOFF.

EARTH CONDUCTION EFFECTS IN TRANSMISSION SYSTEMS. *By* ERLING D. SUNDE.

RADAR SYSTEMS AND COMPONENTS *By* MEMBERS OF THE STAFF OF THE BELL TELEPHONE LABORATORIES; Introduction by M. J. KELLY.

THEORY AND DESIGN OF ELECTRON BEAMS. *By* J. R. PIERCE.

PIEZOELECTRIC CRYSTALS AND THEIR APPLICATION TO ULTRASONICS. *By* WARREN P. MASON.

MICROWAVE ELECTRONICS. *By* JOHN C. SLATER.

TRAVELING-WAVE TUBES. *By* J. R. PIERCE.

PRINCIPLES AND APPLICATIONS OF WAVEGUIDE TRANSMISSION. *By* GEORGE C. SOUTHWORTH.

# TRAVELING-WAVE TUBES

*by*

J. R. PIERCE

*Member of the Technical Staff*
*Bell Telephone Laboratories, Inc.*

1950

D. VAN NOSTRAND COMPANY, INC.

TORONTO       NEW YORK       LONDON

NEW YORK

D. Van Nostrand Company, Inc., 250 Fourth Avenue, New York 3

TORONTO

D. Van Nostrand Company (Canada), Ltd., 228 Bloor Street, Toronto

LONDON

Macmillan & Company, Ltd., St. Martin's Street, London, W.C. 2

PRINTED IN THE UNITED STATES OF AMERICA

*To*
*My Parents*
*and to*
*Harold T. Friis*

# PREFACE

IN WRITING a book about something as new as the traveling-wave tube, it is hopeless to try to be completely up to date. About all that one can hope to do is to treat in an understandable manner matters which seem likely to be of continuing importance.

As specific tube structures seem very likely to change, I have put little about particular tubes or even specific numbers into this book. The emphasis is on general aspects of various wave circuits and their coupling to and interaction with electron flow under various conditions, together with some useful specific features of such interaction.

The book was written in something of a hurry. This put a severe and gratefully acknowledged burden on Miss E. McAlevey, who prepared the manuscript and kept the figures and text under control through numerous changes. I also wish to acknowledge Mrs. M. E. Shannon's contribution in the computation and plotting of curves, checking of equations and general mathematical aid. The figures were prepared by Mr. H. M. Yates and others of the Drafting Department.

I am indebted to Dr. L. M. Field and his students, especially Dr. S. F. Kaisel, for valuable criticisms of the manuscript.

Among my colleagues at the Bell Telephone Laboratories, Dr. R. C. Fletcher, some of whose work I could not resist adding as Appendix VI, made several important corrections as well, and so did Dr. C. F. Quate. I profited, too, from discussions with Mr. C. C. Cutler, with Dr. L. R. Walker, and with many others whose help I can scarcely acknowledge individually.

J. R. PIERCE

# CONTENTS

# CHAPTER I

# INTRODUCTION

ASTRONOMERS are interested in stars and galaxies, physicists in atoms and crystals, and biologists in cells and tissues because these are natural objects which are always with us and which we must understand. The traveling-wave tube is a constructed complication, and it can be of interest only when and as long as it successfully competes with older and newer microwave devices. In this relative sense, it is successful and hence important.

This does not mean that the traveling-wave tube is better than other microwave tubes in all respects. As yet it is somewhat inefficient compared with most magnetrons and even with some klystrons, although efficiencies of over 10 per cent have been attained. It seems reasonable that the efficiency of traveling-wave tubes will improve with time, and a related device, the magnetron amplifier, promises high efficiencies. Still, efficiency is not the chief merit of the traveling-wave tube.

Nor is gain, although the traveling-wave tubes have been built with gains of over 30 db, gains which are rivaled only by the newer double-stream amplifier and perhaps by multi-resonator klystrons.

In noise figure the traveling-wave tube appears to be superior to other microwave devices, and noise figures of around 12 db have been reported. This is certainly a very important point in its favor.

Structurally, the traveling-wave tube is simple, and this too is important. Simplicity of structure has made it possible to build successful amplifiers for frequencies as high as 48,000 megacycles (6.25 mm). When we consider that successful traveling-wave tubes have been built for 200 mc, we realize that the traveling-wave amplifier covers an enormous range of frequencies.

The really vital feature of the traveling-wave tube, however, the new feature which makes it different from and superior to earlier devices, is its tremendous bandwidth.

It is comparatively easy to build tubes with a 20 per cent bandwidth at 4,000 mc, that is, with a bandwidth of 800 mc, and L. M. Field has reported a bandwidth of 3 to 1 extending from 350 mc to 1,050 mc. There seems no reason why even broader bandwidths should not be attained.

As it happens, there is a current need for more bandwidth in the general field of communication. For one thing, the rate of transmission of information by telegraph, by telephone or by facsimile is directly proportional to bandwidth; and, with an increase in communication in all of these fields, more bandwidth is needed.

Further, new services require much more bandwidth than old services. A bandwidth of 4,000 cycles suffices for a telephone conversation. A bandwidth of 15,000 cycles is required for a very-high-fidelity program circuit. A single black-and-white television channel occupies a bandwidth of about 4 mc, or approximately a thousand times the bandwidth required for telephony.

Beyond these requirements for greater bandwidth to transmit greater amounts of information and to provide new types of service, there is currently a third need for more bandwidth. In FM broadcasting, a radio frequency bandwidth of 150 kc is used in transmitting a 15 kc audio channel. This ten-fold increase in bandwidth does not represent a waste of frequency space, because by using the extra bandwidth a considerable immunity to noise and interference is achieved. Other attractive types of modulation, such as PCM (pulse code modulation) also make use of wide bandwidths in overcoming distortion, noise and interference.

At present, the media of communication which have been used in the past are becoming increasingly crowded. With a bandwidth of about 3 mc, approximately 600 telephone channels can be transmitted on a single coaxial cable. It is very hard to make amplifiers which have the high quality necessary for single sideband transmission with bandwidths more than a few times broader than this. In television there are a number of channels suitable for local broadcasting in the range around 100 mc, and amplifiers sufficiently broad and of sufficiently good quality to amplify a single television channel for a small number of times are available. It is clear, however, that at these lower frequencies it would be very difficult to provide a number of long-haul television channels and to increase telephone and other services substantially.

Fortunately, the microwave spectrum, which has been exploited increasingly since the war, provides a great deal of new frequency space. For instance, the entire broadcast band, which is about 1 mc wide, is not sufficient for one television signal. The small part of the microwave spectrum in the wavelength range from 6 to $7\frac{1}{2}$ cm has a frequency range of 1,000 mc, which is sufficient to transmit many simultaneous television channels, even when broad-band methods such as FM or PCM are used.

In order fully to exploit the microwave spectrum, it is desirable to have amplifiers with bandwidths commensurate with the frequency space available. This is partly because one wishes to send a great deal of information in the microwave range: a great many telephone channels and a substantial number of television channels. There is another reason why very broad bands are needed in the microwave range. In providing an integrated nation-wide communication service, it is necessary for the signals to be amplified by many repeaters. Amplification of the single-sideband type of signal used in coaxial systems, or even amplification of amplitude modulated signals, requires a freedom from distortion in amplifiers which it seems almost impossible to attain at microwave frequencies, and a freedom from inter-fering signals which it will be very difficult to attain. For these reasons, it seems almost essential to rely on methods of modulation which use a large bandwidth in order to overcome both amplifier distortion and also inter-ference.

Many microwave amplifiers are inferior in bandwidth to amplifiers avail-able at lower frequencies. Klystrons give perhaps a little less bandwidth than good low-frequency pentodes. The type 416A triode, recently developed at Bell Telephone Laboratories, gives bandwidths in the 4,000 mc range some-what larger than those attainable at lower frequencies. Both the klystron and the triode have, however, the same fundamental limitation as do other conventional tubes. As the band is broadened at any frequency, the gain is necessarily decreased, and for a given tube there is a bandwidth beyond which no gain is available. This is so because the signal must be applied by means of some sort of resonant circuit across a capacitance at the input of the tube.

In the traveling-wave tube, this limitation is overcome completely. There is no input capacitance nor any resonant circuit. The tube is a smooth trans-mission line with a negative attenuation in the forward direction and a positive attenuation in the backward direction. The bandwidth can be limited by transducers connecting the circuit of the tube to the source and the load, but the bandwidth of such transducers can be made very great. The tube itself has a gradual change of gain with frequency, and we have seen that this allows a bandwidth of three times and perhaps more. This means that bandwidths of more than 1,000 mc are available in the microwave range. Such bandwidths are indeed so great that at present we have no means for fully exploiting them.

In all, the traveling-wave tube compares favorably with other microwave devices in gain, in noise figure, in simplicity of construction and in fre-quency range. While it is not as good as the magnetron in efficiency, reason-able efficiencies can be attained and greater efficiencies are to be expected. Finally, it does provide amplification over a bandwidth commensurate with the frequency space available at microwaves.

The purpose of this book is to collect and present theoretical material which will be useful to those who want to know about, to design or to do research on traveling-wave tubes. Some of this material has appeared in print. Other parts of the material are new. The old material and the new material have been given a common notation.

The material covers the radio-frequency aspects of the electronic behavior of the tube and its internal circuit behavior. Matters such as matching into and out of the slow-wave structures which are described are not considered. Neither are problems of producing and focusing electron beams, which have been discussed elsewhere,[1] nor are those of mechanical structure nor of heat dissipation.

In the field covered, an effort has been made to select material of practical value, and to present it as understandably as possible. References to various publications cover some of the finer points. The book refers to experimental data only incidentally in making general evaluations of theoretical results.

To try to present the theory of the traveling-wave tube is difficult without some reference to the overall picture which the theory is supposed to give. One feels in the position of lifting himself by his bootstraps. For this reason the following chapter gives a brief general description of the traveling-wave tube and a brief and specialized analysis of its operation. This chapter is intended to give the reader some insight into the nature of the problems which are to be met. In Chapters III through VI, slow-wave circuits are discussed to give a qualitative and quantitative idea of their nature and limitations. Then, simplified equations for the overall behavior of the tube are introduced and solved, and matters such as overall gain, insertion of loss, a-c space-charge effects, noise figure, field analysis of operation and transverse field operation are considered. A brief discussion of power output is given.

Two final chapters discuss briefly two closely related types of tube; the traveling-wave magnetron amplifier and the double-stream amplifier.

[1] loc. cit.

# CHAPTER II

# SIMPLE THEORY OF
# TRAVELING-WAVE TUBE GAIN

## SYNOPSIS OF CHAPTER

IT IS difficult to describe general circuit or electronic features of traveling-wave tubes without some picture of a traveling-wave tube and traveling-wave gain. In this chapter a typical tube is described, and a simple theoretical treatment is carried far enough to describe traveling-wave gain in terms of an increasing electromagnetic and space-charge wave and to express the rate of increase in terms of electronic and circuit parameters.

In particular, Fig. 2.1 shows a typical traveling-wave tube. The parts of this (or of any other traveling-wave tube) which are discussed are the electron beam and the slow-wave circuit, represented in Fig. 2.2 by an electron beam and a helix.

In order to derive equations covering this portion of the tube, the properties of the helix are simulated by the simple delay line or network of Fig. 2.3, and ordinary network equations are applied. The electrons are assumed to flow very close to the line, so that all displacement current due to the presence of electrons flows directly into the line as an impressed current

For small signals a wave-type solution of the equations is known to exist, in which all a-c electronic and circuit quantities vary with time and distance as $\exp(j\omega t - \Gamma z)$. Thus, it is possible to assume this from the start.

On this basis the excitation of the circuit by a beam current of this form is evaluated (equation (2.10)). Conversely, the beam current due to a circuit voltage of this form is calculated (equation (2.22)). If these are to be consistent, the propagation constant $\Gamma$ must satisfy a combined equation (2.23).

The equation for the propagation constant is of the fourth degree in $\Gamma$, so that any disturbance of the circuit and electron stream may be expressed as a sum of four waves.

Because some quantities are in practical cases small compared with others, it is possible to obtain good values of the roots by making an approximation. This reduces the equation to the third degree. The solutions are expressed in the form

$$-\Gamma = -j\beta_e + \beta_e C\delta$$

Here $\beta_e$ is a phase constant corresponding to the electron velocity (2.16) and $C$ is a gain parameter depending on circuit and beam impedance (2.43). A solution of the equation for the case of an electron speed equal to the speed of the undisturbed wave yields 3 values of $\delta$ which are shown in Fig. 2.4. These represent an increasing, a decreasing and an unattenuated wave. The increasing wave is of course responsible for the gain of the tube. A different approximation yields the missing backward unattenuated wave (2.32).

The characteristic impedance of the forward waves is expressed in terms of $\beta_e$, $C$, and $\delta$ (2.36) and is found to differ little from the impedance in the absence of electrons.

The gain of the increasing wave is expressed in terms of $C$ and the length of the tube in wavelengths, $N$

$$G = 47.3 \, CN \text{ db} \qquad (2.37)$$

It will be shown later that the gain of the tube can be expressed approximately as the sum of the gain of the increasing wave plus a constant to take into account the setting up of the increasing wave, or the boundary conditions (2.39).

Finally, the important gain parameter $C$ is discussed. The circuit part of this parameter is measured by the cube root of an impedance, $(E^2/\beta^2 P)^{\frac{1}{3}}$, which relates the peak field $E$ acting on the electrons, the phase constant $\beta = \omega/v$, and the power flow. $(E^2/\beta^2 P)^{\frac{1}{3}}$ is a measure of circuit goodness as far as gain is concerned.

We should note also that a desirable circuit property is constancy of phase velocity with frequency, for the electron velocity must be near to the circuit phase velocity to produce gain.

Evaluation of the effects of attenuation, of varying the electron velocity and many other matters are treated in later chapters.

## 2.1 DESCRIPTION OF A TRAVELING-WAVE TUBE

Figure 2.1 shows a typical traveling-wave tube such as may be used at frequencies around 4,000 megacycles. Such a tube may operate with a cathode current of around 10 ma and a beam voltage of around 1500 volts. There are two essential parts of a traveling-wave amplifier; one is the helix, which merely serves as a means for producing a slow electromagnetic wave with a longitudinal electric field; and the other is the electron flow. At the input the wave is transferred from a wave guide to the helix by means of a short antenna and similarly at the output the wave is transferred from the helix to a short antenna from which it is radiated into the output wave guide. The wave travels along the wire of the helix with approximately the speed of light. For operation at 1500 volts, corresponding to about $\frac{1}{13}$ the speed of light, the wire in the helix will be about thirteen times as long as the axial length of the helix, giving a wave velocity of about $\frac{1}{13}$ the speed of light along the axis of the helix. A longitudinal magnetic focusing field of a few hundred gauss may be used to confine the electron beam and enable it to pass completely through the helix, which for 4000 megacycle operation may be around a foot long.

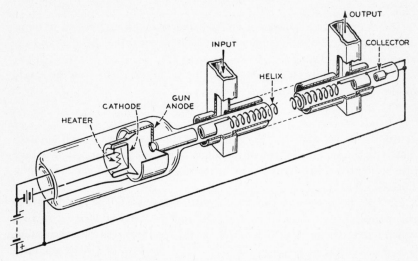

Fig. 2.1—Schematic of the traveling-wave amplifier.

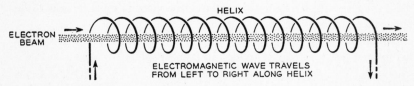

Fig. 2.2—Portion of the traveling-wave amplifier pertaining to electronic interaction with radio-frequency fields and radio-frequency gain.

In analyzing the operation of the traveling-wave tube, it is necessary to focus our attention merely on the two essential parts shown in Fig. 2.2, the circuit (helix) and the electron stream.

## 2.2 THE TYPE OF ANALYSIS USED

A mathematical treatment of the traveling-wave tube is very important, not so much to give an exact numerical prediction of operation as to give a picture of the operation and to enable one to predict at least qualitatively the effect of various physical variations or features. It is unlikely that all of the phenomena in a traveling-wave tube can be satisfactorily described in a theory which is simple enough to yield useful results. Most analyses, for instance, deal only with the small-signal or linear theory of the traveling-wave tube. The distribution of current in the electron beam can have an important influence on operation, and yet in an experimental tube it is often difficult to tell just what this distribution is. Even the more elaborate analyses of linear behavior assume a constant current density across the beam. Similarly, in most practical traveling-wave tubes, a certain fraction of the current is lost on the helix and yet this is not taken into account in the usual theories.

It has been suggested that an absolutely complete theory of the traveling-wave tube is almost out of the question. The attack which seems likely to yield the best numerical results is that of writing the appropriate partial differential equations for the disturbance in the electron stream inside the helix and outside of the helix. This attack has been used by Chu and Jackson[2] and by Rydbeck.[3] While it enables one to evaluate certain quantities which can only be estimated in a simpler theory, the general results do not differ qualitatively and are in fair quantitative agreement with those which are derived here by a simpler theory.

In the analysis chosen here, a number of approximations are made at the very beginning. This not only simplifies the mathematics but it cuts down the number of parameters involved and gives to these parameters a simple physical meaning. In terms of the parameters of this simple theory, a great many interesting problems concerning noise, attenuation and various boundary conditions can be worked out. With a more complicated theory, the working out of each of these problems would constitute essentially a new problem rather than a mere application of various formulae.

There are certain consequences of a more general treatment of a traveling-wave tube which are not apparent in the simple theory presented here. Some of these matters will be discussed in Chapters XII, XIII and XIV.

The theory presented here is a small signal theory. This means that the equations governing electron flow have been linearized by neglecting certain quantities which become negligible when the signals are small. This results in a wave-type solution. Besides the small signal limitation of the analyses presented here, the chief simplifying assumption which has been made is that all the electrons in the electron flow are acted on by the same a-c field, or at least by known fields. The electrons will be acted on by essentially the same field when the diameter of the electron beam is small enough or when

    [2] L. J. Chu and J. D. Jackson, "Field Theory of Traveling-Wave Tubes," *Proc. I. R. E.*, Vol. 36, pp. 853–863, July 1948.
    [3] Olof E. H. Rydbeck, "The Theory of the Traveling-Wave Tube," *Ericsson Technics*, No. 46, 1948.

the electrons form a hollow cylindrical beam in an axially symmetrical circuit, a case of some practical importance.

Besides these assumptions, it is assumed in this section that the electrons are displaced by the a-c field in the axial direction only. This may be approximately true in many cases and is essentially so when a strong magnetic focusing field is used. The effects of transverse motion will be discussed in Chapter XIII.

In this chapter an approximate relation suitable for electron speeds small compared to the velocity of light is used in computing interaction between electrons and the circuit.

A more general relation between impressed current and circuit field, valid for faster waves, will be given in Chapter VI. Non-relativistic equations of motion will, however, be used throughout the book. With whatever speed the waves travel, it will be assumed that the electron speed is always small compared with the speed of light.

We consider here the interaction between an electric circuit capable of propagating a slow electromagnetic wave and a stream of electrons. We can consider that the signal current in the circuit is the result of the disturbed electron stream acting on the circuit and we can consider that the disturbance on the electron stream is the result of the fields of the circuit acting on the electrons. Thus the problem naturally divides itself into two parts.

## 2.3 The Field Caused by an Impressed Current

We will first consider the problem of the disturbance produced in the circuit by a bunched electron stream. In considering this problem in this section in a manner valid for slow waves and small electron velocities, we will use the picture in Fig. 2.3. Here we have a circuit or network with uniformly

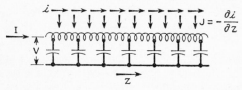

Fig. 2.3—Equivalent circuit of a traveling-wave tube. The distributed inductance and capacitance are chosen to match the phase velocity and field strength of the field acting on the electrons. The impressed current due to the electrons is $-\partial i/\partial z$, where $i$ is the electron convection current.

distributed series inductance and shunt capacitance and with current $I$ and voltage $V$. The circuit extends infinitely in the $z$ direction. An electron convection current $i$ flows along very close to the circuit. The sum of the displacement and convection current into any little volume of the electron beam must be zero. Because the convection current varies with distance in the direction of flow, there will be a displacement current $J$ amperes per meter impressed on the transmission circuit. We will assume that the electron beam is very narrow and very close to the circuit, so that the displacement current along the stream is negligible compared with that from the stream to the circuit. In this case the displacement current to the circuit will be given by the rate of change of the convection current with distance.

If the convection current $i$ and the impressed current $J$ are sinusoidal with time, the equations for the network shown in Fig. 2.3 are

$$\frac{\partial I}{\partial z} = -jBV + J \qquad (2.1)$$

$$\frac{\partial V}{\partial z} = -jXI \qquad (2.2)$$

Here $I$ and $V$ are the current and the voltage in the line, $B$ and $X$ are the shunt susceptance and series reactance per unit length and $J$ is the impressed current per unit length.

It may be objected that these "network" equations are not valid for a transmission circuit operating at high frequencies. Certainly, the electric field in such a circuit cannot be described by a scalar electric potential. We can, however, choose $BX$ so that the phase velocity of the circuit of Fig. 2.3 is the same as that for a particular traveling-wave tube. We can further choose $X/B$ so that, for unit power flow, the longitudinal field acting on the electrons according to Fig. 2.3, that is, $-\partial V/\partial z$, is equal to the true field for a particular circuit. This lends a plausibility to the use of (2.1) and (2.2). The fact that results based on these equations are actually a good approximation for phase velocities small compared with the velocity of light is established in Chapter VI.

We will be interested in cases in which all quantities vary with distance as $\exp(-\Gamma z)$. Under these circumstances, we can replace differentiation with respect to $z$ by multiplication by $-\Gamma$. The impressed current per unit length is given by

$$J = -\frac{\partial i}{\partial z} = \Gamma i \qquad (2.3)$$

Equations (2.1) and (2.2) become

$$-\Gamma I = -jBV + \Gamma i \qquad (2.4)$$

$$-\Gamma V = -jXI \qquad (2.5)$$

If we eliminate $I$, we obtain

$$V(\Gamma^2 + BX) = -j\Gamma Xi \qquad (2.6)$$

Now, if there were no impressed current, the righthand side of (2.6) would be zero and (2.6) would be the usual transmission-line equation. In this case, $\Gamma$ assumes a value $\Gamma_1$, the natural propagation constant of the line, which is given by

$$\Gamma_1 = j\sqrt{BX} \tag{2.7}$$

The forward wave on the line varies with distance as $\exp(-\Gamma_1 z)$ and the backward wave as $\exp(+\Gamma_1 z)$.

Another important property of the line itself is the characteristic impedance $K$, which is given by

$$K = \sqrt{X/B} \tag{2.8}$$

We can express the series reactance $X$ in terms of $\Gamma_1$ and $K$

$$X = -jK\Gamma_1 \tag{2.9}$$

Here the sign has been chosen to assure that $X$ is positive with the sign given in (2.7). In terms of $\Gamma_1$ and $K$, (2.6) may be written

$$V = \frac{-\Gamma\Gamma_1 Ki}{(\Gamma^2 - \Gamma_1^2)} \tag{2.10}$$

In (2.10), the convection current $i$ is assumed to vary sinusoidally with time and as $\exp(-\Gamma z)$ with distance. This current will produce the voltage $V$ in the line. The voltage of the line given by (2.10) also varies sinusoidally with time and as $\exp(-\Gamma z)$ with distance.

## 2.4 CONVECTION CURRENT PRODUCED BY THE FIELD

The other part of the problem is to find the disturbance produced on the electron stream by the fields of the line. In this analysis we will use the quantities listed below, all expressed in M.K.S. units.[4]

$\eta$—charge-to-mass ratio of electrons
 $\eta = 1.759 \times 10^{11}$ coulomb/kg
$u_0$—average velocity of electrons
$V_0$—voltage by which electrons are accelerated to give them the velocity
 $u_0$. $u_0 = \sqrt{2\eta V_0}$
$I_0$—average electron convection current
$\rho_0$—average charge per unit length
 $\rho_0 = -I_0/u_0$
$v$—a-c component of velocity
$\rho$—a-c component of linear charge density
$i$—a-c component of electron convection current

[4] Various physical constants are listed in Appendix I.

The quantities $v$, $\rho$, and $i$ are assumed to vary with time and distance as $\exp(j\omega t - \Gamma z)$.

One equation we have concerning the motion of the electrons is that the time rate of change of velocity is equal to the charge-to-mass ratio times the electric gradient.

$$\frac{d(u_0 + v)}{dt} = \eta \frac{\partial V}{\partial z} \tag{2.11}$$

In (2.11) the derivative represents the change of velocity observed in following an individual electron. There is, of course, no change in the average velocity $u_0$. The change in the a-c component of velocity may be expressed in terms of partial derivatives, $\dfrac{\partial v}{\partial t}$ , which is the rate of change with time of the velocity of electrons passing a given point, and $\dfrac{\partial v}{\partial z}$, which is variation of electron velocity with distance at a fixed time.

$$\frac{dv}{dt} = \frac{\partial v}{\partial t} + \frac{\partial v}{\partial z}\frac{dz}{dt} = \eta \frac{\partial V}{\partial z} \tag{2.12}$$

Equation (2.12) may be rewritten

$$\frac{\partial v}{\partial t} + \frac{\partial v}{\partial z}(u_0 + v) = \eta \frac{\partial V}{\partial z} \tag{2.13}$$

Now it will be assumed that the a-c velocity $v$ is very small compared with the average velocity $u_0$, and $v$ will be neglected in the parentheses. The reason for doing this is to obtain differential equations which are linear, that is, in which products of a-c terms do not appear. Such linear equations necessarily give a wave type of variation with time and distance, such as we have assumed. The justification for neglecting products of a-c terms is that we are interested in the behavior of traveling-wave tubes at small signal levels, and that it is very difficult to handle the non-linear equations. When we have linearized (2.13) we may replace the differentiation with a respect to time by multiplication by $j\omega$ and differentiation with respect to distance by multiplication by $-\Gamma$ and obtain

$$(j\omega - u_0\Gamma)v = -\eta\Gamma V \tag{2.14}$$

We can solve (2.14) for the a-c velocity and obtain

$$v = \frac{-\eta\Gamma V}{u_0(j\beta_e - \Gamma)} \tag{2.15}$$

Where

$$\beta_e = \omega/u_0 \tag{2.16}$$

We may think of $\beta_e$ as the phase constant of a disturbance traveling with the electron velocity.

We have another equation to work with, a relation which is sometimes called the equation of continuity and sometimes the equation of conservation of charge. If the convection current changes with distance, charge must accumulate or decrease in any small elementary distance, and we see that in one dimension the relation obeyed must be

$$\frac{\partial i}{\partial z} = -\frac{\partial \rho}{\partial t} \tag{2.17}$$

Again we may proceed as before and solve for the a-c charge density $\rho$

$$-\Gamma i = -j\omega\rho$$

$$\rho = \frac{-j\Gamma i}{\omega} \tag{2.18}$$

The total convection current is the total velocity times the total charge density

$$-I_0 + i = (u_0 + v)(\rho_0 + \rho) \tag{2.19}$$

Again we will linearize this equation by neglecting products of a-c quantities in comparison with products of a-c quantities and a d-c quantity. This gives us

$$i = \rho_0 v + u_0 \rho \tag{2.20}$$

We can now substitute the value $\rho$ obtained from (2.18) into (2.20) and solve for the convection current in terms of the velocity, obtaining

$$i = \frac{j\beta_e \rho_0 v}{(j\beta_e - \Gamma)} \tag{2.21}$$

Using (2.15) which gives the velocity in terms of the voltage, we obtain the convection current in terms of the voltage

$$i = \frac{jI_0 \beta_e \Gamma V}{2V_0(j\beta_e - \Gamma)^2} \tag{2.22}$$

## 2.5 OVERALL CIRCUIT AND ELECTRONIC EQUATION

In (2.22) we have the convection current in terms of the voltage. In (2.10) we have the voltage in terms of the convection current. Any value of $\Gamma$ for which both of these equations are satisfied represents a natural mode of propagation along the circuit and the electron stream. When we combine 2.22) and (2.10) we obtain as the equation which $\Gamma$ must satisfy:

$$1 = \frac{jKI_0\beta_e\Gamma^2\Gamma_1}{2V_0(\Gamma_1^2 - \Gamma^2)(j\beta_e - \Gamma)^2} \tag{2.23}$$

Equation (2.23) applies for any electron velocity, specified by $\beta_e$, and any wave velocity and attenuation, specified by the imaginary and real parts of the circuit propagation constant $\Gamma_1$. Equation (2.23) is of the fourth degree. This means that it will yield four values of $\Gamma$ which represent four natural modes of propagation along the electron stream and the circuit. The circuit alone would have two modes of propagation, and this is consistent with the fact that the voltages at the two ends can be specified independently, and hence two boundary conditions must be satisfied. Four boundary conditions must be satisfied with the combination of circuit and electron stream. These may be taken as the voltages at the two ends of the helix and the a-c velocity and a-c convection current of the electron stream at the point where the electrons are injected. The four modes of propagation or the waves given by (2.23) enable us to satisfy these boundary conditions.

We are particularly interested in a wave in the direction of electron flow which has about the electron speed and which will account for the observed gain of the traveling-wave tube. Let us assume that the electron speed is made equal to the speed of the wave in the absence of electrons, so that

$$-\Gamma_1 = -j\beta_e \tag{2.24}$$

As we are looking for a wave with about the electron speed, we will assume that the propagation constant differs from $\beta_e$ by a small amount $\xi$, so that

$$-\Gamma = -j\beta_e + \xi$$
$$= -\Gamma_1 + \xi \tag{2.25}$$

Using (2.24) and (2.25) we will rewrite (2.23) as

$$1 = \frac{-KI_0\beta_e^2(-\beta_e^2 - 2j\beta_e\xi + \xi^2)}{2V_0(2j\beta_e\xi - \xi^2)(\xi^2)} \tag{2.26}$$

Now we will find that, for typical traveling-wave tubes, $\xi$ is much smaller than $\beta_e$; hence we will neglect the terms involving $\beta_e\xi$ and $\xi^2$ in the numerator in comparison with $\beta_e^2$ and we will neglect the term $\xi^2$ in the denominator in comparison with the term involving $\beta_e\xi$. This gives us

$$\xi^3 = -j\beta_e^3\frac{KI_0}{4V_0} \tag{2.27}$$

While (2.27) may seem simple enough, it will later be found very convenient to rewrite it in terms of other parameters, and we will introduce them now. Let

$$KI_0/4V_0 = C^3 \tag{2.28}$$

$C$ is usually quite small and is typically often around .02. Instead of $\xi$ we will use a quantity or a parameter $\delta$

$$\xi = \beta_e C \delta \tag{2.29}$$

In terms of $\delta$ and $C$, (2.27) becomes

$$\delta = (-j)^{1/3} = \left(e^{j(2n-1/2)\pi}\right)^{1/3} \tag{2.30}$$

This has three roots which will be called $\delta_1$, $\delta_2$ and $\delta_3$, and these represent three forward waves. They are

$$\delta_1 = e^{-j\pi/6} = \sqrt{3}/2 - j/2$$
$$\delta_2 = e^{-j5\pi/6} = -\sqrt{3}/2 - j/2 \tag{2.31}$$
$$\delta_3 = e^{j\pi/2} = j$$

Figure 2.4 shows the three values of $\delta$. Equation (2.23) was of the fourth degree, and we see that a wave is missing. The missing root was eliminated

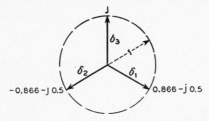

Fig. 2.4—There are three forward waves, with fields which vary with distance as $\exp(-j\beta_e + \beta_e C\delta)z$. The three values of $\delta$ for the case discussed, in which the circuit is lossless and the electrons move with the phase velocity of the unperturbed circuit wave, are shown in the figure.

by the approximations made above, which are valid for forward waves only. The other wave is a backward wave and its propagation constant is found to be

$$-\Gamma = j\beta_e \left(1 - \frac{C^3}{4}\right) \tag{2.32}$$

As $C$ is a small quantity, $C^3$ is even smaller, and indeed the backward wave given by (2.32) is practically the same as the backward wave in the absence of electrons. This is to be expected. In the forward direction, there is a cumulative interaction between wave and the electrons because both are moving at about the same speed. In the backward direction there is no cumulative action, because the wave and the electrons are moving in the opposite directions.

The variation in the $z$ direction for three forward waves is as

$$\exp -\Gamma z = \exp -j\beta_e z \exp \delta C \beta_e z \qquad (2.33)$$

We see that the first wave is an increasing wave which travels a little more slowly than the electrons. The second wave is a decreasing wave which travels a little more slowly than the electrons. The third wave is an un-attenuated wave which travels faster than the electrons. It can be shown generally that when a stream of electrons interacts with a wave, the electrons must go faster than the wave in order to give energy to it.

It is interesting to know the ratio of line voltage to line current, or the characteristic impedance, for the three forward waves. This may be obtained from (2.5). We see that the characteristic impedance $K_n$ for the $n$th wave is given in terms for the propagation constant for the $n$th wave, $\Gamma_n$, by

$$K_n = V/I = jX/\Gamma_n \qquad (2.34)$$

In terms of $\delta_n$ this becomes

$$K_n = K(1 - \beta_e C \delta_n / \Gamma_1) \qquad (2.35)$$

$$K_n = K(1 - jC\delta_n) \qquad (2.36)$$

We see that the characteristic impedance for the forward waves differs from the characteristic impedance in the absence of electrons by a small amount proportional to $C$, and that the characteristic impedance has a small reactive component.

We are particularly interested in the rate at which the increasing wave increases. In a number of wave lengths $N$, the total increase in db is given by

$$20 \log_{10} \exp [(\sqrt{3}/2)(C)(2\pi N)] \text{ db}$$
$$= 47.3 \, CN \text{ db} \qquad (2.37)$$

We will see later that the overall gain of the traveling-wave tube with a uniform helix can be expressed in the form

$$G = A + BCN \text{ db} \qquad (2.38)$$

Here $A$ is a loss relating voltage associated with the increasing wave to the total applied voltage. This loss may be evaluated and will be evaluated later by a proper examination of the boundary conditions at the input of the tube. It turns out that for the case we have considered

$$G = -9.54 + 47.3 \, CN \text{ db} \qquad (2.39)$$

In considering circuits for traveling-wave tubes, and in reformulating the theory in more general terms later on, it is valuable to express $C$ in terms of parameters other than the characteristic impedance. Two physically significant parameters are the power flow in the circuit and the electric field associated with it which acts on the electron stream. The ratio of the square of the electric field to the power can be evaluated by physical measurement even when it cannot be calculated. For instance, Cutler[5] did this by allowing the power from a wave guide to flow into a terminated helix, so that the power in the helix was the same as the power in the wave guide. He then compared the field in the helix with the field in the wave guide by probe measurements. The field strength in the wave guide could be calculated in terms of the power flow, and hence Cutler's measurements enabled him to evaluate the field in the helix for a given power flow.

The magnitude of the field is given in terms of the magnitude of the voltage by

$$E = |\Gamma V|       \tag{2.40}$$

Here $E$ is taken as the magnitude of the field. The power flow in the circuit is given in terms of the circuit voltage by

$$P = |V|^2/2K       \tag{2.41}$$

A quantity which we will use as a circuit parameter is

$$E^2/\beta^2 P = 2K       \tag{2.42}$$

Here it has been assumed that we are concerned with low-loss circuits, so that $\Gamma_1^2$ can be replaced by the phase constant $\beta^2$. Usually, $\beta$ can be taken as equal to $\beta_e$, the electron phase constant, with small error, and in the preceding work this has been assumed to be exactly true in (2.23).

In terms of this new quantity, $C$ is given by

$$C^3 = (2K)(I_0/8V_0) = (E^2/\beta^2 P)(I_0/8V_0)       \tag{2.43}$$

If we call $V_0/I_0$ the beam impedance, $C^3$ is $\frac{1}{4}$ the circuit impedance divided by the beam impedance. It would have been more sensible to use $E^2/2\beta^2 P$ instead of $E^2/\beta^2 P$. Unfortunately the writer feels stuck with his benighted first choice because of the number of curves and published equations which make use of it.

Besides the circuit impedance, another important circuit parameter is the phase velocity. As the electron velocity is made to deviate from the phase velocity of the circuit, the gain falls off. An analysis to be given later

[5] C. C. Cutler, "Experimental Determination of Helical-Wave Properties," *Proc. IRE*, Vol. 36, pp. 230–233, February 1948.

discloses that the allowable range of velocity $\Delta v$ is of the order of

$$\Delta v \approx \pm C u_0 \qquad (2.44)$$

Thus, the allowable difference between the phase velocity of the circuit and the velocity of the electrons increases as circuit impedance and beam current are increased and decreases as voltage is increased.

We have illustrated the general method of attack to be used and have introduced some of the important parameters concerned with the circuit and with the overall behavior of the tube. In later chapters, the properties of various circuits suitable for traveling-wave tubes will be discussed in terms of impedance and phase velocity and various cases of interest will be worked out by the methods presented.

PROBLEMS

1. Draw a vector diagram showing the phase relation between the voltage, the velocity and the current for the 3 forward waves.

2. What is the source of the energy of the amplified wave in the circuit?

3. Suppose that the circuit has a small attenuation. This will mean that $-\Gamma_1$ will have a positive real part $\alpha$. Instead of (2.24), let

$$-\Gamma_1 = \alpha - j\beta_e \qquad (2.24a)$$
$$\alpha << \beta_e$$

Find the equation corresponding to (2.27).

4. Using the equation obtained in Problem 3, find how the roots (2.30) are modified for very small values of $\alpha$.

5. If inductances are connected across the capacitances in Fig. 2.3, the network becomes a band-pass filter. What effect does the added inductance have on the impedance? On the gain of a traveling-wave tube using the circuit?

# CHAPTER III

# THE HELIX

$\text{A}$ NY circuit capable of propagating a slow electromagnetic wave can be used in a traveling-wave tube. The circuit most often used is the helix. The helix is easy to construct. In addition, it is a very good circuit. It has a high impedance and a phase velocity that is almost constant over a wide frequency range.

In this chapter various properties of helices are discussed. An approximate expression for helix properties can be obtained by calculating the properties, not of a helix, but of a helically conducting cylindrical sheet of the same radius and pitch as the helix. An analysis of such a sheet is carried out in Appendix II and the results are discussed in the text.

Parameters which enter into the expressions are the free-space phase constant $\beta_0 = \omega/c$, the axial phase constant $\beta = \omega/v$, where $v$ is the phase velocity of the wave, and the radial phase constant $\gamma$. The arguments of various Bessel functions are, for instance, $\gamma r$ and $\gamma a$, where $r$ is the radial coordinate and $a$ is radius of the helix. The parameters $\beta_0$, $\beta$ and $\gamma$ are related by

$$\beta^2 = \beta_0^2 + \gamma^2$$

For tightly wound helices in which the phase velocity $v$ is small compared with the velocity of light, $\gamma$ is very nearly equal to $\beta$. For instance, at a velocity corresponding to that of 1,000 volt electrons, $\gamma$ and $\beta$ differ by only 0.4%.

Figure 3.1 illustrates two parameters of the helically conducting sheet, the radius $a$ and pitch angle $\psi$. For an actual helix, $a$ will be taken to mean the mean radius, the radius to the center of the wire.

Figure 3.2 shows a single curve which enables one to obtain $\gamma$, and hence $\beta$, for any value of the parameter

$$\beta_0 a \cot \psi = \frac{\omega a \cot \psi}{c}.$$

This parameter is proportional to frequency. The curve is an approximate representation of velocity vs. frequency. At high frequencies $\gamma$ approaches

19

$\beta_0 \cot \psi$ and $\beta$ thus approaches $\beta_0/\sin \psi$; this means that the wave travels with the velocity of light around the sheet in the direction of conduction. In the case of an actual helix, the wave travels along the wire with the velocity of light.

The gain parameter $C$ is given by

$$C = (I_0/8V_0)^{1/3}(E^2/\beta^2 P)^{1/3}$$

Values of $(E^2/\beta^2 P)^{1/3}$ on the axis may be obtained through the use of Fig. 3.4, where an impedance parameter $F(\gamma a)$ is plotted vs. $\gamma a$, and by use of (3.9). For a given helix, $(E^2/\beta^2 P)^{1/3}$ is approximately proportional to $F(\gamma a)$. $F(\gamma a)$ falls as frequency increases. This is partly because at high frequencies and short wavelengths, for which the sign of the field alternates rapidly with distance, the field is strong near the helix but falls off rapidly away from the helix and so the field is weak near the axis. At very high frequencies the field falls off away from the helix approximately as $\exp(-\gamma \Delta r)$, where $\Delta r$ is distance from the helix, and we remember that $\gamma$ is very nearly proportional to frequency. $(E^2/\beta^2 P)^{1/3}$ measured at the helix also falls with increasing frequency.

In many cases, a hollow beam of radius $r$ (the dashed lines of Fig. 3.5 refer to such a beam) or a solid beam of radius $r$ (the solid lines of Fig. 3.5 refer to such a beam) is used. For a hollow beam we should evaluate $E^2$ in $(E^2/\beta^2 P)^{1/3}$ at the beam radius, and for a solid beam we should use the mean square value of $E$ averaged over the beam.

The ordinate in Fig. 3.5 is a factor by which $(E^2/\beta^2 P)^{1/3}$ as obtained from Fig. 3.4 and (3.9) should be multiplied to give $(E^2/\beta^2 P)^{1/3}$ for a hollow or solid beam.

The gain of the increasing wave is proportional to $F(\gamma a)$ times a factor from Fig. 3.5, and times the length of the tube in wavelengths, $N$. $N$ is very nearly proportional to frequency. Also $\gamma$, and hence $\gamma a$, are nearly proportional to frequency. Thus, $F(\gamma a)$ from Fig. 3.4 times the appropriate factor from Fig. 3.5 times $\gamma a$ gives approximately the gain vs. frequency, (if we assume that the electron speed matches the phase velocity over the frequency range). This product is plotted in Fig. 3.6. We see that for a given helix size the maximum gain occurs at a higher frequency and the bandwidth is broader as $r/a$, the ratio of the beam radius to the helix radius, is made larger.

It is usually desirable, especially at very short wavelengths, to make the helix as large as possible. If we wish to design the tube so that gain is a maximum at the operating frequency, we will choose $a$ so that the appropriate curve of Fig. 3.6 has its maximum at the value of $\gamma a$ corresponding to the operating frequency. We see that this value of $a$ will be larger the larger is $r/a$. In an actual helix, the maximum possible value of $r/a$ is less than unity, since the inside diameter of the helix is less than $a$ by the radius of the wire. Further, focusing difficulties preclude attaining a beam radius equal even to the inside radius of the helix.

Experience indicates that at very short wavelengths (around 6 millimeters, say) it is extremely important to have a well-focused electron beam with as large a value of $r/a$ as is attainable.

A characteristic impedance $K_t$ may be defined in terms of a "transverse" voltage $V_t$, obtained by integrating the peak radial field from $a$ to $\infty$, and from the power flow. In Fig. 3.7, $(v/c) K_t$ is plotted vs. $\gamma a$. A "longitudinal" characteristic impedance $K_\ell$ is related to $K_t$ (3.13). For slow waves $K_\ell$ is nearly equal to $K_t$. The impedance parameter $E^2/\beta^2 P$ evaluated at the surface of the cylinder is twice $K_\ell$. We see that $K_\ell$ falls with increasing frequency.

A simplified approach in analysis of the helically conducting sheet is that of "developing" the sheet; that is, slitting it normal to the direction of conduction and flattening it out as in Fig. 3.8. The field equations for such a flattened sheet are then solved. For large values of $\gamma a$ the field is concentrated near the helically conducting sheet, and the fields near the developed sheet are similar to the fields near the cylindrical sheet. Thus the dashed line in Fig. 3.7 is for the developed sheet and the solid line is for a cylindrical sheet.

For the developed sheet, the wave always propagates with the speed of light in the direction of conduction. In a plane normal to the direction of conduction, the field may be specified by a potential satisfying Laplace's equation, as in the case, for instance, of a two-wire or coaxial line. Thus, the fields can be obtained by the solution of an electrostatic problem.

One can develop not only a helically conducting sheet, but an actual helix, giving a series of straight wires, shown in cross-section in Fig. 3.9. In Case I, corresponding to approximately two turns per wavelength, successive wires are $-$, $+$, $-$, $+$ etc.; in case II, corresponding to approximately four turns per wavelength, successive wires are $+$, 0, $-$, 0, $+$, 0 etc.

Figures 3.10 and 3.11 illustrate voltages along a developed sheet and a developed helix.

Figure 3.13 shows the ratio, $R^{1/3}$, of $(E^2/\beta^2 P)^{1/3}$ on the axis to that for a developed helically conducting sheet, plotted vs. $d/p$. We see that, for a large wire diameter $d$, $(E^2/\beta^2 P)^{1/3}$ may be larger on the axis than for a helically conducting sheet with the same mean radius and hence the same pitch angle and phase velocity. This is merely because the thick wires extend nearer to the axis than does the sheet. The actual helix is really inferior to the sheet.

We see this by noting that the highest value of $(E^2/\beta^2 P)^{1/3}$ for a helically conducting sheet is that at the sheet ($r = a$). With a finite wire size, the largest value $r$ can have is the mean helix radius $a$ minus the wire radius. In Fig. 3.14, the ratio of $(E^2/\beta^2 P)^{1/3}$ for this largest allowable radius to $(E^2/\beta^2 P)^{1/3}$ at the surface of the developed sheet is plotted vs. $d/p$. We see that, in terms of maximum available field, $(E^2/\beta^2 P)^{1/3}$ is no more than 0.83 as high as for the sheet for four turns per wavelength and 0.67 as high as for the sheet for two turns per wavelength. We further see that there is an optimum ratio of wire diameter to pitch; about 0.175 for four turns per wavelength and about 0.125 for two turns per wavelength. Because the maxima are so broad, it is probably better in practice to use larger wire, and in most tubes which have been built, $d/p$ has been around 0.5.

In designing tubes it is perhaps best to do so in terms of field on the axis (Fig. 3.13), the allowable value of $r/a$ and the curves of Fig. 3.6.

Figure 3.15 compares the impedance of the developed helix with that of the developed sheet as given by the straight line of Fig. 3.7.

There are factors other than wire size which can cause the value of $E^2/\beta^2 P$ for an actual helix to be less than the value for the helically conducting sheet. An important cause of impedance reduction is the influence of dielectric supporting members. Even small ceramic or glass supporting rods can cause some reduction in helix impedance. In some tubes the helix is supported inside a glass tube, and this can cause a considerable reduction in helix impedance.

When a field analysis seems too involved, it may be possible to obtain some information by considering the behavior of transmission lines having parameters adjusted to make the phase constant and the characteristic impedance equal to those of the helix. For instance, suppose that the presence of dielectric material results in an actual phase constant $\beta_d$ as opposed to a computed phase constant $\beta$. Equation (3.64) gives an estimate of the consequent reduction of $(E^2/\beta^2 P)^{1/3}$ on the axis.

This method is of use in studying the behavior of coupled helices. For instance, concentric helices may be useful in producing radial fields in tubes in which transverse fields predominate in the region of electron flow (see Chapter XIII). A concentric helix structure might be investigated by means of a field analysis, but some interesting properties can be deduced more simply by considering two transmission lines with uniformly distributed self and mutual capacitances and inductances, or susceptance and reactances. The modes of propagation on such lines are affected by coupling in a manner similar to that in which the modes of two resonant circuits are affected by coupling.

If two lines are coupled, their two independent modes of propagation are mixed up to form two modes of propagation in which both lines participate. If the original phase velocities differ greatly, or if the coupling between the lines is weak, the fields and velocity of one of these modes will be almost like the original fields and velocity of one line, and the fields and velocity of the other mode will be almost like the original fields and velocity of the other line. However, if the coupling is strong enough compared with the original separation of phase velocities, both lines will participate almost equally in each mode. One mode will be a "longitudinal mode" for which the excitations on the two lines are substantially equal, and the other mode will be a "transverse" mode for which the excitations are substantially equal and opposite.

The ratios of the voltages on the lines for the two modes are given by (3.75). Here it is assumed that the series reactances $X$ and shunt susceptances $B$ of the lines are almost equal, differing only enough to make a difference $\Delta \Gamma_0$ in the propagation constants. $B_{12}$ and $X_{12}$ are the mutual susceptance and reactance. We see that to make the voltages on the two lines nearly equal or equal and opposite, $B_{12}$ and $X_{12}$ should have the same sign, so that capacitive and inductive couplings add.

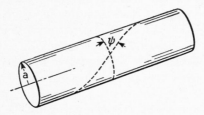

Fig. 3.1—A helically conducting sheet of radius $a$. The sheet is conducting along helical paths making an angle $\psi$ with a plane normal to the axis.

Increasing the coupling increases the velocity separation between the two modes, and this is desirable. When there is a substantial difference in velocity, operation in the desired mode can be secured by making the electron velocity equal to the phase velocity of the desired mode.

To make the capacitive and inductive couplings add in the case of concentric helices (Fig. 3.17), the helices should be wound in opposite directions.

## 3.1 THE HELICALLY CONDUCTING SHEET

In computing the properties of a helix, the actual helix is usually replaced by a helically conducting cylindrical sheet of the same mean radius. Such a sheet is illustrated in Fig. 3.1. This sheet is perfectly conducting in a helical direction making an angle $\psi$, the pitch angle, with a plane normal to the axis (the direction of propagation), and is non-conducting in a helical direction normal to this $\psi$ direction, the direction of conduction. Appropriate solutions of Maxwell's equations are chosen inside and outside of the cylindrical sheet. At the sheet, the components of the electric field in the $\psi$ direction are made zero, and those normal to the $\psi$ direction are made equal inside and outside. Since there can be no current in the sheet normal to the $\psi$ direction, the components of magnetic field in the $\psi$ direction must be the same inside and outside of the sheet. When these boundary conditions are imposed, one can solve for the propagation constant and $E^2/\beta^2 P$ can then be obtained by integrating the Poynting vector.

The helically conducting sheet is treated mathematically in Appendix II. The results of this analysis will be presented here.

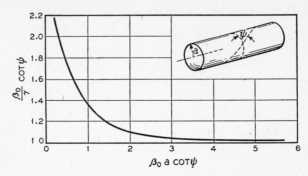

Fig. 3.2—The radial propagation constant is $\gamma^2 = (\beta^2 - \beta_0^2)^{1/2}$. Here $(\beta_0/\gamma) \cot \psi$ is plotted vs $\beta_0 a \cot \psi$, a quantity proportional to frequency. For slow waves the ordinate is roughly the ratio of the wave velocity to the velocity the wave would have if it traveled along the helically conducting sheet with the speed of light in the direction of conduction.

### 3.1a *The Phase Velocity*

The results for the helically conducting sheet are expressed in terms of three phase or propagation constants. These are

$$\beta_0 = \omega/c, \qquad \beta = \omega/v \qquad (3.1)$$

$$\gamma = \sqrt{\beta^2 - \beta_0^2} \qquad (3.2)$$

$$\gamma = \beta\sqrt{1 - (v/c)^2} \qquad (3.3)$$

Here $c$ is the velocity of light and $v$ is the phase velocity of the wave. $\beta_0$ is the phase constant of a wave traveling with the speed of light, which would vary with distance in the $z$ direction as $\exp(-j\beta_0 z)$. The actual axial phase constant is $\beta$, and the fields vary with distance as $\exp(-j\beta z)$.

$\gamma$ is the radial propagation constant. Various field components vary as modified Bessel functions of argument $\gamma r$, where $r$ is the radius. Particularly, the longitudinal electric field, which interacts with the electrons, varies as $I_0(\gamma r)$.

For the phase velocities usually used, $\gamma$ is very nearly equal to $\beta$, as may be seen from the following table of accelerating voltages $V_0$ (to give an electron the velocity $v$), $v/c$ and $\gamma/\beta$.

| $V$ | $v/c$ | $\gamma/\beta$ |
|---|---|---|
| 100 | .0198 | 1.000 |
| 1,000 | .0625 | .998 |
| 10,000 | .1980 | .980 |

Figure 3.2 gives information concerning the phase velocity of the wave in the form of a plot of $(\beta_0/\gamma) \cot \psi$ as a function of $\beta_0\, a \cot \psi$.

The ratio of the phase velocity $v$ to the velocity of light $c$ may be expressed

$$v/c = \beta_0/\beta = (\gamma/\beta)(\beta_0/\gamma) \cot \psi \tan \psi \qquad (3.4)$$

$$v/c = (\gamma/\beta) \tan \psi \, [(\beta_0/\gamma) \cot \psi \,]$$

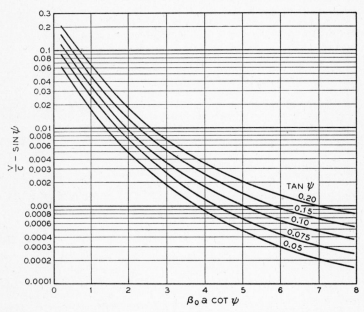

Fig. 3.3—From these curves one can obtain $v/c$, the ratio of the phase velocity of the wave to the velocity of light, for various values of $\tan \psi$ and $\beta_0 a \cot \psi$.

From Fig. 3.2 we see that, for large values of $\beta_0 a \cot \psi$, $(\beta_0/\gamma) \cot \psi$ approaches unity. For slow waves $\gamma/\beta$ approaches unity. Under these circumstances, very nearly

$$v/c = \tan \psi \qquad (3.5)$$

If the wave traveled in the direction of conduction with the speed of light we would have

$$v/c = \sin \psi$$

This is essentially the same as (3.5) for small pitch angles $\psi$. Thus, for large values of the abscissa in Fig. 3.2, the phase velocity is just about that corresponding to propagation along the sheet in the direction of conduction with the speed of light and hence in the axial direction at a much reduced speed. For helices of smaller radius compared with the wavelength, the speed is greater.

The bandwidth of a traveling-wave tube is in part determined by the range over which the electrons keep in step with the wave. The abscissa of Fig. 3.2 is proportional to frequency, but the ordinate is not strictly proportional to phase velocity. Hence, it seems desirable to have a plot which does show velocity directly. To obtain this we can assign various values to cot $\psi$.

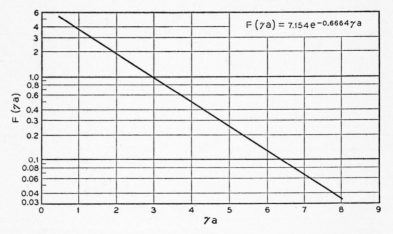

Fig. 3.4—A curve giving the impedance function $F(\gamma a)$ vs. $\gamma a$. On the axis, $(E^2/\beta^2 P)^{1/3} = (\beta/\beta_0)^{1/3}(\gamma/\beta)^{4/3}F(\gamma a)$.

The ordinate $(\beta_0/\gamma)$ cot $\psi$ then gives us $\gamma/\beta_0$ and from (3.2) we see that

$$v/c = \beta_0/\beta = (1 + (\gamma/\beta_0)^2)^{-1/2} \qquad (3.6)$$

We have seen that, for large values of $\beta_0 a$ cot $\psi$, $(\beta_0/\gamma)$ cot $\psi$ approaches unity, and $v/c$ approaches a value

$$v/c = (1 + \cot^2 \psi)^{-1/2} = \sin \psi \qquad (3.7)$$

To emphasize the change in velocity with frequency it seems best to plot the difference between the actual velocity ratio and this asymptotic velocity ratio on a semi-log scale. Accordingly, Fig. 3.3 shows $(v/c) - \sin \psi$ vs. $\beta_0 a$ cot $\psi$ for tan $\psi$ = .05, .075, .1, .15, .2.

For large values of the abscissa the velocities are those corresponding to about 640 volts (tan $\psi$ = .05), 1,400 volts (.075), 2,500 volts (.1), 5,600 volts (.15), 9,800 volts (.2).

### 3.1b *The Impedance Parameter* $(E^2/\beta^2 P)$

Figure 3.4 shows a plot of a quantity $F(\gamma a)$ vs. $\gamma a$. This quantity is computed from a very complicated expression (Appendix II), but it is accurately given over the range shown by the empirical relation

$$F(\gamma a) = 7.154 \, e^{-.6664\gamma a} \tag{3.8}$$

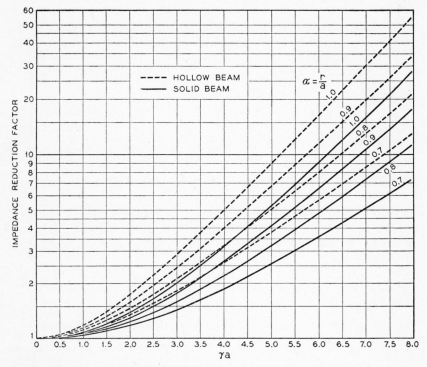

Fig. 3.5—Factors by which $(E^2/\beta^2 P)^{1/3}$ on the axis should be multiplied to give the correct value for hollow and solid beams of radius $r$.

For the field on the axis of the helix,

$$(E^2/\beta^2 P)^{1/3} = (\beta/\beta_0)^{1/3}(\gamma/\beta)^{4/3}F(\gamma a) \tag{3.9}$$

We should remember that $\beta/\beta_0 = c/v$ and that $\gamma/\beta$ is nearly unity for velocities small compared with the velocity of light.

In the expression for the gain parameter $C$, the square of the field $E$ is multiplied by the current $I_0$ (2.28). If we were to assume that two electron streams of different currents, $I_1$ and $I_2$, were coupled to the circuit through transformers, so as to be acted on by fields $E_1$ and $E_2$, but that the streams did not interact directly with one another, we would find the effective value of $C^3$ to be given by

$$C^3 = (E_1^2/\beta^2 P)(I_1/8V_0) + (E_2^2/\beta^2 P)(I_2/8V_0)$$

Thus, if we neglect the direct interaction of electron streams through fields due to local space charge, we can obtain an effective value of $C^3$ by integrating $E^2 dI_0$ over the beam. If we assume a constant current density, we can merely use the mean square value of $E$ over the area occupied by electron flow.

The axial component of electric field at a distance $r$ from the axis is $I_0(\gamma r)$ times the field on the axis. Hence, if we used a tubular beam of radius $r$, we should multiply $(E^2/\beta^2 P)^{1/3}$ as obtained from Fig. 3.4 by $[I_0(\gamma r)]^{2/3}$. The quantity $[I_0(\gamma r)]^{2/3}$ is plotted vs. $\gamma a$ for several values of $r/a$ as the dashed lines in Fig. 3.5.

Suppose the current density is uniform out to a radius $r$ and zero beyond this radius. The average value of $E^2$ is greater than the value on the axis by a factor $[I_0^2(\gamma r) - I_1(\gamma r)]$ and $(E^2/\beta^2 P)^{1/3}$ from Fig. 3.4 should in this case be multiplied by this factor to the $\frac{1}{3}$ power. The appropriate factor is plotted vs. $\gamma a$ as the solid lines of Fig. 3.5.

We note from (2.39) that the gain contains a term proportional to $CN$, where $N$ is the number of wavelengths. For slow waves and usual values of $\gamma a$, very nearly, $N$ will be proportional to the frequency and hence to $\gamma$, while $C$ is proportional to $(E^2/\beta^2 P)^{1/3}$. We can obtain $(E^2/\beta^2 P)^{1/3}$ from Figs. 3.4 and 3.5. The gain of the increasing wave as a function of frequency will thus be very nearly proportional to this value of $(E^2/\beta^2 P)^{1/3}$ times $\gamma$, or, times $\gamma a$ if we prefer.

In Fig. 3.6, $\gamma a F(\gamma a)$ is plotted vs. $\gamma a$ for hollow beams of radius $r$ for various values of $r/a$ (dashed lines) and for uniform density beams of radius $r$ for various values of $r/a$ (solid lines). If we assume that the electron speed is adjusted to equal the phase velocity of the wave, we can take the ordinate as proportional to gain and the abscissa as proportional to frequency.

We see that the larger is $r/a$, the larger is the value of $\gamma a$ for maximum gain. For one typical 7.5 cm wavelength traveling-wave tube, $\gamma a$ was about 2.8. For this tube, the ratio of the inside radius of the helix to the mean radius of the helix was 0.87. We see from Fig. 3.6 that, if a solid beam just filled this helix, the maximum gain should occur at about the operating wavelength. As a matter of fact, the beam was somewhat smaller than the inside diameter of the helix, and there was an observed increase of gain with an increase in wavelength (a higher gain at a lower frequency). In a particular tube for 0.625 cm wavelength, it was felt desirable to use a relatively large helix diameter. Accordingly, a value of $\gamma a$ of 6.7 was chosen. We see that, unless $r/a$ is 0.9 or larger, this must result in an appreciable increase in gain at some frequency lower than operating frequency. It was only by use of great care in focusing the beam that gain was attained at 0.625 cm wavelength, and there was a tendency toward oscillation, presumably at longer wavelengths. This discussion of course neglects the effect of transmission

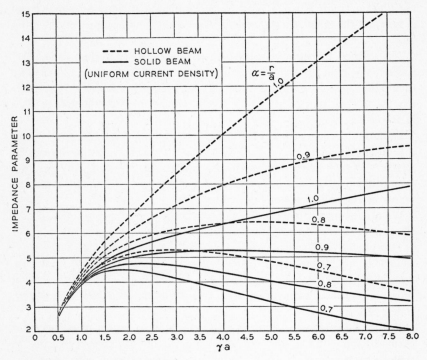

Fig. 3.6—The ordinate is $\gamma a F(\gamma a)$ times the parameters from Fig. 3.5. For a fixed current and voltage it is nearly proportional to gain per unit length, and hence the curves give roughly the variation of gain with frequency.

loss or gain. Usually the loss decreases when the frequency is decreased, and this favors oscillation at low frequencies.

### 3.1c *Impedance of the Helix*

No impedance which can be assigned to the helically conducting sheet can give full information for matching a helix to a waveguide or transmission line. As in the case of transducers between a coaxial line and a waveguide or between waveguides of different cross-section, the impedance is important, but discontinuity effects are also important. However, a suitably defined helix impedance is of some interest.

Figure 3.7 presents the impedance as defined on a voltage-power basis. The peak "transverse" voltage $V_t$ is obtained by integrating the radial electric field from the radius $a$ of the helically conducting sheet to $\infty$. The "transverse" characteristic impedance $K_t$ is defined by the relation

$$P = (\tfrac{1}{2})(V_t^2/K_t)$$

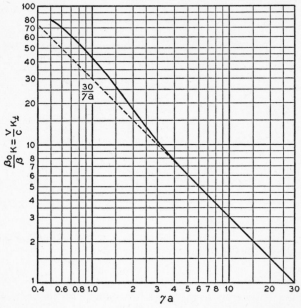

Fig. 3.7—Curves giving the variation of transverse impedance, $K_t$, with $\gamma a$.

The impedance is found to be given by

$$\left(\frac{\beta}{\gamma}\right)^2 \left(\frac{\beta_0}{\beta}\right) K_t = \frac{120 I_0^2}{(\gamma a)^2}\left[\left(1 + \frac{I_0 K_1}{I_1 K_0}\right)(I_1^2 - I_0 I_2)\right.$$
$$\left. + \left(\frac{I_0}{K_0}\right)^2 \left(1 + \frac{I_1 K_0}{I_0 K_1}\right)(K_0 K_2 - K_1^2)\right]^{-1}$$

(3.10)

The $I$'s and $K$'s are modified Bessel functions of argument $\gamma a$.

The dashed line on Fig. 3.7 is a plot of $30/\gamma a$ vs. $\gamma a$. It may be seen that, for large values of $\gamma a$, very nearly

$$K_t = (\beta/\beta_0)(\gamma/\beta)^2(30/\gamma a)$$

(3.11)

and in the whole range shown the impedance differs from this value by a factor less than 1.5.

We might have defined a "longitudinal" voltage $V\ell$ as half of the integral of the longitudinal component of electric field at the surface of the helically conducting sheet for a half wavelength (between successive points of zero field). We find that

$$V_\ell = \sqrt{1 - (v/c)^2}\ V_t = (\gamma/\beta)V_t \qquad (3.12)$$

and, accordingly, the "longitudinal impedance" $K\ell$ will be

$$K_\ell = [1 - (v/c)^2]K_t = (\gamma/\beta)^2 K_t \qquad (3.13)$$

Our impedance parameter, $E^2/\beta^2 P$, is just twice this "longitudinal impedance."

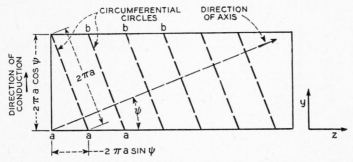

Fig. 3.8—A "developed" helically conducting sheet. The sheet has been slit along a line normal to the direction of conduction and flattened out.

The transverse voltage $V_t$ is greater than the longitudinal voltage $V\ell$ because of the circumferential magnetic flux outside of the helix. For slow waves $V\ell$ is nearly equal to $V_t$ and the fields are nearly curl-free solutions of Laplace's equation. In this case the circumferential magnetic flux is small compared with the longitudinal flux inside of the helix.

For the circuit of Fig. 2.3 the transverse and longitudinal voltages are equal, and it is interesting to note that this is approximately true for slow waves on a helix. For very fast waves, the longitudinal voltage becomes small compared with the transverse voltage.

For a typical 4,000-megacycle tube, for which $\gamma a = 2.8$, Fig. 3.7 indicates a value of $K_t$ of about 150 ohms.

## 3.2 THE DEVELOPED HELIX

For large helices, i.e., for large values of $\gamma a$, the fields fall off very rapidly away from the wire. Under these circumstances we can obtain quite accurate results by slitting the helically conducting sheet along a spiral line normal to the direction of conduction and flattening it out. This gives us the plane conducting sheet shown in Fig. 3.8. The indicated coordinates are $z$ to the right and $y$ upward: $x$ is positive into the paper. The fields about the developed sheet approximate those about the helically conducting sheet for distances always small compared with the original radius of curvature.

The straight dashed line shown on the helix impedance curve of Fig. 3.7 can be obtained as a solution for the "developed helix." We see that it is within 10% of the true curve for values of $\gamma a$ greater than 2.8. We might note that a 10% error in impedance means only a $3\frac{1}{3}\%$ error in the gain parameter $C$.

In solving for the fields around the sheet, the developed surface can be extended indefinitely in the plus and minus $y$ directions. In order that the fields may match when the sheet is rolled up, they must be the same at $y = 0$, $z = 2\pi a \sin \psi$ and $y = 2\pi a \cos \psi$, $z = 0$. The appropriate solutions are plane electromagnetic waves traveling in the $y$ direction with the speed of light.

For positive values of $x$, the appropriate electric and magnetic fields are

$$E_x = E_0 e^{-\gamma x} e^{-j\gamma z} e^{-j\beta_0 y}$$

$$E_z = jE_0 e^{-\gamma x} e^{-j\gamma z} e^{-j\beta_0 y} \tag{3.14}$$

$$E_y = 0$$

We should note that the $x$ and $z$ components of the field can be obtained as gradients of a function

$$\Phi = -(E_0/\gamma)e^{-\gamma x} e^{-j\gamma z} e^{-j\beta_0 y} \tag{3.15}$$

where

$$E_x = -\partial\Phi/\partial z$$
$$E_z = -\partial\Phi/\partial y \tag{3.16}$$

$$\partial^2\Phi/\partial x^2 + \partial^2\Phi/\partial z^2 = 0 \tag{3.17}$$

Thus, in the $xz$ plane, $\Phi$ satisfies Laplace's equation.

The magnetic field is given by the curl[6] of the electric field times $j/\omega\mu$. Its components are:

$$H_x = \frac{j}{\mu c} E_0 e^{-\gamma x} e^{-j\gamma z} e^{-j\beta_0 y}$$

$$H_z = \frac{-1}{\mu c} E_0 e^{-\gamma x} e^{-j\gamma z} e^{-j\beta_0 y} \tag{3.18}$$

$$H_y = 0$$

[6] Maxwell's equations are given in Appendix I.

The fields in the $-x$ direction may be obtained by substituting $\exp(\gamma x)$ for $\exp(-\gamma x)$.

If the sheet is to roll up properly, the points $a$ on the bottom coinciding with the points $b$ on the top, we have

$$2\pi\gamma a \sin\psi - 2\pi\beta_0 a \cos\psi = 2n\pi \qquad (3.19)$$

where $n$ is an integer.

The solution corresponding most nearly to the wave on a singly-wound helix is that for $n = 0$. The others lead to a variation of field by $n$ cycles along a circumferential line. These can be combined with the $n = 0$ solution to give a solution for a developed helix of thin tape, for instance. Or, appropriate combinations of them can represent modes of helices wound of several parallel wires. For instance, we can imagine winding a balanced transmission line up helically. One of the modes of propagation will be that in which the current in one wire is 180° out of phase with the current in the other. This can be approximated by a combination of the $n = +1$ and $n = -1$ solutions. This mode should not be confused with a fast wave, a perturbation of a transverse electromagnetic wave, which can exist around an unshielded helix.

Usually, we are interested in the slow wave on a singly-wound helix, and in this case we take $n = 0$ in (3.19), giving

$$\gamma \sin\psi - \beta_0 \cos\psi = 0$$
$$\tan\psi = \beta_0/\gamma \qquad (3.20)$$

$$\sin\psi = \frac{\beta_0}{(\gamma^2 + \beta_0^2)^{1/2}} \qquad (3.21)$$

$$\cos\psi = \frac{\gamma}{(\gamma^2 + \beta_0^2)^{1/2}} \qquad (3.22)$$

Let us evaluate the propagation constant in the axial direction. From Fig. 3.8 we see that, in advancing unit distance in the axial direction, we proceed a distance $\cos\psi$ in the $z$ direction and $\sin\psi$ in the y direction. Hence, the phase constant $\beta$ in the axial direction must be

$$\beta = \beta_0 \sin\psi + \gamma \cos\psi \qquad (3.23)$$

Using (3.23) and (3.19), we obtain

$$\beta = (\beta_0^2 + \gamma^2)^{1/2} \qquad (3.24)$$

$$\gamma = (\beta^2 - \beta_0^2)^{1/2} \qquad (3.25)$$

These are just relations (3.2, 3.3).

The power flow along the axis is that crossing a circumferential circle, represented by lines *a-b* in Fig. 3.8. As the power flows in the $y$ direction, this is the power associated with a distance $2\pi a \sin \psi$ in $z$ direction. Also, the power flow in the $+x$ region will be equal to the power flow in the $-x$ region. Hence, the power flow in the helix will be twice that in the region $x = 0$ to $x = +\infty$, $z = 0$ to $z = 2\pi a \sin \psi$.

$$P = 2 \int_{z=0}^{2\pi a \sin \psi} \int_{x=0}^{\infty} (\tfrac{1}{2})(E_z H_x^* - E_x H_z^*) \, dx \, dz \qquad (3.26)$$

This is easily integrated to give

$$P = \frac{2\pi a \sin \psi E_0^2}{\gamma \mu c} \qquad (3.27)$$

The magnitude $E$ of the axial component of field is

$$E = E_0 \cos \psi \qquad (3.28)$$

Using (3.21), (3.22), (3.24) and (3.28) in connection with (3.27) we obtain

$$(E^2/\beta^2 P) = (\gamma/\beta)^4 (\beta/\beta_0)(\mu c/2\pi\gamma a) \qquad (3.29)$$

We have

$$\mu c = \mu/\sqrt{\mu\epsilon} = \sqrt{\mu/\epsilon} = 377 \text{ ohms}$$

Thus

$$E^2/\beta^2 P = (\gamma/\beta)^4 (\beta/\beta_0)(60/\gamma a) \qquad (3.30)$$

The longitudinal impedance is half this, and the transverse impedance is $(\beta/\gamma)^2$ times the longitudinal impedance.

### 3.3 Effect of Wire Size

An actual helix of round wire, as used in traveling-wave tubes, will of course differ somewhat in properties from the helically conducting sheet for which the foregoing material applies.

One might expect a small difference if there were many turns per wavelength, but actual tubes often have only a few turns per wavelength. For instance, a typical 4,000 mc tube has about 4.8 turns per wavelength, while a tube designed for 6 mm operation has 2.4 turns per wavelength.

If the wire is made very small there will be much electric and magnetic energy very close to the wire, which is not associated with the desired field component (that which varies as $\exp(-j\beta z)$ in the $z$ direction). If the wire is very large the internal diameter of the helix becomes considerably less than the mean diameter, and the space available for electron flow is reduced. As the field for the helically conducting sheet is greatest at the sheet, this means that the maximum available field is reduced. Too, the impedance will depend on wire size.

It thus seems desirable to compare in some manner an actual helix and the helically conducting sheet. It would be very difficult to solve the problem of an actual helix. However, we can make an approximate comparison by a method suggested by R. S. Julian.

In doing this we will develop the helix of wires just as the helically con-

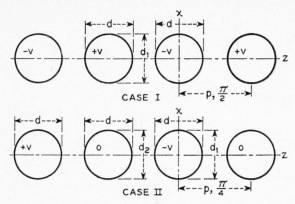

Fig. 3.9—The wires of a developed helix with about two turns per wavelength (case I) and about four turns per wavelength (case II). In the analysis used, the wires are not quite round.

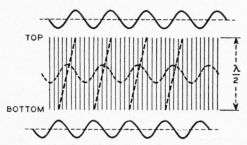

Fig. 3.10—Voltages on a developed helically conducting sheet for two turns per wavelength.

ducting sheet was developed, by slitting it along a helical line normal to the wires. We will then consider two special cases, one in which the wires of the developed helix are one half wavelength long and the other in which the wires are one quarter wavelength long.

The waves propagated on the developed helix are transverse electromagnetic waves propagated in the direction of the wires, and the electric fields normal to the direction of propagation can be obtained from a solution of Laplace's equation in two dimensions (as in (3.15)–(3.17)).

It is easy to make up two-dimensional solutions of Laplace's equation with equipotentials or conductors of approximately circular form, as shown in Fig. 3.9. In case I, the conductors are alternately at potentials $-V, +V$, $-V$, etc.; and in case II, the potentials are $-V$, 0, $+V$, 0, $-V$, 0, $+V$, etc. Far away in the $x$ direction from such a series of conductors, the field will vary sinusoidally in the $z$ direction and will vary in the same manner with $x$ as in the developed helically conducting sheet. Hence, we can make the distant fields of the conductors of cases I and II of Fig. 3.9 equal to the distant fields of developed helically conducting sheets, and compare the $E^2/\beta^2 P$ and the impedance for the different systems. Case I would correspond to a helix of approximately two turns per wavelength and case II to four turns per wavelength.

### 3.3a *Two Turns per Wavelength*

Figure 3.10 is intended to illustrate the developed helically conducting sheet. The vertical lines indicate the direction of conduction. The dashed slanting lines are intersections of the original surface with planes normal to the axis. That is, on the original cylindrical surface they were circles about the surface, and they connect positions along the top and bottom which should be brought together in rolling up the flattened surface to reconstitute the helically conducting sheet.

Waves propagate on the developed sheet of Fig. 3.10 vertically with the speed of light. The vertical dimension of the sheet is in this case taken as $\lambda/2$, where $\lambda$ is the free-space wavelength.[7] The sine waves above and below Fig. 3.10 indicate voltages at the top and the bottom and are, of course, 180° out of phase. As is necessary, the voltages at the ends of the dashed slanting lines, (really, the voltages at the same point before the sheet was slit) are equal.

A wave sinusoidal at the bottom of the sheet, zero half way up and 180° out of phase with the bottom at the top would constitute along any horizontal line a standing wave, not a traveling wave. Actually, this is only one component of the field. The other is a wave 90° out of phase in both the horizontal and vertical directions. Its maximum voltage is half-way up, and it is indicated by the dotted sine wave in Fig. 3.10. The voltage of this component is zero at top and bottom. It may be seen that these two components propagating upward together constitute a wave traveling to the right. The two components are orthogonal spatially, and the total power is twice the power of either component taken separately.

Figure 3.11 indicates an array of wires obtained by developing an actual

---

[7] Section 3.3a is referred to as "two turns per wavelength." This is not quite accurate; it is in error by the difference between the lengths of the vertical and the slanting lines in Fig. 3.10.

helix which has been slit along a helical line normal to the wire of which the helix is wound. The dashed slanting lines again connect points which were the same point before the helix was slit and developed. Again we assume a height of a half wavelength. Thus, if the polarities are maximum $+$, $-$, $+$ $-$ etc. as shown at the bottom, they will be maximum $-$, $+$, $-$, $+$, $-$, $+$ etc. as shown at the top, and zero half-way up. In this case the field is a standing wave along any horizontal line, and no other component can be introduced to make it a traveling wave. Half of the field strength can be regarded as constituting a component traveling to the right and half as a component traveling to the left.

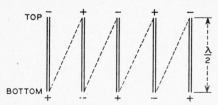

Fig. 3.11—Voltages on a developed helix for two turns per wavelength.

The equipotentials used to represent the field about the wires of Fig. 3.9, Case I and Fig. 3.10 belong to the field

$$V + j\psi = \ln \tan (z + jx) \tag{3.31}$$

Here $V$ is potential and $\psi$ is a stream function. There are negative equipotentials about $z = x = 0$ and positive equipotentials about $x = 0$, $z = \pm\pi/2$. For an equipotential coinciding with the surface of a wire of $z$-diameter, $2 z_{\text{wire}}$, $d/p$ is thus

$$d/p = \frac{z_{\text{wire}}}{\pi/4} \tag{3.32}$$

at $x = 0$, $z < \pi/4$

$$V = \ln \tan z \tag{3.33}$$

at $z = 0$

$$V = \ln \tanh x \tag{3.34}$$

Hence, for an equipotential on the wire with an $z$-diameter $2z$, the $x$-diameter $2x$ can be obtained from (3.33) and (3.34) as

$$2x = 2 \tanh^{-1} \tan z \tag{3.35}$$

Of course, the ratio of the $x$-diameter $d_1$ to the pitch is given by

$$d_1/p = \frac{x}{\pi/4} \tag{3.36}$$

where $x$ is obtained from (3.35).

In Fig. 3.12, $d_1/d$ is plotted vs. $d/p$ by means of (3.35) and (3.36). This shows that for wire diameters up to $d/p = .5$ (open space equal to wire diameter) the equipotentials representing the wire are very nearly round.

The total electric flux from each wire is $2\pi\epsilon$ and the potential of a wire of $z$-diameter $2z$ is $V = -\ln \tan z$. Hence, the stored energy $W_1$ per unit length per wire, half the product of the charge and the voltage, is

$$W_1 = -\pi\epsilon \ln \tan z \qquad (3.37)$$

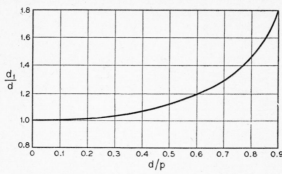

Fig. 3.12—Ratio of the two diameters of the wire of a helix for two turns per wavelength (see Fig. 3.9) vs. the ratio of one of the diameters to the pitch.

The total distant field and the useful field component are given by expanding (3.31) in Fourier series and taking the fundamental component, giving

$$V = -2 \cos 2z e^{\mp 2x} \qquad (3.38)$$

The $-$ sign applies for $x > 0$ and the $+$ sign for $x < 0$. Half of this can be regarded as belonging to a field moving to the right and half to a field moving to the left.

For a field equal to half that specified by (3.38), which might be part of the field of a developed helically conducting sheet, the stored energy $W_2$ per unit depth can be obtained by integrating $(E_z^2 + E_x^2)\,\epsilon/2$ from $x = -\infty$ to $x = +\infty$ and from $z = -\pi/4$ to $+\pi/4$, and it turns out to be

$$W_2 = \tfrac{1}{2}\pi\epsilon \qquad (3.39)$$

If we add another field component similar to half of (3.38), but in quadrature with respect to $z$ and $t$, we will have the traveling wave of a helically conducting sheet with the same distant traveling field component as given by (3.31). Hence, the ratio $R$ of the stored energy for the developed sheet to the stored energy for the developed helix is

$$R = 2W_2/W_1 = -\frac{1}{\ln \tan z} \qquad (3.40)$$

$R$ is the ratio of the stored energies, and hence of the power flows (since the waves both propagate with the speed of light) of a developed helically conducting sheet and a developed helix with the same distant traveling fundamental field components. Hence, at a given distance $(E^2/\beta^2 P)^{1/3}$ for the helix is $R^{1/3}$ times as great as for the helically conducting sheet. In Fig. 3.13, $R^{1/3}$ is plotted vs. $d/p$.

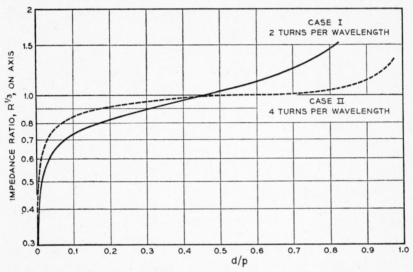

Fig. 3.13—Ratio $R^{1/3}$ of $(E^2/\beta^2 P)^{1/3}$ for a helix to the value for a helically conducting sheet for the distant field.

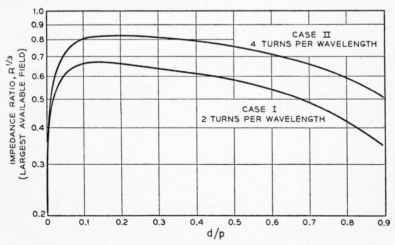

Fig. 3.14—Ratio $R^{1/3}$ of $(E^2/\beta^2 P)^{1/3}$ for a helix to the value for a helically conducting sheet, field at the inside diameter of the helix or sheet.

The maximum available field for the developed helically conducting sheet (equation (3.38)) is that for $x = 0$. The maximum available field for the developed helix (equation (3.31)) is that for an electron grazing the helix inner or outer diameter, that is, an electron at a value of $x$ given by (3.35). The fundamental sinusoidal component of the field varies as $\exp(-2x)$ for both the sheet and the helix, and hence there is a loss in $E^2$ by a factor $\exp(-4x)$ because of this. We wish to make a comparison on the basis of $E^2$ and power or energy. Hence, on basis of maximum available field squared we would obtain from (3.40)

$$R = -\frac{1}{\ln \tan z} e^{-4x} \qquad (3.41)$$

where $x$ is obtained from (3.35). Figure 3.14 was obtained from (3.32), (3.35) and (3.41).

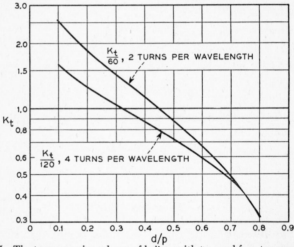

Fig. 3.15—The transverse impedance of helices with two and four turns per wavelength vs. the ratio of wire diameter to pitch.

In a transmission line the characteristic impedance is given by

$$K = \sqrt{\frac{L}{C}} \qquad (3.42)$$

Here $L$ and $C$ are the inductance and capacitance per unit length. This impedance should be identified with the transverse impedance of the helix. We also have for the velocity of propagation, which will be the velocity of light, $c$,

$$c = \frac{1}{\sqrt{LC}} = \frac{1}{\sqrt{\mu\epsilon}} \qquad (3.43)$$

From (3.42) and (3.43) we obtain

$$K_t = \sqrt{\mu\epsilon}/C = \sqrt{\mu/\epsilon}(\epsilon/C)$$
$$= 377\ \epsilon/C \tag{3.44}$$

Now $C$ is the charge $Q$ divided by the voltage $V$. Hence

$$K_t = 377\ \epsilon V/Q \tag{3.45}$$

In this case we have

$$K_t = \frac{337\epsilon \ln \tan z}{2\pi\epsilon}$$
$$K_t = -60 \ln \tan z \tag{3.46}$$

To obtain the impedance of the corresponding helically conducting sheet we assume, following (3.30)

$$K_t = (\gamma/\beta)\ (\gamma/\beta_0)\ (30/\gamma a) \tag{3.47}$$

and assuming a slow wave, let $\gamma = \beta$, so that

$$K_t = 30/\beta_0 a \tag{3.48}$$

If we are to have $n$ turns per wavelength, and the speed of light in the direction of conduction, then we must have

$$\beta_0 a = 1/n \tag{3.49}$$

whence

$$K_t = 30n \tag{3.50}$$

For $n = 2$ (two turns per wavelength), $K = 60$. In Fig. 3.15, the characteristic impedance $K_t$ as obtained from (3.46) divided by 60 (from (3.50)) is plotted vs. $d/p$.

### 3.3b *Four Turns per Wavelength*

In this case there are enough wires so that we can add a quadrature component as in Fig. 3.10 and thus produce a traveling wave rather than a standing wave. Thus, we can make a more direct comparison between the developed sheet and the developed helix.

For the developed helix we have

$$V + j\psi = \ln \tan (z + jx) + \frac{A}{\cos 2\ (z + jx)} \tag{3.15}$$

If we transform this to new coordinates $z_1$, $x_1$ about an origin at $z = 0$, $x = \pi/4$ we obtain

$$V + j\psi = \ln \left( \frac{1 + \tan(z_1 + jx_1)}{1 - \tan(z_1 + jx_1)} \right) - \left( \frac{A}{\sin 2(z_1 + jx_1)} \right) \qquad (3.52)$$

We can now adjust $A$ to give a zero equipotential of diameter $2z_1$ about $x = x_1 = 0$, $z_1 = 0$ $(z = \pi/4)$ by letting

$$A = (\sin 2z_1) \ln \left( \frac{1 + \tan z_1}{1 - \tan z_1} \right) \qquad (3.53)$$

If $A$ is so chosen, there will be roughly circular equipotentials of $z$-diameter $2z_1$ about $z = \pm \pi/4$, etc. There will also be roughly circular equipotentials of the same $z$-diameter about $z = 0$, $\pm\pi/2$, etc., of potential $\pm V$. That about $z = 0$ has a potential

$$V = \ln \left( \frac{1 + \tan z_1}{1 - \tan z_1} \right) \frac{A}{\cos 2z_1} \qquad (3.54)$$

where $A$ is taken from (3.53).

The distance between centers of equipotentials is $p = \pi/4$, so that the ratio of $z$-diameter of the equipotentials to pitch is

$$d/p = 2z_1/(\pi/4) = z_1/(\pi/8) \qquad (3.55)$$

The $x$-diameter of the equipotential about $z = 0$ (and of those about $z = \pm\frac{\pi}{2}$ etc.) can be obtained as $2x$ by letting $V$ have the value given by (3.54) and setting $z = 0$ in (3.51), giving

$$V = \ln \tanh x + \frac{A}{\cosh 2x} \qquad (3.56)$$

The ratio of this $x$-diameter to the pitch, $d_1/p$, is

$$d_1/p = y/(\pi/8), \qquad (3.57)$$

$x$ is obtained from (3.56).

To obtain the $x$-diameter of the 0 potential electrodes we take the derivative (3.52) with respect to $z_1$, giving the gradient in the $z$ direction

$$\frac{\partial V}{\partial z_1} + j \frac{\partial \psi}{\partial z_1} = \frac{\sec^2(z_1 + jx_1)}{1 + \tan(z_1 + jx_1)} + \frac{\sec^2(z_1 + jx_1)}{1 - \tan(z_1 + jx_1)}$$
$$- \frac{2A \cos 2(z_1 + jx_1)}{\sin 2(z_1 + jx_1)} \qquad (3.58)$$

We then let $z_1 = 0$ and find the value of $x_1$ for which $\partial V/\partial z_1 = 0$. When $z_1 = 0$, (3.58) becomes

$$A = \sinh 2x_1 \tanh 2x_1 \frac{(1 - \tanh^2 x_1)}{(1 + \tanh^2 x_1)} \tag{3.59}$$

As $A$ is given by (3.53), we can obtain $x$, from (3.57), and the ratio of the $x$-diameter $d_2$ to the pitch is

$$d_2/p = x_1/(\pi/8) \tag{3.60}$$

Figure 3.16 shows $d_1/d$ and $d_2/d$ vs. $d/p$.

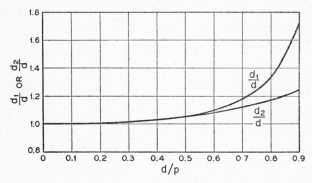

Fig. 3.16—Ratios of the wire diameters for the four turns per wavelength analysis.

The ratios $R$ and the impedance are obtained merely by comparing the power flow for the developed sheet with a single sinusoidally distributed component with the power flow for case II for the same distant field. In a comparison with the helically conducting sheet, $n = 2$ is used in (3.50). The results are shown in Figs. 3.13, 3.14, 3.15. We see that on the basis of the largest available field, the best wire size is $d/p = .19$.

### 3.4 TRANSMISSION LINE EQUATIONS AND HELICES

It is of course possible at any frequency to construct a transmission line with a distributed shunt susceptance $B$ per unit length and a distributed shunt reactance $X$ per unit length and, by adjusting $B$ and $X$ to make the phase velocity and $E^2/\beta^2 P$ the same for the artificial line as for the helix. In simulating the helix with the line, $B$ and $X$ must be changed as frequency is changed. Indeed, it may be necessary to change $B$ and $X$ somewhat in simulating a helix with a forced wave on it, as, the wave forced by an electron stream. Nevertheless, a qualitative insight into some problems can be obtained by use of this type of circuit analogue.

### 3.4a Effect of Dielectric on Helix Impedance Parameter

One possible application of the transmission line equivalent is in estimating the lowering of the helix impedance parameter $(E^2/\beta^2 P)^{1/3}$.

In the case of a transmission line of susceptance $B$ and reactance $X$ per unit length, we have for the phase constant $\beta$ and the characteristic impedance $K$

$$\beta = \sqrt{BX} \tag{3.61}$$

$$K = \sqrt{X/B} \tag{3.62}$$

Now, suppose that $B$ is increased by capacitive loading so that $\beta$ has a larger value $\beta_d$. Then we see that $K$ will have a value $K_d$

$$K_d = (\beta/\beta_d)K \tag{3.63}$$

Where should $K$ be measured? It is reasonable to take the field at the surface of the helix or the helically conducting sheet as the point at which the field should be evaluated. The field at the axis will, then, be changed by a different amount, for the field at the surface of the helix is $I_0(\gamma a)$ times the field at the axis.

Suppose, then, we design a helix to have a phase constant $\beta$ (a phase velocity $\omega/\beta$) and, in building it, find that the dielectric supports increase the phase constant to a value $\beta_d$ giving a smaller phase velocity $\omega/\beta_d$. Suppose $\beta/\beta_0$ is large, so that $\gamma$ is nearly equal to $\beta$. How will we estimate the actual axial value of $(E^2/\beta^2 P)^{1/3}$? We make the following estimate:

$$(E^2/\beta^2 P)_d^{1/3} = \left(\frac{\beta}{\beta_d}\right)^{1/3} \left(\frac{I_0(\beta a)}{I_0(\beta_d a)}\right)^{2/3} (E^2/\beta^2 P)^{1/3} \tag{3.64}$$

Here the factor $(\beta/\beta_d)^{1/3}$ is concerned with the reduction of impedance measured at the helix surface, and the other factor is concerned with the greater falling-off of the field toward the center of the helix because of the larger value of $\gamma$ (taken equal to $\beta$ and $\beta_d$ in the two cases).

The writer does not know how good this estimate may be.

### 3.4b Coupled Helices

Another case in which the equivalent transmission line approach is particularly useful is in considering the problem of concentric helices. Such configurations have been particularly suggested for producing slow transverse fields. They can be analyzed in terms of helically conducting cylinders or in terms of developed cylinders. A certain insight can be gained very quickly, however, by the approach indicated above.

We will simulate the helices by two transmission lines of series impedances $jX_1$ and $jX_2$, of shunt admittances $jB_1$ and $jB_2$ coupled by series mutual impedance and shunt mutual admittance $jX_{12}$ and $jB_{12}$. If we consider a wave which varies as $\exp(-j\Gamma z)$ in the $z$ direction we have

$$\Gamma I_1 \ - jB_1V_1 - jB_{12}V_2 = 0 \tag{3.65}$$

$$\Gamma V_1 - jX_1I_1 - jX_{12}I_2 = 0 \tag{3.66}$$

$$\Gamma I_2 \ - jB_2V_2 - jB_{12}V_1 = 0 \tag{3.67}$$

$$\Gamma V_2 - jX_2I_2 - jX_{12}I_1 = 0 \tag{3.68}$$

If we solve (3.65) and (3.67) for $I_1$ and $I_2$ and eliminate these, we obtain

$$\frac{V_2}{V_1} = \frac{-(\Gamma^2 + X_1 B_1 + X_{12} B_{12})}{X_1 B_{12} + B_2 X_{12}} \tag{3.69}$$

$$\frac{V_1}{V_2} = \frac{-(\Gamma^2 + X_2 B_2 + X_{12} B_{12})}{X_2 B_{12} + B_1 X_{12}} \tag{3.70}$$

Multiplying these together we obtain

$$\Gamma^4 + (X_1 B_1 + X_2 B_2 + 2X_{12} B_{12})\Gamma^2$$
$$+ (X_1 X_2 - X_{12}^2)(B_1 B_2 - B_{12}^2) = 0 \tag{3.71}$$

We can solve this for the two values of $\Gamma^2$

$$\Gamma^2 = -\tfrac{1}{2}(X_1 B_1 + X_2 B_2 + 2X_{12} B_{12})$$
$$\pm \tfrac{1}{2} [(X_1 B_1 - X_2 B_2)^2 + 4(X_1 B_1 + X_2 B_2)(X_{12} B_{12}) \tag{3.72}$$
$$+ 4(X_1 X_2 B_{12}^2 + B_1 B_2 X_{12}^2)]^{1/2}$$

Each value of $\Gamma^2$ represents a normal mode of propagation involving both transmission lines. The two square roots of each $\Gamma^2$ of course indicate waves going in the positive and negative directions.

Suppose we substitute (3.72) into (3.69). We obtain

$$\frac{V_2}{V_1} = \frac{-(X_1 B_1 - X_2 B_2) \pm [(X_1 B_1 - X_2 B_2)^2 + 4(X_1 B_1 + X_2 B_2)(X_{12} B_{12}) + 4(X_1 X_2 B_{12}^2 + B_1 B_2 X_{12}^2)]^{1/2}}{2(X_1 B_{12} + B_2 X_{12})} \tag{3.73}$$

We will be interested in cases in which $X_1B_1$ is very nearly equal to $X_2B_2$. Let

$$\Delta\Gamma_0^2 = X_1B_1 - X_2B_2 \tag{3.74}$$

and in the parts of (3.73) where the difference of (3.74) does not occur use

$$X_1 = X_2 = X$$
$$B_1 = B_2 = B \tag{3.75}$$

Then, approximately

$$\frac{V_2}{V_1} = \frac{-\Delta\Gamma_0^2 \pm [(\Delta\Gamma_0^2)^2 + 4(XB_{12} + BX_{12})^2]^{1/2}}{2(XB_{12} + BX_{12})} \qquad (3.76)$$

Let us assume that $\Delta\Gamma^2$ is very small and retains terms up to the first power of $\Delta\Gamma^2$

$$\frac{V_2}{V_1} = \pm 1 + \frac{\Delta\Gamma_0^2}{2(XB_{12} + BX_{12})} \qquad (3.77)$$

Let

$$\Gamma_0^2 = -XB \qquad (3.78)$$

$$\frac{V_2}{V_1} = \pm 1 - \frac{\Delta\Gamma_0^2/\Gamma_0^2}{2(B_{12}/B + X_{12}/X)} \qquad (3.79)$$

Let us now interpret (3.79). This says that if $\Delta\Gamma_0^2$ is zero, that is, if $X_1B_1 = X_2B_2$ exactly, there will be two modes of transmission, a *longitudinal* mode in which $V_2/V_1 = +1$ and a *transverse* mode in which $V_2/V_1 = -1$. If we excite the transverse mode it will persist. However, if $\Delta\Gamma_0^2 \neq 0$, there will be two modes, one for which $V_2 > V_1$ and the other for which $V_2 < V_1$; in other words, as $\Delta\Gamma_0^2$ is increased, we approach a condition in which one mode is nearly propagated on one helix only and the other mode nearly propagated on the other helix only. Then if we drive the pair with a transverse field we will excite both modes, and they will travel with different speeds down the system.

We see that to get a good transverse field we must make

$$\frac{\Delta\Gamma_0^2}{\Gamma_0^2} \ll 2(B_{12}/B + X_{12}/X) \qquad (3.80)$$

In other words, the stronger the coupling ($B_{12}$, $X_{12}$) the more the helices can afford to differ (perhaps accidentally) in propagation constant and the pair still give a distinct transverse wave.

Thus, it seems desirable to couple the helices together as tightly as possible and especially to see that $B_{12}$ and $X_{12}$ have the same signs.

Let us consider two concentric helices wound in opposite directions, as in Fig. 3.17. A positive voltage $V_1$ will put a positive charge on helix 1 while a positive voltage $V_2$ will put a negative charge on helix 1. Thus, $B_{12}/B$ is negative. It is also clear that the positive current $I_2$ will produce flux linking helix 1 in the opposite direction from the positive current $I_1$, thus making $X_{12}/X$ negative. This makes it clear that to get a good transverse field between concentric helices, the helices should be wound in opposite directions. If the helices were wound in the same direction, the "transverse" and "longitudinal" modes would cease to be clearly transverse and longitudinal should the phase velocities of the two helices by accident differ a little. Further, even if the phase velocities were the same, the transverse and longitudinal modes would have almost the same phase velocity, which in itself may be undesirable.

Field analyses of coupled helices confirm these general conclusions.

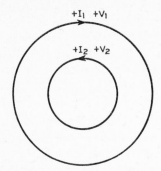

Fig. 3.17—Currents and voltages of concentric helices.

## 3.5 About Loss in Helices

The loss of helices is not calculated in this book. Some matters concerning deliberately added loss will be considered, however.

Loss is added to helices so that the backward loss of the tube (loss for a wave traveling from output to input) will be greater than the forward gain. If the forward gain is greater than the backward loss, the tube may oscillate if it is not terminated at each end in a good broad-band match.

In some early tubes, loss was added by making the helix out of lossy wire, such as nichrome or even iron, which is much lossier at microwave frequencies because of its ferromagnetism. Most substances are in many cases not lossy enough. Iron is very lossy, but its presence upsets magnetic focusing.

When the helix is supported by a surrounding glass tube or by parallel ceramic or glass rods, loss may be added by spraying aquadag on the inside or outside of the glass tube or on the supporting rods. This is advantageous in that the distribution of loss with distance can be controlled.

It is obvious that for lossy material a finite distance from the helix there is a resistivity which gives maximum attenuation. A perfect conductor would introduce no dissipation and neither would a perfect insulator.

If lossy material is placed a little away from the helix, loss can be made greater at lower frequencies (at which the field of the helix extends out into the lossy material) than at higher frequencies (at which the fields of the helix are crowded near the helix and do not give rise to much current in the lossy material. This construction may be useful in preventing high-frequency tubes from oscillating at low frequencies.

Loss may be added by means of tubes or collars of lossy ceramic which fit around the helix.

## PROBLEMS

1. Suppose a variation in phase velocity of $\pm 1\%$ is allowable in the bandwidth of amplification. Let the nominal beam voltage be 1,600 volts. What will be the bandwidth if at the center of the band for $\gamma a = 1, 2, 3, 4, 5$?

2. Suppose that at a given frequency one can make a beam of given current any diameter he wishes. What helix diameter will give the highest gain?

3. Obtain approximate propagation constants for concentric helices of the same pitch in terms of the pitch and the separation by developing them and solving the problem in rectangular coordinates (a) for helices wound in the same direction, (b) for helices wound in opposite directions.

4. Using the developed helix method, find the effect on (a) propagation constant (b) impedance, if the space outside the helix is filled with medium or higher dielectric constant than vacuum.

# CHAPTER IV
# FILTER-TYPE CIRCUITS

SYNOPSIS OF CHAPTER

ASIDE FROM HELICES, the circuits most commonly used in traveling-wave tubes are iterated or filter-type circuits, composed of linear arrays of coupled resonant slots or cavities.

Sometimes the geometry of such structures is simple enough so that an approximate field solution can be obtained. In other cases, the behavior of the circuits can be inferred by considering the behavior of lumped-circuit analogues, and the behavior of the circuits with frequency can be expressed with varying degrees of approximation in terms of parameters which can be computed or experimentally evaluated.

In this chapter the field approach will be illustrated for some very simple circuits, and examples of lumped-circuit analogues of other circuits will be given. The intent is to present methods of analyzing circuits rather than particular numerical results, for there are so many possible configurations that a comprehensive treatment would constitute a book in itself.

Readers interested in a wider and more exact treatment of field solutions are referred to the literature.[1,2]

The circuit of Fig. 4.1 is one which can be treated by field methods. This "corrugated waveguide" type of circuit was first brought to the writer's attention by C. C. Cutler. It is composed of a series of parallel equally spaced thin fins of height $h$ projecting normal to a conducting plane. The case treated is that of propagation of a transverse magnetic wave, the magnetic field being parallel to the length of the fins. It is assumed that the spacing $\ell$ is small compared with a wavelength. In Fig. 4.2, $\beta h$ is plotted vs. $\beta_0 h$. Here $\beta$ is the phase constant and $\beta_0 = \omega/c$ is a phase constant corresponding to the velocity of light.

For small values of $\beta_0 h$, that is, at low frequencies, very nearly $\beta = \beta_0$; that is, the phase velocity is very near to the velocity of light. The field decays slowly away from the circuit. The longitudinal electric field is small compared with the transverse electric field. In fact, as the frequency approaches zero, the wave approaches a transverse electromagnetic wave traveling with the speed of light.

---

[1] E. L. Chu and W. W. Hansen, "The Theory of Disk-Loaded Wave Guides," *Journal of Applied Physics*, Vol. 18, pp. 999–1008, Nov. 1947.

[2] L. Brillouin, "Wave Guides for Slow Waves," *Journal of Applied Physics*, Vol. 19, pp. 1023–1041, Nov. 1948.

At high frequencies the wave falls off rapidly away from the circuit, and the transverse and longitudinal components of electric field are almost equal. The wave travels very slowly. As the wavelength gets so short that the spacing $\ell$ approaches a half wavelength ($\beta\ell = \pi$) the simple analysis given is no longer valid. Actually, $\beta\ell = \pi$ specifies a cutoff frequency; the circuit behaves as a lowpass filter.

Figure 4.3 shows two opposed sets of fins such as those of Fig. 4.1. Such a circuit propagates two modes, a transverse mode for which the longitudinal electric field is zero at the plane of symmetry and a longitudinal mode for which the transverse electric field is zero at the plane of symmetry.

At low frequencies, the longitudinal mode corresponds to the wave on a loaded transmission line. The fins increase the capacitance between the conducting planes to which they are attached but they do not decrease the inductance. Figure 4.6 shows $\beta h$ vs. $\beta_0 h$ for several ratios of fin height, $h$, to half-separation, $d$. The greater is $h/d$, the slower is the wave (the larger is $\beta/\beta_0$).

The longitudinal mode is like a transverse magnetic waveguide mode; it propagates only at frequencies above a cutoff frequency, which increases as $h/d$ is increased. Figure 4.7 shows $\beta h$ vs. $\beta_0 h = (\omega/c)h$ for several values of $h/d$. The cutoff, for which $\beta\ell = \pi$, occurs for a value of $\beta_0 h$ less than $\pi/2$. Thus, we see that the longitudinal mode has a band pass characteristic. The behavior of the longitudinal mode is similar to that of a longitudinal mode of the washer-loaded waveguide shown in Fig. 4.8. The circuit of Fig. 4.8 has been proposed for use in traveling-wave tubes.

The transverse mode of the circuit of Fig. 4.3 can also exist in a circuit consisting of strips such as those of Fig. 4.1 and an opposed conducting plane, as shown in Fig. 4.5. This circuit is analogous in behavior to the disk-on-rod circuit of Fig. 4.9. The circuit of Fig. 4.5 may be thought of as a loaded parallel strip line. That of Fig. 4.9 may be thought of as a loaded coaxial line.

Wave-analysis makes it possible to evaluate fairly accurately the transmission properties of a few simple structures. However, iterated or repeating structures have certain properties in common: the properties of filter networks.

For instance, a mode of propagation of the loaded waveguide of Fig. 4.10 or of the series of coupled resonators of Fig. 4.11 can be represented accurately at a single frequency by the ladder networks of Fig. 4.12. Further, if suitable lumped-admittance networks are used to represent the admittances $B_1$ and $B_2$, the frequency-dependent behavior of the structures of Figs. 4.10 and 4.11 can be approximated.

It is, for instance, convenient to represent the shunt admittances $B_2$ and the series admittances $B_1$ in terms of a "longitudinal" admittance $B_L$ and a "transverse" admittance $B_T$. $B_L$ and $B_T$ are admittances of shunt resonant circuits, as shown in Fig. 4.15, where their relation to $B_1$ and $B_2$ and approximate expressions for their frequency dependence are given. The resonant frequencies of $B_L$ and $B_T$, that is, $\omega_L$ and $\omega_T$, have simple physical meanings. Thus, in Fig. 4.10, $\omega_L$ is the frequency corresponding to equal and opposite voltages across successive slots, that is, the $\pi$ mode frequency. $\omega_T$ is the frequency corresponding to zero slot voltage and no phase change along the filter, that is, the zero mode frequency.

If $\omega_L$ is greater than $\omega_T$, the phase characteristic of this lumped-circuit analogue is as shown in Fig. 4.17. The phase shift is zero at the lower cutoff frequency $\omega_T$ and rises to $\pi$ at the upper cutoff frequency $\omega_L$. If $\omega_T$ is greater than $\omega_L$, the phase shift starts at $-\pi$ at the lower cutoff frequency $\omega_L$ and rises to zero at the upper cutoff frequency $\omega_T$, as shown in Fig. 4.19. In this case the phase velocity is negative. Figure 4.20 shows a measure of $(E^2/\beta^2 P)$ plotted vs. $\omega$ for $\omega_L > \omega_T$. This impedance parameter is zero at $\omega_T$ and rises to infinity at $\omega_L$.

The structure of Fig. 4.11 can be given a lumped-circuit equivalent in a similar manner. In this case the representation should be quite accurate. We find that $\omega_L$ is always greater than $\omega_T$ and that one universal phase curve, shown in Fig. 4.27, applies. A curve giving a measure of $(E^2/\beta^2 P)$ vs. frequency is shown in Fig. 4.28. In this case the impedance parameter goes to infinity at both cutoff frequencies.

The electric field associated with iterated structures does not vary sinusoidally with distance but it can be analyzed into sinusoidal components. The electron stream will interact strongly with the circuit only if the electron velocity is nearly equal to the phase velocity of one of these field components. If $\theta$ is the phase shift per section and $L$ is the section length, the phase constant $\beta_m$ of a typical component is

$$\beta_m = (\theta + 2m\pi)/L$$

where $m$ is a positive or negative integer. The field component for which $m = 0$ is called the fundamental; for other values of $m$ the components are called *spatial harmonics*. Some of these components have negative phase velocities and some have positive phase velocities.

The peak field strength of any field component may be expressed

$$E = -M(V/L)$$

Here $V$ is the peak gap voltage, $L$ is the section spacing and $M$ is a function of $\beta$ (or $\beta_m$) and of various dimensions. For the electrode systems of Figs. 4.29, 4.30, 4.31 and 4.32 $M$ is given by (4.69), (4.71), (4.72) and (4.73), respectively.

The factor $M$ may be indifferently regarded as a factor by which we multiply the a-c beam current to give the induced current at the gap, or, as a factor by which we multiply the gap voltage in obtaining the field. We can go further, evaluate $E^2/\beta^2 P$ in terms of gap voltage, and use $M^2 I_0$ as the effective current, or we can use the current $I_0$ and take the effective field in the impedance parameter as

$$E^2 = M^2(V/\ell)^2$$

It is sometimes desirable to make use of a spatial harmonic ($m \neq 0$) instead of a fundamental, usually to (1) allow a greater resonator spacing (2) to obtain a positive phase velocity when the fundamental has a negative phase velocity (3) to obtain a phase curve for which the phase angle is nearly a constant times frequency; that is, a phase curve for which the group velocity does not change much with frequency and hence can be matched by the electron velocity over a considerable frequency range. Figure 4.33 shows how $\theta + 2\pi$ (the phase shift per section for $m = 1$) can be nearly a constant times $\omega$ even when $\theta$ is not.

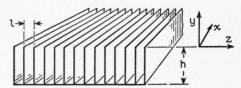

Fig. 4.1—A corrugated or finned circuit with filter-like properties.

## 4.1 FIELD SOLUTIONS

An approximate field analysis will be made for two very simple two-dimensional structures. The first of these, which is shown in Fig. 4.1, is empty space for $y > 1$ and consists of very thin conducting partitions in the $y$ direction from $y = 0$ to $y = -h$; the partitions are connected together by a conductor in the $z$ direction at $y = -h$. These conducting partitions are spaced a distance $\ell$ apart in the $z$ direction. The structure is assumed to extend infinitely in the $+x$ and $-x$ directions.

In our analysis we will initially assume that the wavelength of the propagated wave is long compared with $\ell$. In this case, the effect of the partitions is to prevent the existence of any $y$ component of electric field below the $z$ axis, and the conductor at $y = -h$ makes the $z$ component of electric field zero at $y = -z$.

In some perfectly conducting structures the waves propagated are either transverse electric (no electric field component in the direction of propagation, that is, $z$ direction) or transverse magnetic (no magnetic field component in the $z$ direction). We find that for the structure under consideration there is a transverse magnetic solution. We can take it either on the basis of other experience or as a result of having solved the problem that the correct form for the $x$ component of magnetic field for $y > 0$ is

$$H_x = H_0 e^{(-\gamma y - j\beta z)} \tag{4.1}$$

Expressing the electric field in terms of the curl of the magnetic field, we have

$$j\omega\epsilon E_x = \frac{\partial Hz}{\partial y} - \frac{\partial Hy}{\partial z} = 0$$

$$j\omega\epsilon E_y = \frac{\partial Hx}{dz} - \frac{\partial Hz}{\partial x} \tag{4.2}$$

$$E_y = -\frac{\beta}{\omega\epsilon} H_0 e^{(-\gamma y - j\beta z)} \tag{4.3}$$

$$j\omega\epsilon E_z = \frac{\partial Hy}{\partial x} - \frac{\partial Hx}{\partial y} \tag{4.4}$$

$$E_z = -j\frac{\gamma}{\omega\epsilon} H_0 e^{(-\gamma y - j\beta z)} \tag{4.5}$$

We can in turn express $H_x$ in terms of $E_y$ and $E_z$

$$-j\omega\mu H_x = \frac{\partial Ez}{\partial y} - \frac{\partial Ey}{\partial z} \tag{4.6}$$

This leads to the relation

$$\beta^2 - \gamma^2 = \omega^2\mu\epsilon \tag{4.7}$$

Now, $1/\sqrt{\mu\epsilon}$ is the velocity of light, and $\omega$ divided by the velocity of light has been called $\beta_0$, so that

$$\beta^2 - \gamma^2 = \beta_0{}^2 \tag{4.8}$$

Between the partitions, the field does not vary in the $z$ direction. In any space between from $y = 0$ to $y = -h$, the appropriate form for the magnetic field is

$$H_x = H_0 \frac{\cos \beta_0(y + h)}{\cos \beta_0 h} \tag{4.9}$$

From this we obtain by means of (4.4)

$$E_z = -\frac{j\beta_0}{\omega\epsilon} H_0 \frac{\sin \beta_0(y + h)}{\cos \beta_0 h} \tag{4.10}$$

Application of (4.6) shows that this is correct.

Now, at $y = 0$ we have just above the boundary

$$E_z = -j \frac{\gamma}{\omega \epsilon} H_0 e^{-j\beta z} \tag{4.11}$$

The fields in the particular slot just below the boundary will be in phase with these (we specify this by adding a factor exp $-j\beta z$ to 4.10) and hence will be

$$E_z = -\frac{j\beta_0}{\omega \epsilon} H_0 e^{-j\beta z} \tan \beta_0 h \tag{4.12}$$

From (4.11) and (4.12) we see that we must have

$$\beta_0 h \tan \beta_0 h = \gamma h \tag{4.13}$$

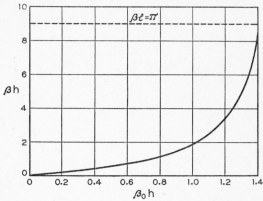

Fig. 4.2—The approximate variation of the phase constant $\beta$ with frequency (proportional to $\beta_0 h$) for the circuit of Fig. 4.1. The curve is in error as $\beta \ell$ approaches $\pi$, and there is a cutoff at $\beta \ell = \pi$.

Using (4.8), we obtain

$$\beta h = \frac{\pm \beta_0 h}{\cos \beta_0 h} \tag{4.14}$$

In Fig. 4.2, $\beta h$ has been plotted vs $\beta_0 h$, which is, of course, proportional to frequency. This curve starts out as a straight line, $\beta = \beta_0$; that is, for low frequencies the speed is the speed of light. At low frequencies the field falls off slowly in the $y$ direction, and as the frequency approaches zero we have essentially a plane electromagnetic wave. At higher frequencies, $\beta > \beta_0$, that is, the wave travels with less than the speed of light, and the field falls off rapidly in the $y$ direction. According to (4.14), $\beta$ goes to infinity at $\beta_0 h = \pi/2$.

As a matter of fact, the match between the fields assumed above and below the boundary becomes increasingly bad as $\beta \ell$ becomes larger. The most rapid alteration we can have below the boundary is one in which fields in alternate spaces follow a $+, -, +, -$ pattern. Thus, the rapid variations of field above the boundary predicted by (4.14) for values of $\beta_0 h$ which make $\beta \ell$ greater than $\pi$ cannot be matched below the boundary. The frequency at which $\beta \ell = \pi$ constitutes the cutoff frequency of the structure regarded as a filter. There is another pass band in the region $\pi < \beta_0 h < 3\pi/2$, in which the ratio of $E$ to $H$ below the boundary has the same sign as the ratio of $E$ to $H$ above the boundary.

A more elaborate matching of fields would show that our expression is considerably in error near cutoff. This matter will not be pursued here; the behavior of filters near cutoff will be considered in connection with lumped circuit representations.

We can obtain the complex power flow $P$ by integrating the Poynting vector over a plane normal to the $z$ direction in the region $y > 0$. Let us consider the power flow over a depth $W$ normal to the plane of the paper. Then

$$P = \frac{1}{2} \int_0^\infty \int_0^W (E_x H_y^* - E_y H_x^*) \, dx \, dy \tag{4.15}$$

Using (4.1) and (4.3), we obtain

$$P = \frac{W}{2} \int_0^\infty \frac{\beta H_0^2}{\omega \epsilon} e^{-2\gamma y} \, dy$$

$$P = \frac{1}{4} \frac{H_0^2 \beta W}{\omega \epsilon \gamma} \tag{4.16}$$

We will express this in terms of $E$ the magnitude of the $z$ component of the field at $y = 0$, which, according to (4.5), is

$$E = \frac{\gamma}{\omega \epsilon} H_0 \tag{4.17}$$

We will also note that

$$\omega \epsilon = \omega \sqrt{\mu \epsilon} / \sqrt{\mu/\epsilon}$$

$$= (\omega/c) / \sqrt{\mu/\epsilon} = \beta_0 / \sqrt{\mu/\epsilon} \tag{4.18}$$

and that

$$\sqrt{\mu/\epsilon} = 377 \text{ ohms} \tag{4.19}$$

By using (4.17)–(4.18) in connection with (4.16), we obtain

$$E^2/\beta^2 P = (4/\beta_0 W)(\gamma/\beta)^3 \sqrt{\mu/\epsilon} \tag{4.20}$$

We notice that this impedance is very small for low frequencies, at which the velocity of the wave is high, and the field extends far in the $y$ direction and becomes higher at high frequencies, where the velocity is low and the field falls off rapidly.

We will next consider a symmetrical array of two opposed sets of slots (Fig. 4.3) similar to that shown in Fig. 4.1. Two modes of propagation will be of interest. In one the field is symmetrical about the axis of physical symmetry, and in the other the fields at positions of physical symmetry are equal and opposite.

In writing the equations, we need consider only half of the circuit. It is convenient to take the $z$ axis along the boundary, as shown in Fig. 4.4.

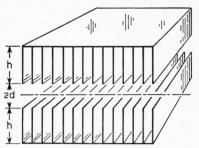

Fig. 4.3—A double finned structure which will support a transverse mode (no longitudinal electric field on axis) and a longitudinal mode (no transverse electric field on axis).

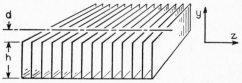

Fig. 4.4—The coordinates used in connection with the circuit of Fig. 4.3.

This puts the axis of symmetry at $y = +d$, and the slots extend from $y = 0$ to $y = -h$.

For negative values of $y$, (4.9), (4.10), (4.12) hold.

Let us first consider the case in which the fields above are opposite to the fields below. This also corresponds to waves in a series of slots opposite a conducting plane, as shown in Fig. 4.5. In this case the appropriate form of the magnetic field above the boundary is

$$H_x = H_0 \frac{\cosh \gamma(d - y)}{\cosh \gamma d} e^{-j\beta z} \tag{4.21}$$

From Maxwell's equations we then find

$$E_y = -\frac{\beta}{\omega \epsilon} H_0 \frac{\cosh \gamma(d - y)}{\cosh \gamma d} e^{-j\beta z} \tag{4.22}$$

$$E_z = -j \frac{\gamma}{\omega\epsilon} H_0 \frac{\sinh \gamma(d - y)}{\cosh \gamma d} e^{-j\beta z} \qquad (4.23)$$

$$\beta_0^2 = \beta^2 - \gamma^2 \qquad (4.24)$$

At $y = 0$ we have from (4.23) and (4.12)

$$E_z = -j \frac{\gamma}{\omega\epsilon} H_0 e^{-j\beta z} \tanh \gamma d \qquad (4.25)$$

$$E_z = -j \frac{\beta_0}{\omega\epsilon} H_0 e^{-j\beta z} \tan \beta_0 h \qquad (4.12)$$

Hence, we must have

$$\gamma h \tanh ((d/h)\gamma h) = \beta_0 h \tan \beta_0 h \qquad (4.26)$$

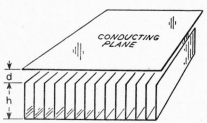

Fig. 4.5—The transverse mode of the circuit of Fig. 4.3 exists in this circuit also.

Here we have added parameter, $(d/h)$. For any value of $d/h$, we can obtain $\gamma h$ vs $\beta_0 h$; and we can obtain $\beta h$ in terms of $\gamma h$ by means of 4.24

$$\beta h = ((\gamma h)^2 + (\beta_0 h)^2)^{1/2} \qquad (4.27)$$

We see that for small values of $\beta_0 h$ (low frequencies)

$$\gamma^2 = (h/d) \beta_0^2 \qquad (4.28)$$

$$\beta = \beta_0 \left(\frac{h + d}{d}\right)^{1/2} \qquad (4.29)$$

If we examine Fig. 4.5, to which this applies, we find (4.28) easy to explain. At low frequencies, the magnetic field is essentially constant from $y = d$ to $y = -h$, and hence the inductance is proportional to the height $h + d$. The electric field will, however, extend only from $y = 0$ to $y = d$; hence the capacitance is proportional to $1/d$. The phase constant is proportional to $\sqrt{LC}$, and hence (4.29). At higher frequencies the electric and magnetic fields vary with $y$ and (4.29) does not hold.

We see that (4.26) predicts infinite values of $\gamma$ for $\beta h = \pi/2$. As in the previous cases, cutoff occurs at $\beta \ell = \pi$.

As an example of the phase characteristic of the circuit, $\beta h$ from (4.26) and (4.27) is plotted vs $\beta_0 h$ for $h/d = 0$, 10, 100 in Fig. 4.6. The curve for $h/d = 0$ is of course the same as Fig. 4.2.

If we integrate Poynting's vector from $y = 0$ to $y = d$ and for a distance $W$ in the $x$ direction, and multiply by 2 to take the power flow in the other half of the circuit into account, we obtain

$$E^2/\beta^2 P = (2/\beta_0 W)(\gamma/\beta)^3 \left(\frac{\sinh^2 \gamma d}{\sinh \gamma d \cosh \gamma d + \gamma d}\right) \sqrt{\mu/\epsilon} \quad (4.30)$$

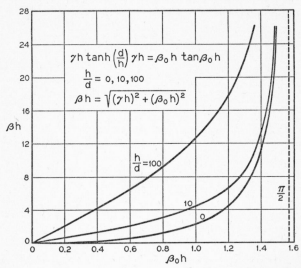

Fig. 4.6—The variation of $\beta$ with frequency (proportional to $\beta_0 h$) for the transverse mode of the circuit of Fig. 4.3. Again, the curves are in error near the cutoff at $\beta\ell = \pi$.

At very low frequencies, at which (4.28) and (4.29) hold, we have

$$E^2/\beta^2 P = (\gamma^4/\beta_0\beta^3)(d/W) \sqrt{\mu/\epsilon}$$
$$E^2/\beta^2 P = (h/d)^{1/2} (1 + d/h)^{3/2} (d/W) \sqrt{\mu/\epsilon} \quad (4.31)$$

At high frequencies, for which $\gamma d$ is large, (4.30) approaches $\frac{1}{2}$ of the value given by (4.20). There is twice as much power because there are two halves to the circuit.

Let us now consider the case in which the field is symmetrical and $E_z$ does not go to zero on the axis. In this case the appropriate field for $y > 0$ is

$$H_x = H_0 \frac{\sinh \gamma(d - y)}{\sinh \gamma d} e^{-j\beta z} \quad (4.32)$$

Proceeding as before, we find

$$\frac{\gamma h}{\tanh\left((d/h)\,\gamma h\right)} = \beta_0\, h\, \tan \beta_0\, h \qquad (4.33)$$

We see that, in this case, for small values of $\gamma h$ we have

$$\beta_0 h \tanh \beta_0 h = h/d \qquad (4.33a)$$

There is no transmission at all for frequencies below that specified by (4.33). As the frequency is increased above this lower cutoff frequency, $\gamma h$ and hence $\beta h$ increase, and approach infinity at $\beta_0 h = \pi/2$. Actually, of course, the upper cutoff occurs at $\beta\ell = \pi$. In Fig. 4.7 $\beta h$ is plotted vs $\beta_0 h$ for $h/d = 0$,

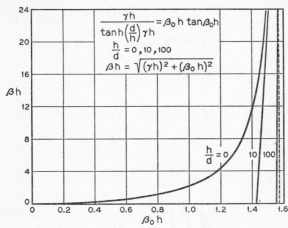

Fig. 4.7—The variation of $\beta$ with frequency (proportional to $\beta_0 h$) for the longitudinal mode of the circuit of Fig. 4.3. This mode has a band pass characteristic; the band narrows as the opening of width 2d is made small compared with the fin height. Again, the curves are in error near the upper cutoff at $\beta\ell = \pi$.

10, 100. This illustrates how the band is narrowed as the opening between the slots is decreased.

By the means used before we obtain

$$E^2/\beta^2 P = (2/\beta_0 W)(\gamma/\beta)^3 \left(\frac{\cosh^2 \gamma d}{\sinh \gamma d \cosh \gamma d - \gamma d}\right) \sqrt{\mu/\epsilon} \qquad (4.34)$$

We see that this goes to infinity at $\gamma d = 0$. For large values of $\gamma d$ it becomes the same as (4.30).

## 4.2 Practical Circuits

Circuits have been proposed or used in traveling-wave tubes which bear a close resemblance to those of Figs. 4.1, 4.3, 4.5 and which have very similar properties[3]. Thus Field[4] describes an apertured disk structure (Fig. 4.8) which has band-pass properties very similar to the symmetrical mode of the circuit of Fig. 4.3. In this case there is no mode similar to the other mode, with equal and opposite fields in the two halves. Field also shows a disk-on-rod structure (Fig. 4.9) and describes a tube using it. This structure has low-

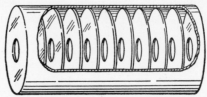

Fig. 4.8—This loaded waveguide circuit has band-pass properties similar to those of Fig. 4.7.

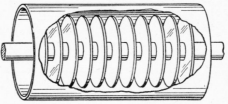

Fig. 4.9—This disk-on-rod circuit has properties similar to those of Fig. 4.6.

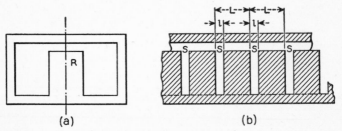

(a)                                    (b)

Fig. 4.10—A circuit consisting of a ridged waveguide with transverse slots or resonators in the ridge.

pass properties very similar to those of the circuit of Fig. 4.5, which are illustrated in Fig. 4.6.

Figure 4.10 shows a somewhat more complicated circuit. Here we have a rectangular waveguide, shown end on in *a* of Fig. 4.10, loaded by a longitudinal ridged portion *R*. In *b* of Fig. 4.10 we have a longitudinal cross sec-

---

[3] F. B. Llewellyn, *U. S. Patents* 2,367,295 and 2,395,560.
[4] Lester M. Field, "Some Slow-Wave Structures for Traveling-Wave Tubes," *Proc. I.R.E.*, Vol. 37, pp. 34–40, Jan. 1949.

tion, showing regularly spaced slots $S$ cut in the ridge $R$. The slots $S$ may be thought of as resonators.

Figure 4.11 shows in cross section a circuit made of a number of axially symmetrical reentrant resonators $R$, coupled by small holes $H$ which act as inductive irises.

It would be very difficult to apply Maxwell's equations directly in deducing the performance of the structures shown in Figs. 4.10 and 4.11. Moreover, it is apparent that we can radically change the performance of

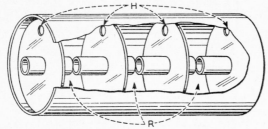

Fig. 4.11—A circuit consisting of a number of resonators inductively coupled by means of holes.

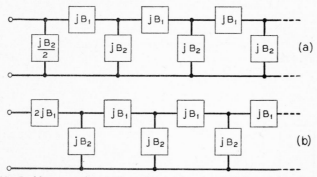

Fig. 4.12—Ladder networks terminated in $\pi$ (above) and $T$ (below) half sections. Such networks can be used in analyzing the behavior of circuits such as those of Figs. 4.10 and 4.11.

such structures by minor physical alterations as, by changing the iris size, or by using resonant irises in the circuit of Fig. 4.11, for instance.

As a matter of fact, it is not necessary to solve Maxwell's equations afresh each time in order to understand the general properties of these and other circuits.

## 4.3 LUMPED ITERATED ANALOGUES

Consider the ladders of lossless admittances or susceptances shown in Fig. 4.12. Susceptances rather than reactances have been chosen because the elements we shall most often encounter are shunt resonant near the frequencies considered; their susceptance is near zero and changing slowly but their reactance is near infinity.

If these ladders are continued endlessly to the right (or terminated in a reflectionless manner) and if a signal is impressed on the left-hand end, the voltages, currents and fields at corresponding points in successive sections will be in the ratio exp(-$\Gamma$) so that we can write the voltages,

$$V_n = V_0 e^{-n\Gamma} \tag{4.35}$$

If the admittances $Y_1$ and $Y_2$ are pure susceptances (lossless reactors), $\Gamma$ is either purely real (an exponential decay with distance) or purely imaginary (a pass band). In this case $\Gamma$ is usually replaced by $j\beta$. In order to avoid confusion of notation, we will use $j\theta$ instead, and write for the lossless case in the pass band

$$V_n = V_0 e^{-jn\theta} \tag{4.35a}$$

Thus, $\theta$ is the phase lag in radians in going from one section to the next. In terms of the susceptances,*

$$\cos \theta = 1 + B_2/2B_1 \tag{4.36}$$

We will henceforward assume that all elements are lossless.

Two characteristic impedances are associated with such iterated networks. If the network starts with a shunt susceptance $B_1/2$, as in $a$ of Fig. 4.12, then we see the mid-shunt characteristic impedance $K_\pi$

$$K_\pi = 2(-B_2(B_2 + 4B_1))^{-1/2} \tag{4.37}$$

If the network starts with a series susceptance $2B_1$ we see the mid-series characteristic impedance $K_T$

$$K_T = \pm(1/2B_1)(-(B_2 + 4B_1)/B_2)^{1/2} \tag{4.38}$$

Here the sign is chosen to make the impedance positive in the pass band.

When such networks are used as circuits for a traveling-wave tube, the voltage acting on the electron stream may be the voltage across $B_2$ or the voltage across $B_1$ or the voltage across some capacitive element of $B_2$ or $B_1$. We will wish to relate this peak voltage $V$ to the power flow $P$. If the voltage across $B_2$ acts on the electron stream

$$V^2/P = 2K_\pi \tag{4.39}$$

If the voltage across $Y_1$ acts on the electron stream

$$V = I/jB_1$$

---

* The reader can work such relations out or look them up in a variety of books or handbooks. They are in Schelkunoff's Electromagnetic Waves.

where $I$ is the current in $B_1$

$$P = |I^2| K_T/2$$

and hence

$$V^2/P = 2/B_1^2 K_T \tag{4.40}$$

$$V^2/P = -4(B_2/B_1)(-B_2(B_2 + 4B_1))^{-1/2} \tag{4.41}$$

$$V^2/P = -2(B_2/B_1)K_\pi \tag{4.42}$$

Here the sign has been chosen so as to make $V^2/P$ positive in the pass band.

Let us now consider as an example the structure of Fig. 4.10. We see that two sorts of resonance are possible. First, if all the slots are shorted, or if no voltage appears between them, we can have a resonance in which the field between the top of the ridge $R$ and the top of the waveguide is constant

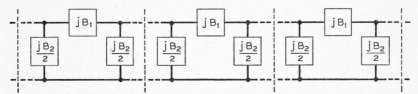

Fig. 4.13—A ladder network broken up into $\pi$ sections.

all along the length, and corresponds to the cutoff frequency of the ridged waveguide. There are no longitudinal currents (or only small ones near the slots $S$) and hence there is no voltage across the slots and their admittance (the slot depth, for instance) does not affect the frequency of this resonance. Looking at Fig. 4.12, we see that this corresponds to a condition in which all shunt elements are open, or $B_2 = 0$. We will call the frequency of this resonance $\omega_T$, the $T$ standing for transverse.

There is another simple resonance possible; that in which the fields across successive slots are equal and opposite. Looking at Fig. 4.12, we see that this means that equal currents flow into each shunt element from the two series elements which are connected to it. We could, in fact, divide the network up into unconnected $\pi$ sections, associating with each series element of susceptance $B_1$ half of the susceptance of a shunt element, that is, $B_2/2$, at each end, as shown in Fig. 4.13, without affecting the frequency of this resonance. This resonance, then, occurs at the frequency $\omega_L$ ($L$ for longitudinal) at which

$$B_1 + B_2/4 = 0. \tag{4.43}$$

We have seen that the transverse resonant frequency, $\omega_T$, has a clear meaning in connection with the structure of Fig. 4.10; it is (except for small errors due to stray fields near the slots) the cutoff frequency of the waveguide without slots. Does the longitudinal frequency $\omega_L$ have a simple meaning?

Suppose we make a model of one section of the structure, as shown in Fig. 4.14. Comparing this with $b$ of Fig. 4.10, we see that we have included the section of the ridged portion between two slots, and one half of a slot at each end, and closed the ends off with conducting plates $C$. The resonant frequency of this model is $\omega_L$, the longitudinal resonant frequency defined above.

We will thus liken the structure of Fig. 4.10 to the filter network of Fig.

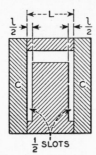

Fig. 4.14—A section which will have a resonant frequency corresponding to that for $\pi$ radians phase shift per section in the circuit of Fig. 4.10.

$$B_L = B_1 + \frac{B_2}{4} \qquad C_L \qquad\qquad B_T = B_2 \qquad C_T$$

$$B_L = 2C_L(\omega - \omega_L) \qquad\qquad B_T = 2C_T(\omega - \omega_T)$$

Fig. 4.15—The approximate variation with frequency (over a narrow band) of the longitudinal ($B_L$) transverse ($B_T$) susceptances of a filter network.

4.12, and express the susceptances $B_1$ and $B_2$ in terms of two susceptances $B_T$ and $B_L$ associated with the transverse and longitudinal resonances and defined below

$$B_T = B_2 \tag{4.44}$$

$$B_L = B_1 + B_2/4 \tag{4.45}$$

At the transverse resonant frequency $\omega_T$, $B_T = 0$, and at the longitudinal resonant frequency $\omega_L$, $B_L = 0$. So far, the lumped-circuit representation of the structure of Fig. 4.14 can be considered exact in the sense that at any frequency we can assign values to $B_T$ and $B_L$ which will give the correct values for $\theta$ and for $V^2/P$ for the voltage across either the shunt or the series elements (whichever we are interested in).

We will go further and assume that near resonances these values of $B_T$ and $B_L$ behave like the admittances of shunt resonant circuits, as indicated in Fig. 4.15. Certainly we are right by our definition in saying that $B_T = 0$ at $\omega_T$, and $B_L = 0$ at $\omega_L$. We will assume near these frequencies a linear variation of $B_T$ and $B_L$ with frequency, which is very nearly true for shunt resonant circuits near resonance*

$$B_T = 2C_T(\omega - \omega_T) \tag{4.46}$$

$$B_L = 2C_L(\omega - \omega_L) \tag{4.47}$$

Here $C_T$ can mean twice the peak stored electric energy per section length for unit peak voltage between the top of the guide and the top of the ridge $R$ when the structure resonates in the transverse mode, and $C_L$ can mean twice the stored energy per section length $L$ for unit peak voltage across the top

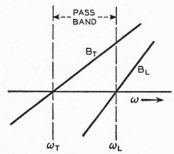

Fig. 4.16—Longitudinal and transverse susceptances which give zero radians phase shift at the lower cutoff ($\omega = \omega_T$) and $\pi$ radians phase shift at the upper cutoff ($\omega = \omega_L$).

of the slot when the structure resonates in the longitudinal mode.

In terms of $B_T$ and $B_L$, expression (4.36) for the phase angle $\theta$ becomes

$$\cos \theta = \frac{4B_L + B_T}{4B_L - B_T} \tag{4.48}$$

We see immediately that for real values of $\theta$ ($\cos \theta \leq 1$), $B_T$ and $B_L$ must have opposite signs, making the denominator greater than the numerator.

Figure 4.16 shows one possible case, in which $\omega_T < \omega_L$. In this case the pass band ($\theta$ real) starts at the lower cutoff frequency $\omega = \omega_T$ at which $B_T$ is zero, $\cos \theta = 1$ (from (4.48)) and $\theta = 0$, and extends up to the upper cutoff frequency $\omega = \omega_L$ at which $B_L = 0$, $\cos \theta = -1$ and $\theta = \pi$.

* In case the filter has a large fractional bandwidth, it may be worth while to use the accurate lumped-circuit forms

$$B_T = \omega_T C_T(\omega/\omega_T - \omega_T/\omega) \tag{4.46a}$$

$$B_L = \omega_L C_L(\omega/\omega_L - \omega_L/\omega) \tag{4.46b}$$

The shape of the phase curves will depend on the relative rates of variation of $B_T$ and $B_L$ with frequency. Assuming the linear variations with frequency of (4.46) and (4.47) the shapes can be computed. This has been done for $C_L/C_T = 1, 3, 10$ and the results are shown in Fig. 4.17.

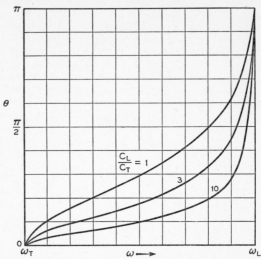

Fig. 4.17—Phase shift per section, $\theta$, vs radian frequency $\omega$ for the conditions of Fig. 4.16.

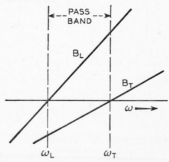

Fig. 4.18—Longitudinal and transverse susceptances which give $-\pi$ radians phase shift at the lower cutoff ($\omega = \omega_L$) and 0 degrees phase shift at the upper cutoff ($\omega = \omega_T$). This means a negative phase velocity.

It is of course possible to make $\omega_L > \omega_T$. In this case the situation is as shown in Fig. 4.18, the pass band extending from $\omega_L$ to $\omega_T$. At $\omega = \omega_L$, $\cos \theta = -1$, $\theta = -\pi$. At $\omega = \omega_T$, $\cos \theta = 1$ and $\theta = 0$. In Fig. 4.19, assuming (4.46) and (4.47), $\theta$ has been plotted vs $\omega$ for $C_L/C_T = 1, 3, 10$.

The curves of Figs. 4.17 and 4.18 are not exact for any physical structure of the type shown in Fig. 4.10. In lumped circuit terms, they neglect coupling betweer slots. They will be most accurate for structures with slots longitudinally far apart compared with the transverse dimensions, and least accurate for structures with slots close together. They do, however, form a valuable guide in understanding the performance of such structures and in evaluating the effect of the ratio of energies stored in the fields at the two cut-off frequencies.

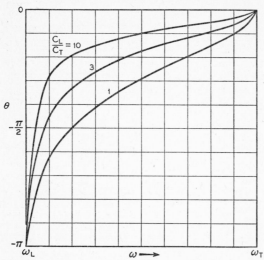

Fig. 4.19—Phase shift per section, $\theta$, vs radian frequency, $\omega$, for the conditions of Fig 4.18.

It is most likely that the voltages across the slots would be of most interest in connection with the circuit shown in Fig. 4.10. We can rewrite (4.41) in terms of $B_T$ and $B_L$

$$V^2/P = \frac{1}{2(1 - 4B_L/B_T)(-B_T B_L)^{1/2}} \qquad (4.49)$$

We see that $V^2/P$ goes to 0 at $B_T = 0$ ($\omega = \omega_T$) and to infinity at $B_L = 0$ ($\omega = \omega_L$). In Fig. 4.20 assuming (4.46) and (4.47), $(V^2/P)(\omega_L C_L \omega_T C_T)$ is plotted vs $\omega$ for $C_L/C_T = 1, 3, 10$.

Let us consider another circuit, that shown in Fig. 4.11. We see that this consists of a number of resonators coupled together inductively. We might draw the equivalent circuits of these resonators as shown in Fig. 4.21. Here $L$ and $C$ are the effective inductance and the effective capacitance of the resonators without irises. They are chosen so that the resonant frequency $\omega_0$ is given by

$$\omega_0 = \sqrt{LC} \qquad (4.50)$$

and the variation of gap susceptance $B$ with frequency is

$$\partial B / \partial \omega = 2C \qquad (4.51)$$

The arrows show directions of current flow when the currents in the gap capacitances are all the same.

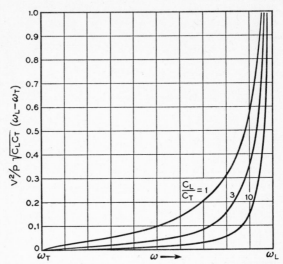

Fig. 4.20—A quantity proportional to $(E^2/\beta^2 P)$ vs $\omega$ for the conditions of Figs. 4.16 and 4.17.

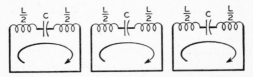

Fig. 4.21—A representation of the resonators of Fig. 4.11.

We can now represent the circuit of Fig. 4.11 by interconnecting the circuits of Fig. 4.21 by means of inductances $L_M$ of Fig. 4.22. This gives a suitable representation, but one which is open to a minor objection: the gap capacitance does not appear across either a shunt or a series arm.

It is important to notice that there is another equally good representation, and there are probably many more. Suppose we draw the resonators as shown in Fig. 4.23 instead of as in Fig. 4.21. The inductance $L$ and capacitance $C$ are still properly given by 4.50 and 4.51. We can now interconnect the resonators inductively as shown in Fig. 4.24.

We should note one thing. In Fig. 4.21, the currents which are to flow in the common inductances of Fig. 4.22 flow in opposite directions when the gap currents are in the same directions. In the representation of Fig. 4.23 the currents which will flow in the common inductances of Fig. 4.24 have been drawn in opposite directions, and we see that the currents in the gap capacitances flow alternately up and down. In other words, in Fig. 4.24, every other gap appears inverted. This can be taken into account by adding a phase angle $-\pi$ to $\theta$ as computed from (4.48).

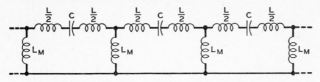

Fig. 4.22—The resonators of Fig. 4.11 coupled inductively.

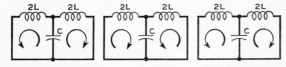

Fig. 4.23—Another representation of the resonators of Fig. 4.11.

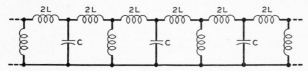

Fig. 4.24—Figure 4.23 with inductive coupling added.

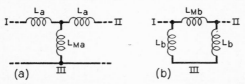

Fig. 4.25—A $T - \pi$ transformation used in connection with the circuit of Fig. 4.24.

Now, the $T$ configuration of inductances in $a$ of Fig. 4.25 can be replaced by the $\pi$ configuration, $b$ of Fig. 4.25. Imagine I and II to be connected together and a voltage to be applied between them and III. We see that

$$L_b = L_a + 2L_{Ma} \qquad (4.52)$$

Imagine a voltage to be applied between I and II. We see that

$$1/L_a = 1/L_b + 2/L_{Mb} \qquad (4.53)$$

If $L_{Ma} \ll L_a$, then $L_b$ will be nearly equal to $L_a$ and $L_{Mb} \gg L_b$.

By means of such a $T - \pi$ transformation we can redraw the equivalent circuit of Fig. 4.24 as shown in Fig. 4.26. The series susceptance $B_1$ is now that of $L_1$, and the shunt susceptance is now that of the shunt resonant circuit consisting of $C_2$ (the effective capacitance of the resonators) and $L_2$.

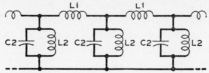

Fig. 4.26—The final representation of the circuit of Fig. 4.11.

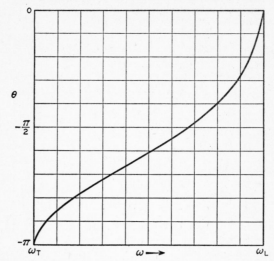

Fig. 4.27—The phase characteristic of the circuit of Fig. 4.11.

The transverse resonance, $B_2 = 0$, occurs at a frequency

$$\omega_T = \sqrt{C_2 L_2} \tag{4.54}$$

Near this frequency the transverse susceptance is given by

$$B_T = 2C_2(\omega - \omega_T) \tag{4.55}$$

The longitudinal resonance occurs at a frequency

$$\omega_L = \sqrt{2C_2 L_1 L_2 / (L_1 + 2L_2)} \tag{4.56}$$

and near $\omega_L$,

$$B_L = C_2(\omega - \omega_L) \tag{4.57}$$

These are just the forms we found in connection with the structure of Fig. 4.10; but we see that, in the case of the circuit of Fig. 4.11, the effective transverse capacitance is always twice the effective longitudinal capacitance ($C_L/C_T = 1/2$ in Fig. 4.19), and that $\omega_L > \omega_T$ for attainable volume of $L_1$.

We obtain $\theta$ vs $\omega$ by adding $-\pi$ to the phase angle from 4.48, using (4.55) and (4.57) in obtaining $B_T$ and $B_L$. The phase angle vs. frequency is shown in Fig. 4.27. As the irises are made larger, the bandwidth, $\omega_L - \omega_T$, becomes larger, largely by a decrease in $\omega_L$.

The voltage of interest is that across $C_2$, that is, that across the gap. From (4.37), (4.44), (4.45), (4.55) and (4.57) we obtain

$$V^2/P = 2/(-B_T B_L)^{1/2} \qquad (4.58)$$

$$V^2/P = (\sqrt{2}/C_2)((\omega_L - \omega)(\omega - \omega_T))^{-1/2} \qquad (4.59)$$

This goes to infinity at both $\omega = \omega_L$ and $\omega = \omega_T$. In Fig. 4.28, $(V^2/P)C_2\sqrt{\omega_L \omega_T}$ is plotted vs $\omega$. This curve represents the performance of all narrow band structures of the type shown in Fig. 4.11.

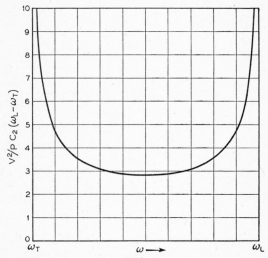

Fig. 4.28—A quantity proportional to $(E^2/\beta^2 P)$ for the circuit of Fig. 4.11, plotted vs radian frequency $\omega$.

In a structure such as that shown in Fig. 4.11, there is little coupling between sections which are not adjacent, and hence the lumped-circuit representation used is probably quite accurate, and is certainly more accurate than in structures such as that shown in Fig. 4.10.

Other structures could be analyzed, but it is believed that the examples given above adequately illustrate the general procedures which can be employed.

## 4.4 Traveling Field Components

Filter-type circuits produce fields which are certainly not sinusoidal with distance. Indeed, with a structure such as that shown in Fig. 4.11, the electrons are acted upon only when they are very near to the gaps. It is possible to analyze the performance of traveling-wave tubes on this basis[5]. The chief conclusion of such an analysis is that highly accurate results can be obtained by expressing the field as a sum of traveling waves and taking into account only the wave which has a phase velocity near to the electron velocity. Of course this is satisfactory only if the velocities of the other components are quite different from the electron velocity (that is, different by a fraction several times the gain parameter $C$).

As an example, consider a traveling-wave tube in which the electron stream passes through tubular sections of radius $a$, as shown in Fig. 4.29, and is acted upon by voltages appearing across gaps of length $\ell$ spaced $L$ apart.

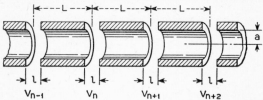

Fig. 4.29—A series of gaps in a tube of inside radius $a$. The gaps are $\ell$ long and are spaced $L$ apart. Voltages $V_n$, etc., act across them.

A wave travels in some sort of structure and produces voltages across the gaps such that that across the $n$th gap, $V$, is

$$V_n = V_0 e^{-jn\theta} \tag{4.60}$$

where $n$ is any integer.

We analyze this field into traveling-wave components which vary with distance as $\exp(-j\beta_m z)$ where

$$\beta_m = (\theta + 2m\pi)/L \tag{4.61}$$

where $m$ is any positive or negative integer. Thus, the total field will be

$$E = \sum_{m=-\infty}^{\infty} E_m = \sum_{m=-\infty}^{\infty} A_m e^{-j\beta_m z} I_0(\gamma_m r) \tag{4.62}$$

$$\gamma_m^2 = \beta_m^2 - \beta_0^2 \tag{4.63}$$

Here $I_0(\gamma_m r)$ is a modified Bessel function, and $\gamma_m$ has been chosen so that (4.62) satisfies Maxwell's equations.

[5] J. R. Pierce and Nelson Wax, "A Note on Filter-Type Traveling-Wave Amplifiers," *Proc. I.R.E.*, Vol. 37, pp. 622–625, June, 1949.

We will evaluate the coefficients by the usual means of Fourier analysis. Suppose we let $z = 0$ at the center of one of the gaps. We see that

$$\int_{-L/2}^{L/2} EE^* \, dz = \sum_{m=-\infty}^{\infty} \int_{-L/2}^{L/2} A_m A_m^* I_0^2(\gamma_m r) \, dz$$

$$= \sum_{m=-\infty}^{\infty} A_m A_m^* I_0^2(\gamma_m r) L \tag{4.64}$$

All of the terms of the form $E_m E_p$, $p \neq m$ integrate to zero because the integral contains a term $\exp(-j2\pi(p - m)/L)z$.

Let us consider the field at the radius $r$. This is zero along the surface of the tube. We will assume with fair accuracy that it is constant and has a value $-V/\ell$ across the gap. Thus we have also at $r = a$,

$$\int_{-L/2}^{L/2} EE^* \, dz = -(V/\ell) \sum_{m=-\infty}^{\infty} \int_{-\ell/2}^{\ell/2} A_m^* e^{-j\beta_m z} I_0(\gamma_m a) \, dz$$

$$= -(V/\ell) \sum_{m=-\infty}^{\infty} (A_m^*) I_0(\gamma_m a) \left( \frac{e^{-j\beta_m \ell/2} - e^{j\beta_m \ell/2}}{j\beta} \right) \tag{4.65}$$

We can rewrite this

$$\int_{-L/2}^{L/2} EE^* \, dz = -(V/\ell) \sum_{m=-\infty}^{\infty} A_m^* I_0(\gamma_m a) \frac{\sin(\beta_m \ell/2)}{(\beta_m \ell/2}) \tag{4.66}$$

By comparison with (4.64) we see that

$$A_m = -(V/L)(\sin(\beta_m \ell/2)/(\beta_m \ell/2))(1/I_0(\gamma a)) \tag{4.67}$$

This is the magnitude of the $m$th field component on the axis. The magnitude of the field at a radius $r$ would be $I_0(\gamma r)$ times this.

The quantity $\beta_m \ell$ is an angle which we will call $\theta_g$, the gap angle. Usually we are concerned with only a single field component, and hence can merely write $\gamma$ instead of $\gamma_m$. Thus, we say that the magnitude $E$ of the travelling field produced by a voltage $V$ acting at intervals $L$ is

$$E = -M(V/L) \tag{4.68}$$

$$M = \frac{\sin(\theta g/2)}{(\theta g/2)} \frac{I_0(\gamma r)}{I_0(\gamma a)} \tag{4.69}$$

$$\theta g = \beta \ell \tag{4.70}$$

The factor $M$ is called the gap factor or the modulation coefficient*. For slow waves, $\gamma$ is very nearly equal to $\beta$, and we can replace $\gamma r$ and $\gamma a$ by $\beta r$ and $\beta a$. For unattenuated waves, $M$ is a real positive number; and,

---

* This factor is often designated by $\beta$, but we have used $\beta$ otherwise.

for the slowly varying waves with which we deal, we will always consider $M$ as a real number.

The gap factor for some other physical arrangements is of interest. At a distance $y$ above the two-dimensional array of strip electrodes shown in Fig. 4.30

$$M = \frac{\sin (\theta g/2)}{(\theta g/2)} e^{-\gamma y} \tag{4.71}$$

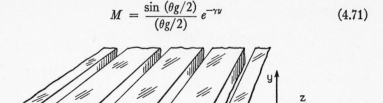

Fig. 4.30—A series of slots $\theta_g$ radians long separated by walls $L$ long.

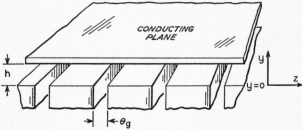

Fig. 4.31—A system similar to that of Fig. 4.30 but with the addition of an opposed conducting plane.

If we add a conducting plane $a$ at $y = h$, as in Fig. 4.31,

$$M = \frac{\sin (\theta g/2)}{(\theta g/2)} \frac{\sinh \gamma(h - y)}{\sinh \gamma h} \tag{4.72}$$

For a symmetrical two-dimensional array, as shown in Fig. 4.32, with a separation of $2\,h$ in the $y$ direction and the fields above equal to the fields below

$$M = \frac{\sin (\theta g/2)}{(\theta g/2)} \frac{\cosh \gamma y}{\cosh \gamma h} \tag{4.73}$$

### 4.5 Effective Field and Effective Current

In Section 4.4 we have expressed a field component or "effective field" in terms of circuit voltage by means of a gap-factor or modulation coefficient $M$. This enables us to make calculations in terms of fields and currents at the electron stream.

The gap factor can be used in another way. A voltage appears across a gap, and the electron stream induces a current at the gap. At the electron stream the power $P_1$, produced in a distance $L$ by a convection current $i$ with the same $z$-variation as the field component considered, acting on the field component is

$$P_1 = -Ei^*L$$

$$= +(MV)i^* \qquad (4.74)$$

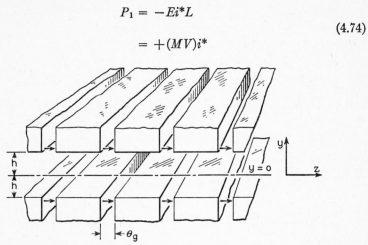

Fig. 4.32—A system of two opposed sets of slots.

At the circuit we observe some impressed current $I$ flowing against the voltage $V$ to produce a power

$$P_2 = VI^* \qquad (4.75)$$

By the conservation of energy, these two powers must be the same, and we deduce that

$$I^* = Mi^* \qquad (4.76)$$

or, since we take $M$ as a real number

$$I = Mi \qquad (4.77)$$

Thus, we have our choice of making calculations in terms of the beam current and a field component or effective field, or in terms of circuit voltage and an effective current, and in either case we make use of the modulation coefficient $M$.

Our gain parameter $C^3$ will be

$$C^3 = (V/L)^2 M^2 I_0 / 8\beta^2 V_0$$

where $V$ is circuit voltage. We can regard this in two ways. We can think of $-(V/L)M$ as the effective field at the location of the current $I_0$, or we can think of $M^2 I_0$ as the effective current referred to the circuit.

If we have a broad beam of electrons and a constant current density $J_0$ we compute (essentially as in Chapter III) a value of $C^3$ by integrating

$$C^3 = (1/8\beta^2 V_0) J_0 (V/L)^2 \int M^2 \, d\sigma \tag{4.78}$$

where $d\sigma$ is an element of area. We can think of the result in terms of an effective field $E_e$

$$E_e^2 = (V/L)^2 \frac{\int M^2 \, d\sigma}{\sigma} \tag{4.79}$$

where $\sigma$ is the total beam area, and a total current $\sigma J_0$, or we can think of the integral (4.77) in terms of an effective current $I_0$ given by

$$I_0 = J_0 \int M^2 \, d\sigma \tag{4.80}$$

and the voltage at the circuit.

Of course, these same considerations apply to distributed circuits. Sometimes it is most convenient to think in terms of the total current and an effective field (as we did in connection with helices in Chapter III) and sometimes it is most convenient to think of the field at the circuit and an effective current. Either concept refers to the same mathematics.

### 4.6 HARMONIC OPERATION

Of the field components making up $E$ in (4.62) it is customary to regard the $m = 0$ component, for which $\beta = \theta/L$, as the *fundamental* field component, and the other components as *harmonic* components. These are sometimes called *Hartree harmonics*. If the electron speed is so adjusted that the interaction is with the $m = 0$ or fundamental component we have fundamental operation; if the electron speed is adjusted so that we have interaction with a harmonic component, we have harmonic operation.

There are several reasons for using harmonic operation in connection with filter-type circuits. For one thing the fundamental component may appear to be traveling backwards. Thus, for circuits of the type shown in Fig. 4.11, we see from Fig. 4.27 that $\theta$ is always negative. Now, in terms of the velocity $v$

$$\beta = \omega/v = \theta/L \tag{4.81}$$

and if $\theta$ is negative, $v$ must be negative. However, consider the $m = 1$ component

$$\beta = \omega/v = (2\pi + \theta)/L \tag{4.82}$$

We see that, for this component, $v$ is positive.

The interaction of electrons with backward-traveling field components will be considered later. Here it will merely be said that, in order to avoid interaction with waves traveling in both directions, one must avoid having the electron speed lie near both the speed of a forward component and the speed of a backward component.

In order that the fundamental component be slow, $\theta$ must be large or $L$ must be small. The largest value of $\theta$ is that near one edge of the band, where $\theta$ approaches $\pi$. Thus, the largest fundamental value of $\beta$ is $\pi/L$, and to make

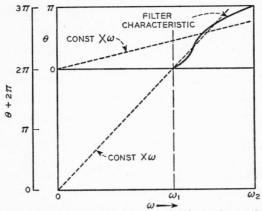

Fig. 4.33—The variation of phase with frequency for the fundamental (0 to $\pi$ over the band) and a spatial harmonic ($2\pi$ to $3\pi$ over the band). The dotted lines show $\omega$ divided by the electron velocity for the two cases. For amplification over a broad band the dotted curve should not depart much from the filter characteristic.

$\beta$ large with $m = 0$ we must make $L$ small and put the resonators very close together. This may be physically difficult or even impossible in tubes for very high frequencies. The alternative is to use a harmonic component, for which $\beta = (2m\pi + \theta)/L$.

Another reason for using harmonic operation is to achieve broad-band operation. The phase of a filter-type circuit changes by $\pi$ radians between the lower cutoff frequency $\omega_1$ and the upper cutoff frequency $\omega_2$†. Now, for the wave velocity to be near to the electron velocity over a good part of the band, $\beta$ must be nearly a constant times $\omega$. Figure 4.33 shows how this can be approximately true for the $m = 1$ component even when it obviously won't be for the $m = 0$ or fundamental component. Similarly, for a filter with a narrower fractional bandwidth and hence a steeper curve of $\theta$ vs $\omega$, a larger value of $m$ might give a nearly constant value of $v$.

† The phase of some filters changes more than this, but they don't seem good candidates for traveling-wave tube circuits.

PROBLEMS

1. Solve for the propagation constant of the structure of Fig. 4.8 using assumptions similar to those made in connection with the structures of Figs. 4.1 and 4.3.

2. What would be the chief effect on the phase curve of Fig. 4.27 of using capacitive rather than inductive irises to couple the resonators of Fig. 4.11. How can this be done?

3. Suppose that a circuit similar to that of Fig. 4.10 is to be used in an $m = 1$ spatial harmonic (see (4.61)). Let $\omega_L > \omega_T$. Draw a diagram similar to Fig. 4.33 using the actual phase curves for $C_L/C_T = .2, .5, 1$.

4. Do as in Problem 3 for $\omega_L < \omega_T$.

5. In a circuit of Fig. 1, the space outside of the circuit is filled with electron flow of current density $J_0$. What is the effective current referred to the edge of the fins? (See (4.80)).

# CHAPTER V

# GENERAL CIRCUIT CONSIDERATIONS

SYNOPSIS OF CHAPTER

IN CHAPTERS III AND IV, helices and filter-type circuits have been considered. Other slow-wave circuits have been proposed, as, for instance, wave guides loaded continuously with dielectric material. One may ask what the best type of circuit is, or, indeed, in just what way do bad circuits differ from good circuits.

So far, we have as one criterion for a good circuit a high impedance, that is, a high value of $E^2/\beta^2 P$. If we want a broad-band amplifier we must have a constant phase velocity; that is, $\beta$ must be proportional to frequency. Thus, two desirable circuit properties are: high impedance and constancy of phase velocity.

Now, $E^2/\beta^2 P$ can be written in the form

$$E^2/\beta^2 P = E^2/\beta^2 W v_g$$

where $W$ is the stored energy per unit length for a field strength $E$, and $v_g$ is the group velocity.

One way of making $E^2/\beta^2 P$ large is to make the stored energy for a given field strength small. In an electromagnetic wave, half of the stored energy is electric and half is magnetic. Thus, to make the total stored energy for a given field strength small we must make the energy stored in the electric field small. The energy stored in the electric field will be increased by the presence of material of a high dielectric constant, or by the presence of large opposed metallic surfaces, as in the circuits of Figs. 4.8 and 4.9. Thus, such circuits are poor as regards circuit impedance, however good they may be in other respects.

If the stored energy for a given field strength is held constant, $E^2/\beta^2 P$ may be increased by decreasing the group velocity. It is the phase velocity $v$ which should match the electron speed. The group velocity $v_g$ is given in terms of the phase velocity by (5.12). We see that the group velocity may be much smaller than the phase velocity if $-\partial v/\partial \omega$ is large. It is, for instance, a low group velocity near cutoff that accounts for the high impedance regions exhibited in Figs. 4.20 and 4.28. We remember, however, that, if the phase velocity of the circuit of a traveling-wave tube changes with frequency, the tube will have a narrow bandwidth, and thus the high

79

impedances attained through large values of $-\partial v/\partial \omega$ are useful over a narrow range of frequency only.

If we consider a broad electron stream of current density $J_0$, the highest effective value of $E^2/\beta^2 P$, and hence the highest value of $C$, will be attained if there is current everywhere that there is electric field, and if all of the electric field is longitudinal. This leads to a limiting value of $C$, which is given by (5.23). There $\lambda_0$ is the free-space wavelength. The nearest practical approach to this condition is perhaps a helix of fine wire flooded inside and outside with electrons.

In many cases, it is desirable to consider circuits for use with a narrow beam of electrons, over which the field may be taken as constant. As the helix is a common as well as a very good circuit, it might seem desirable to use it as a standard for comparison. However, the group velocity of the helix differs a little from the phase velocity, and it seems desirable instead to use a sort of hypothetical circuit or field for which the stored energy is almost the same as in the helix, but for which the group velocity is the same as the phase velocity. This has been referred to in the text as a "forced sinusoidal field." In Fig. 5.3, $(E^2/\beta^2 P)^{1/3}$ for the forced sinusoidal field is compared with $(E^2/\beta^2 P)^{1/3}$ for the helix.

Several other circuits are compared with this: the circular resonators of Fig. 5.4 (the square resonators of Fig. 5.4 give nearly the same impedance) and the resonant quarter-wave and half-wave wires of Figs. 5.6 and 5.7. The comparison is made in Fig. 5.8 for three voltages, which fix three phase velocities. In each case it is assumed that in some way the group velocity has been made equal to the phase velocity. Thus, the comparison is made on the basis of stored energies. The field is taken as the field at radius $a$ (corresponding to the surface of the helix) in the case of the forced sinusoidal field, and at the point of highest field in the case of the resonators.

We see from Figs. 5.8 and 5.3 that a helix of small radius is a very fine circuit.

In circuits made up of a series of resonators, the group velocity can be changed within wide limits by varying the coupling between resonators, as by putting inductive or capacitive irises between them. Thus, even circuits with a large stored energy can be made to have a high impedance by sacrificing bandwidth.

The circuits of Fig. 5.4 have a large stored energy because of the large opposed surfaces. The wires of Fig. 5.6 have a small stored energy associated entirely with "fringing fields" about the wires. The narrow strips of Fig. 5.5 have about as much stored energy between the opposed flat surfaces as that in the fringing field, and are about as good as the half-wave wires of Fig. 5.7.

An actual circuit made up of resonators such as those of Fig. 5.4 will be worse than Fig. 5.8 implies. Thus, there is a decrease of $(E^2/\beta^2P)^{1/3}$ due to wall thickness. Thickening the flat opposed walls of the resonators decreases the spacing between the opposed surfaces, increases the capacitance and hence increases the stored energy for a given gap voltage. In Fig. 5.9 the factor $f$ by which $(E^2/\beta^2P)^{1/3}$ is reduced is plotted vs. the ratio of the wall thickness $t$ to the resonator spacing $L$.

There is a further reduction of effective field because of the electrical length, $\theta$ in radians, of the space between opposed resonator surfaces. The lower curve in Fig. 5.10 gives a factor by which $(E^2/\beta^2P)^{1/3}$ is reduced because of this. If the resonator spacing, $\theta_t$ in radians, is greater than 2.33 radians, it is best to make the opening, or space between the walls, only 2.33 radians long by making the opposed disks forming the walls very thick.

There is of course a further loss in effective field, both in the helix and in circuits made up of resonators, because of the falling-off of the field toward the center of the aperture through which the electrons pass. This was discussed in Chapter IV.

Finally, it should be pointed out that the fraction of the stored energy dissipated in losses during each cycle is inversely proportional to the $Q$ of the circuit or of the resonators forming it. The distance the energy travels in a cycle is proportional to the group velocity. Thus, for a given $Q$ the signal will decay more rapidly with distance if the group velocity is lowered (to increase $E^2/\beta^2P$). Equations (5.38), (5.42) and (5.44) pertain to attenuation expressed in terms of group velocity. The table at the end of the chapter shows that a circuit made up of resonators and having a low enough group velocity to give it an impedance comparable with that of a helix can have a very high attenuation.

## 5.1 GROUP AND PHASE VELOCITY

Suppose we use a broad video pulse $F(t)$, containing radian frequencies $p$ lying in the range 0 to $p_0$, to modulate a radio-frequency signal of radian frequency $\omega$ which is much larger than $p_0$, so as to give a radio-frequency pulse $f(t)$

$$f(t) = e^{j\omega t}F(t) \tag{5.1}$$

the functions $F(t)$ and $f(t)$ are indicated in Fig. 5.1.

$F(t)$, which is a real function of time, can be expressed by means of its Fourier transform in terms of its frequency components

$$F(t) = \int_{-p_0}^{p_0} A(p)e^{jpt}\,dp \tag{5.2}$$

Here $A(p)$ is a complex function of $p$, such that $A(-p)$ is the complex conjugate of $A(p)$ (this assures that $F(t)$ is real).

With $F(t)$ expressed as in (5.2), we can rewrite (5.1)

$$f(t) = \int_{-p_0}^{p_0} A(p)e^{j(\omega+p)t}\,dp \qquad (5.3)$$

Now, suppose, as indicated in Fig. 5.2, we apply the r-f pulse $f(t)$ to the input of a transmission system of length $L$ with a phase constant $\beta$ which

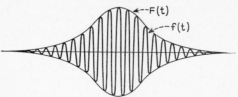

Fig. 5.1—A radio-frequency pulse varying with time as $f(t)$. The envelope varies with time as $F(t)$. The pulse might be produced by modulating a radio-frequency source with $F(t)$.

PHASE CONSTANT $\beta(\omega)$

Fig. 5.2—When the pulse of Fig. 5.1 is applied to a transmission system of length $L$ and phase constant $\beta(\omega)$ (a function of $\omega$), the output pulse $g(t)$ has an envelope $G(t)$.

is a function of frequency. Let us assume that the system is lossless. The output $g(t)$ will then be

$$g(t) = \int_{-p_0}^{p_0} A(p)e^{j((\omega+p)t-\beta L)}\,dp \qquad (5.4)$$

We have assumed that $p_0$ is much smaller than $\omega$. Let us assume that over the range $\omega - p_0$ to $\omega + p_0$, $\beta$ can be adequately represented by

$$\beta = \beta_0 + \frac{\partial\beta}{\partial\omega}\,p \qquad (5.5)$$

In this case we obtain

$$g(t) = e^{j(\omega t-\beta_0 L)} \int_{-p_0}^{p_0} A(p)\,e^{jp(t-(\partial\beta/\partial\omega)L)}\,dp \qquad (5.6)$$

The envelope at the output is

$$G(t) = \int_{-p_0}^{p_0} A(p)\,e^{jp(t-(\partial\beta/\partial\omega)L)}\,dp \qquad (5.7)$$

By comparing this with (5.2) we see that

$$G(t) = F\left(t - \frac{\partial \beta}{\partial \omega} L\right) \tag{5.8}$$

In other words, the envelope at the output is of the same shape as at the input, but arrives a time $\tau$ later

$$\tau = \frac{\partial \beta}{\partial \omega} L \tag{5.9}$$

This implies that it travels with a velocity $v_g$

$$v_g = L/\tau = \left(\frac{\partial \beta}{\partial \omega}\right)^{-1} \tag{5.10}$$

This velocity is called the group velocity, because in a sense it is the velocity with which the group of frequency components making up the pulse travels down the circuit. It is certainly the velocity with which the energy stored in the electric and magnetic fields of the circuit travels; we could observe physically that, if at one time this energy is at a position $x$, a time $t$ later it is at a position $x + v_g t$.

If the attenuation of the transmission circuit varies with frequency, the pulse shape will become distorted as the pulse travels and the group velocity loses its clear meaning. It is unlikely, however, that we shall go far wrong in using the concept of group velocity in connection with actual circuits.

We have used earlier the concept of phase velocity, which we have designated simply as $v$. In terms of phase velocity,

$$\beta = \frac{\omega}{v} \tag{5.11}$$

We see from (5.10) that in terms of phase velocity $v$ the group velocity $v_g$ is

$$v_g = v\left(1 - \frac{\omega}{v}\frac{\partial v}{\partial \omega}\right)^{-1} \tag{5.12}$$

For interaction of electrons with a wave to give gain in a traveling-wave tube, the electrons must have a velocity near the phase velocity $v$. Hence, for gain over a broad band of frequencies, $v$ must not change with frequency; and if $v$ does not change with frequency, then, from (5.12), $v_g = v$.

We note that the various harmonic components in a filter-type circuit have different phase velocities, some positive and some negative. The group velocity is of course the same for all components, as they are all aspects of one wave. Relation (4.61) is consistent with this:

$$\beta_m = (\theta + 2m\pi)/L \tag{4.61}$$

$$1/v_g = \partial\beta_m/\partial\omega = (\partial\theta/\partial\omega)/L \tag{5.13}$$

## 5.2 Gain and Bandwidth in a Traveling-Wave Tube

We can rewrite the impedance parameter $E^2/\beta^2 P$ in terms of stored energy per unit length $W$ for a field strength $E$, and a group velocity $v_g$. If $W$ is the stored energy per unit length, the power flow $P$ is

$$P = Wv_g \tag{5.14}$$

and, accordingly, we have

$$E^2/\beta^2 P = E^2/\beta^2 Wv_g \tag{5.15}$$

And, for the gain parameter, we will have

$$C = (E^2/\beta^2 Wv_g)^{1/3}(I_0/8V_0)^{1/3} \tag{5.16}$$

For example, we see from Fig. 4.20 that $E^2/\beta^2 P$ for the circuit of Fig. 4.10 goes to infinity at the upper cut-off. From Fig. 4.17 we see that $\partial\theta/\partial\omega$, and hence $1/v_g$, go to infinity at the upper cutoff, accounting for the infinite impedance. We see also that $\partial\theta/\partial\omega$ goes to infinity at the lower cutoff, but there the slot voltage and hence the longitudinal field also go to zero and hence $E^2/\beta^2 P$ does not go to infinity but to zero instead.

In the case of the circuit of Fig. 4.11, the gap voltage and hence the longitudinal field are finite for unit stored energy at both cutoffs. As $\partial\theta/\partial\omega$ is infinite at both cutoffs, $V^2/P$ and hence $E^2/\beta^2 P$ go to infinity at both cutoffs, as shown in Fig. 4.28.

To get high gain in a traveling-wave tube at a given frequency and voltage (the phase velocity is specified by voltage) we see from (5.16) that we must have either a small stored energy per unit length for unit longitudinal field, or a small group velocity, $v_g$.

To have amplification over a broad band of frequencies we must have the phase velocity $v$ substantially equal to the electron velocity over a broad band of frequencies. This means that for very broad-band operation, $v$ must be substantially constant and hence in a broad-band tube the group velocity will be substantially the same as the phase velocity.

If the group velocity is made smaller, so that the gain is Increased, the range of frequencies over which the phase velocity is near to the electron velocity is necessarily decreased. Thus, for a given phase velocity, as the group velocity is made less the gain increases but the bandwidth decreases.

Particular circuits can be compared on the basis of $(E^2/\beta^2 P)$ and bandwidth. We have discussed the impedance and phase or velocity curves in Chapters III and IV. Field[1] has compared a coiled waveguide structure with a series of apertured disks of comparable dimensions. Both of these structures must have about the same stored energy for a given field strength. He found the coiled waveguide to have a low gain and broad bandwidth as compared with the apertured disks. We explain this by saying that the particular coiled waveguide he considered had a higher group velocity than did the apertured disk structure. Further, if the coiled waveguide could be altered in some way so as to have the same group velocity as the apertured disk structure it would necessarily have substantially the same gain and bandwidth.

In another instance, Mr. O. J. Zobel of these Laboratories evaluated the effect of broad-banding a filter-type circuit for a traveling-wave tube by $m$-derivation. He found the same gain for any combination of $m$ and bandwidth which made $v = v_g(\partial v/\partial \omega = 0)$. We see this is just a particular instance of a general rule. The same thing holds for any type of broadbanding, as, by harmonic operation.

## 5.3 A COMPARISON OF CIRCUITS

The group velocity, the phase velocity and the ratio of the two are parameters which are often easily controlled, as, by varying the coupling between resonators in a filter composed of a series of resonators. Moreover, these parameters can often be controlled without much affecting the stored energy per unit length. For instance, in a series of resonators coupled by loops or irises, such as the circuit of Fig. 4.11, the stored energy is not much affected by the loops or irises unless these are very large, but the phase and group velocities are greatly changed by small changes in coupling.

Let us, then, think of circuits in terms of stored energy, and regard the phase and group velocities and their ratio as adjustable parameters. We find that, when we do this, there are not many essentially different configurations which promise to be of much use in traveling-wave tubes, and it is easy to make comparisons between extreme examples of these configurations.

### 5.3a Uniform Current Density throughout Field

Suppose we have a uniform current density $J_0$ wherever there is longitudinal electric field. We might approximate this case by flooding a helix of very fine wire with current inside and outside, or by passing current through a series of flat resonators whose walls were grids of fine wire.

[1] Lester M. Field, "Some Slow-Wave Structures for Traveling-Wave Tubes," *Proc. I.R.E.*, Vol. 37, pp. 34–40, January 1949.

In the latter case, if resonators had parallel walls of very fine mesh normal to the direction of electron motion there would be substantially no transverse electric field. All the electric field representing stored energy would act on the electron stream. In this case, we would have

$$W = \frac{\epsilon}{2} \int E^2 \, d\Sigma \qquad (5.17)$$

Here $d\Sigma$ is an elementary area normal to the direction of propagation. $W$ given by this expression is the total electric and magnetic stored energy per unit length. Where $E$ is less than its peak value, the magnetic energy makes up the difference.

In evaluating $E^2 I_0$ in (5.16) we will have as an effective value

$$(EI_0)_{\text{eff}} = J_0 \int E \, d\Sigma \qquad (5.18)$$

Hence, we will have for the gain parameter $C$

$$C = \left( \frac{J_0 \int E^2 \, d\Sigma}{\left(\frac{\omega}{v}\right)^2 \left(\frac{\epsilon}{2} \int E^2 \, d\Sigma\right) v_g (8V_0)} \right)^{1/3}$$

$$C = \left( \frac{J_0}{4 \left(\frac{\omega}{v}\right)^2 \epsilon v_g V_0} \right)^{1/3} \qquad (5.19)$$

It is of interest to put this in a slightly different form. Suppose $\lambda_0$ is the free-space wavelength. Then

$$\frac{\omega}{v} = \frac{2\pi}{\lambda_0} \frac{c}{v} \qquad (5.20)$$

where $c$ is the velocity of light

$$c = 3 \times 10^{10} \text{ cm/sec} = 3 \times 10^8 \text{ m/sec}$$

Further, we have for synchronism between the electron velocity $u_0$ and the phase velocity $v$

$$v^2 = 2\eta V_0 \qquad (5.21)$$

Also

$$c = 1/\sqrt{\mu \epsilon}$$

$$\epsilon = 1/c\sqrt{\mu/\epsilon} \qquad (5.22)$$

$$\sqrt{\mu/\epsilon} = 377 \text{ ohms}$$

Using (5.20), (5.21), (5.22) in connection with (5.19), we obtain

$$C = \left( \frac{\eta \sqrt{\mu/\epsilon} \; J_0 \lambda_0^2}{16\pi^2 c v_g} \right)^{1/3} \tag{5.23}$$

$$= 11.16 \; (J_0 \lambda_0^2 / v_g)^{1/3}$$

We have in (5.23) an expression for the gain parameter $C$ in case longitudinal fields only are present and in case there is a uniform current density $J_0$ wherever there is a longitudinal field.

In a number of cases, as in case of a large-diameter helix, or of a resonator with large apertures, the stored energy due to the transverse field is about equal to that due to the longitudinal field and $C$ will be $2^{-1/3}$ times as great as the value of $C$ given by (5.23). Thus, the value of $C$ given by (5.23), or even $2^{-1/3}$ times this, represents an unattainable ideal. It is nevertheless of interest in indicating how limiting behavior depends on various parameters. For instance, we see that if the wavelength $\lambda_0$ is made shorter, a higher current density must be used if $C$ is not to be lowered; for a constant $C$ the current density must be such as to give a constant current through a square a wavelength on a side.

In the table below, some values of $C$ have been computed from (5.23) for various wavelengths and current densities. The broad-band condition of equal phase and group velocities has been assumed, and the voltage has been taken as 1,000 volts.

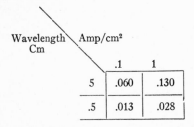

| Wavelength Cm \ Amp/cm² | .1 | 1 |
|---|---|---|
| 5 | .060 | .130 |
| .5 | .013 | .028 |

For larger voltages, $C$ will be smaller. $C$ can of course be made larger by making the group velocity smaller than the phase velocity.

Of course, if the electron stream does not pass through some portions of the field, $C$ will be smaller than given by (5.23). $C$ will also be less if there are "harmonic" field components which do not vary in the $z$ direction as $\exp(j\omega z/v)$.

### 5.3b Narrow Beams

Usually, no attempt is made to fill the entire field with electron flow even though this is necessary in getting a large value of $C$ for a given current density. Instead a narrow electron beam is shot through a region of high field. We then wish to relate the peak field strength to the stored energy in comparing various circuits.

Let us first consider a helically conducting sheet of radius $a$. The upper curve of Fig. 5.3 shows $(E^2/\beta^2 P)^{1/3}(v/c)^{1/3}$ vs. $\beta a$. In obtaining this curve it was assumed that $v \ll c$, so that $\gamma$ can be taken as equal to $\beta$. The field $E$ is the longitudinal field at the surface of the helically conducting cylinder. Figure 5.3 can be obtained from Fig. 3.4 by multiplying $F(\gamma a)$ by $(I_0(\gamma a))^{2/3}$ to give a curve valid for the field at $r = a$.

The helix has a very small circumferential electric field which represents "useless" stored energy. The lower curve of Fig. 5.3 is based on the stored electric energy of an axially symmetrical sinusoidal field impressed at the radius $a$.† This field has no circumferential component but is otherwise the

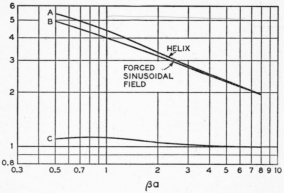

Fig. 5.3—The impedance parameter $(E^2/\beta^2 P)^{1/3}$ compared for a helically conducting sheet ($A$) and a forced sinusoidal field ($B$) with a group velocity equal to the phase velocity. The helix has a higher impedance because the phase velocity is higher than the group velocity by a radio shown to the ⅓ power by curve $C$.

same as the electric field of the helix (again assuming $v \ll c$). We can imagine such a field propagating because of an inductive sheet at the radius $a$, which provides stored magnetic energy enough to make the electric and magnetic energies equal. The quantity plotted vs. $\beta a$ is $(E^2/\beta^2 P)^{1/3} (v/c)^{1/3} (v_g/v)^{1/3}$.

The forced sinusoidal field is not the field of some particular circuit for which a certain group velocity $v_g$ corresponds to a given phase velocity $v$. Hence, the factor $(v_g/v)^{1/3}$ is included in the ordinate, so that the curve will be the same no matter what group velocity is assumed. For the helically conducting sheet, a definite group velocity goes with a given phase velocity. In Fig. 5.3, the ordinate of the curve for the helically conducting sheet does not contain the factor $(v_g/v)^{1/3}$. If, for instance, we assume $v_g = v$

† See Appendix III.

in connection with the curve for the forced sinusoidal field, then the two ordinates are both $(E^2/\beta^2 P)^{1/3}$ $(v/c)^{1/3}$ and the curve for the sheet is higher than that for the forced field because, for the helically conducting sheet,

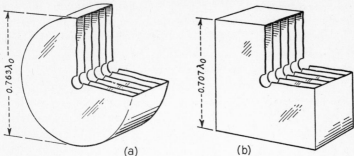

(a)                    (b)

Fig. 5.4—Pillbox and rectangular resonators. When a number of resonators are coupled one to the next, a filter-type circuit is formed.

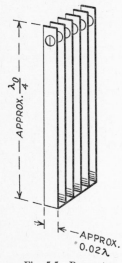

Fig. 5.5—Resonators with the opposing parallel surfaces reduced to lower stored energy and increase impedance.

$v_g < v$ for small values of $\gamma a$. Curve $C$ shows $(v/v_g)^{1/3}$ for the sheet vs. $\beta a$. Aside from the influence of group velocity, we might have expected the curve for the sheet to be a little lower than that for the forced field because of the energy associated with the transverse electric field component of the sheet. This, however, becomes small in comparison with the transverse magnetic component when $v \ll c$, as we have assumed.

Various other circuits will be compared, using the impressed sinusoidal field as a sort of standard of reference.

One of the circuits which will be considered is a series of flat resonators coupled together to make a filter. Figure 5.4a shows a series of very thin pillboxes with walls of negligible thickness. A small central hole is provided for the electron stream, and the field $E$ is to be measured at the edge of this hole. The diameter is chosen to obtain resonance at a wavelength $\lambda_0$. Figure 5.4b shows a similar series of flat square resonators.

For the round resonators it is found that*

$$(E^2/\beta^2 P)^{1/3} = 5.36 \ (v/c)^{1/3} \ (v/v_g)^{1/3} \tag{5.24}$$

for the square resonators*

$$(E^2/\beta^2 P)^{1/3} = 5.33 \ (v/c)^{1/3} \ (v/v_g)^{1/3} \tag{5.25}$$

For practical purposes these are negligibly different.

* See Appendix III.

Suppose we wanted to improve on such circuits by reducing the stored energy. An obvious procedure would be to cut away most of the flat opposed surfaces as shown in Fig. 5.5. This reduces the energy stored between the resonator walls, but results in energy storage outside of the open edges, energy associated with a "fringing field."

Going to an extreme, we might consider an array of closely spaced very fine wires, as shown in Fig. 5.6. Here there are no opposed flat surfaces, and all of the electric field is a fringing field; we have reached an irreducible minimum of stored energy in paring down the resonator.

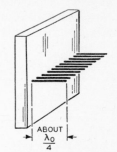

The structure of Fig. 5.6 has not been analyzed exactly, but that of Fig. 5.7 has. In Fig. 5.7, we have an array of fine, closely spaced half-wave wires between parallel planes.* This should have roughly twice the stored energy of Fig. 5.6, and we will estimate $(E^2/\beta^2 P)^{1/3}$ for Fig. 5.6 on this basis. We obtain in Appendix III:

For the half-wave wires,

Fig. 5.6—Quarter-wave wires, which have a minimum of stored energy.

$$(E^2/\beta^2 P)^{1/3} = 6.20 \; (v/v_g)^{1/3} \qquad (5.25)$$

and hence for the quarter-wave wires, approximately

$$(E^2/\beta^2 P)^{1/3} = 7.81 \; (v/v_g)^{1/3} \qquad (5.26)$$

As we have noted, $(v/c)$, which appears in the expression for $(E^2/\beta^2 P)^{1/3}$ for the sinusoidal field impressed at radius $a$ and in (5.24) and (5.25), is a

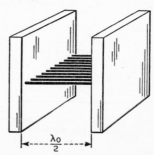

Fig. 5.7—Half-wave wires between parallel planes. The stored energy can be calculated for this configuration, assuming the wires to be very fine. The circuit does not propagate a wave unless added coupling is provided.

function of the accelerating voltage. Figure 5.8 makes a comparison between the sinusoidal field impressed at a radius $a$, curve $A$; the flat resonators, either circular or square, $B$; the half-wave wires, $C$; and the quarter-

---

* There is no transverse magnetic wave propagation along such a circuit unless extra coupling or loading is provided. Behavior of nonpropagating circuits in the presence of an electron stream is considered in Section 4 of Chapter XIV.

wave wires $C'$. In all cases, it is assumed that the coupling is so adjusted as to make $(v_g/v) = 1$ (broad-band condition).

What sort of information can we get from the curves of Fig. 5.8? Consider the curves for 1,000 volts. Suppose we want to cut down the opposed areas of resonators, as indicated in Fig. 5.5, so as to make them as good as half-wave wires (curve $C$). The edge capacitance in Fig. 5.5 will be about equal to that for quarter-wave wires (curve $C'$). Curve $C'$ is about 3.7 times as high as curve $B$, and hence represents only about $(1/3.7)^3 = .02$ as much capacitance. If we make the opposed area in Fig. 5.5 about .01 that in Fig. 5.4a or b, the capacitance* between opposed surfaces will equal the edge

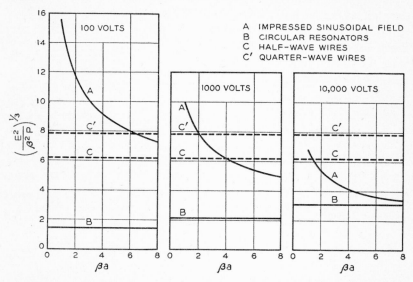

Fig. 5.8—Comparisons in terms of impedance parameter of an impressed sinusoidal field ($A$), circular resonators ($B$), half-wave wires ($C$) and quarter-wave wires ($C'$) assuming the group and phase velocities to equal the electron velocity. The radius of the impressed sinusoidal field is $a$.

capacitance and the total stored energy will be twice that for quarter-wave wires, or equal to that for half-wave wires. This area is shown approximately to scale relative to Fig. 5.4 in Fig. 5.5. Thus, at 1,000 volts the resonant strips of Fig. 5.5 are about as good as fine, closely spaced half-wave wires.

Suppose again that we wish at 1,000 volts to make the gain of the resonators of Fig. 5.4 (or of a coiled waveguide) as good as that for a helix with $\beta a = 3$. For $\beta a = 3$ the helix curve $A$ is about 3.2 times as high as the resona-

---

* This takes into account a difference in field distribution—that in Fig. 5.4b.

tor curve $B$. As $(E^2/\beta^2 P)^{1/3}$ varies as $(v/v_g)^{1/3}$, we must adjust the coupling between resonators so as to make

$$v_g = v/(3.2)^3 = .031\ v$$

in order to make $(E^2/\beta^2 P)^{1/3}$ the same for the resonators as for the helix. From (5.12) we see that this means that a change in frequency by a fraction .002 must change $v$ by a fraction .06. Ordinarily, a fractional variation of $v$ of $\pm.03$ would cause a very serious falling off in gain. At 3,000 mc the total frequency variation of .002 times in $v$ would be 6 mc. This is then a measure of the bandwidth of a series of resonators used in place of a helix for which $\beta a = 3$ and adjusted to give the same gain.

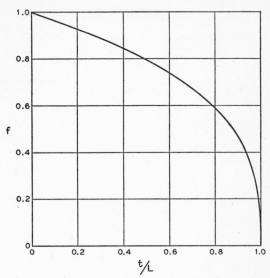

Fig. 5.9—The factor $f$ by which $(E^2/\beta^2 P)^{1/3}$ for a series of resonators such as those of Fig. 5.4 is reduced because of wall thickness $t$, in relation to gap spacing $L$.

## 5.4 Physical Limitations

In Section 3.3b the resonators were assumed to be very thin and to have walls of zero thickness. Of course the walls must have finite thickness, and it is impractical to make the resonators extremely thin. The wall thickness and the finite transit time across the resonators both reduce $E^2/\beta^2 P$.

### 5.4a Effect of Wall Thickness

Consider the resonators of Fig. 5.4. Let $L$ be the spacing between resonators ($1/L$ resonators per unit length), and $t$ be the wall thickness. Thus, the gap length is $(L - t)$. Suppose we keep $L$ and the voltage across each resonator constant, so as to keep the field constant, but vary $t$. The capacitance will be proportional to $(L - t)^{-1}$ and, as the stored energy is the voltage squared times the capacitance, we see that $(E^2/\beta^2 P)^{1/3}$ will be reduced by a factor $f$,

$$f = (1 - t/L)^{1/3} \qquad (5.27)$$

The factor $f$ is plotted vs. $t/L$ in Fig. 5.9.

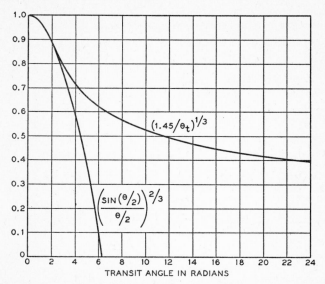

Fig. 5.10—The lower curve shows the factor by which $E^2/\beta^2 P$ is reduced by gap length, $\theta$ in radians. If the gap spacing is greater than 2.33 radians, it is best to make the gap 2.33 radians long. Then the upper curve applies.

## 5.4b Transit Time

As it is impractical to make the resonators infinitely thin, there will be some transit angle $\theta_g$ across the resonator, where

$$\theta_g = \beta \ell \qquad (5.28)$$

Here $\ell$ is the space between resonator walls, or, the length of the gap. If we assume a uniform electric field between walls, the gap factor $M$, that is, the ratio of peak energy gained in electron volts to peak resonator voltage, or the ratio of the magnitude of the sinusoidal field component produced to that which would be produced by the same number of infinitely thin gaps with the same voltages, will be (from (4.69) with $r = a$)

$$M = \frac{\sin (\theta_g/2)}{\theta_g/2} \qquad (5.29)$$

For a series of resonators $\theta_g$ long with infinitely thin walls $E^2/\beta^2 P$ will be less than the values given by (5.24) and (5.25) by a factor $M^{2/3}$. This is plotted vs. $\theta_g$ in Fig. 5.10.

### 5.4c Fixed Gap Spacing

Suppose it is decided in advance to put only one gap in a length specified by the transit angle $\theta_t$. How wide should the gap be made, and how much will $E^2/\beta^2 P$ be reduced below the value for very thin resonators and infinitely thin walls?

Let us assume that all the stored energy is energy stored between parallel planes separated by the gap thickness, expressed in radians as $\theta$ or in distance as $L$

$$\theta_t = \beta \ell$$

$$\theta_g = \beta L$$

Here $\ell$ is the gap spacing and $L$ is the spacing between resonators.

From Section 4.4 of Chapter IV we see that if $V$ is the gap voltage, the field strength $E$ is given by

$$E = MV/L$$

The stored energy per unit length, $W$, will be

$$W = W_0 V^2/\ell L \tag{5.30}$$

Here $W_0$ is a constant depending on the cross-section of the resonators. Thus, for unit field strength, the stored energy will be

$$W = W_0 L/\ell M^2$$
$$W = W_0(\theta_t/\theta_g)(\theta_g/2)^2/\sin^2(\theta_g/2) \tag{5.31}$$

We see that $W_0$ is merely the value of $W$ when $\theta_t = \theta_g$ and $\theta_g = 0$, or, for zero wall thickness and very thin resonators. Thus, the ratio $W/W_0$ relates the actual stored energy per unit length per unit field to this optimum stored energy for resonators of the same cross section.

For $\theta_t < 2.33$, $W/W_0$ is smallest (best) for $\theta_g = \theta_t$ (zero wall thickness). For larger values of $\theta_t$, the optimum value of $\theta_g$ is 2.33 radians and for this optimum value

$$(W_0/W)^{1/3} = (1.450/\theta_t)^{1/3} \tag{5.32}$$

If $\theta_t < 2.33$, it is thus best to make $\theta_g = \theta_t$. Then $(E^2/\beta^2 P)^{1/3}$ is reduced by the factor $[\sin(\theta/2)/(\theta/2)]^{2/3}$, which is plotted in Fig. 5.10. If $\theta_t > 2.33$, it is best to make $\theta = 2.33$. Then $(E^2/\beta^2 P)^{1/3}$ is reduced from the value for thin resonators with infinitely thin walls by a factor given by (5.32), which is plotted vs. $\theta_t$ in Fig. 5.10.

If there are edge effects, the optimum gap spacing and the reduction in $(E^2/\beta^2 P)^{1/3}$ will be somewhat different. However, Fig. 5.10 should still be a useful guide.

In case of wide gap separation (large $\theta_t$), there would be some gain in using reentrant resonators, as shown in Fig. 4.11, in order to reduce the capacitance. How good can such a structure be? Certainly, it will be worse than a helix. Consider merely the sections of metal tube with short gaps, which surround the electron beam. The shorter the gaps, the greater the capacitance. The space outside the beam has been capacitively loaded, which tends to reduce the impedance. This capacitance can be thought of as being associated with many spatial harmonics in the electric field, which do not contribute to interaction with the electrons.

## 5.5 ATTENUATION

Suppose we have a circuit made up of resonators with specified unloaded $Q$.† The energy lost per cycle is

$$W_L = 2\pi W_S/Q \qquad (5.33)$$

In one cycle, however, a signal moves forward a distance $L$, where

$$L = v_g/f \qquad (5.34)$$

The fractional energy loss per unit distance, which we will call $2\alpha$, is

$$2\alpha = \frac{W_L}{W_S} \frac{1}{L} \qquad (5.35)$$

whence

$$\alpha = \frac{\omega}{2Qv_g} \qquad (5.36)$$

So defined, $\alpha$ is the attenuation constant, and the amplitude will decay along the circuit as $\exp(-\alpha z)$.

The wavelength, $\lambda$, is given by

$$\lambda = v/f = 2\pi v/\omega \qquad (5.37)$$

The loss per wavelength in db is

$$\text{db/wavelength} = 20 \log_{10} \exp(\alpha\lambda)$$

$$\text{db/wavelength} = \frac{27.3}{Q} \frac{v}{v_g} \qquad (5.38)$$

† Disregarding coupling losses, the circuit and the resonantors will both have this same $Q$.

We see that, for given values of $v$ and $Q$, decreasing the group velocity, which increases $E^2/\beta^2 P$, also increases the attenuation per wavelength.

### 5.5a Attenuation of Circuits

For various structures, $Q$ can be evaluated in terms of surface resistivity, $R$, the intrinsic resistance of space, $\sqrt{\mu/\epsilon} = 377$ ohms, and varous other parameters. For instance, Schelkunoff[2] gives for the $Q$ of a pill-box resonator

$$Q = \frac{1.20\,(\sqrt{\mu/\epsilon}/R)}{1 + a/h} \tag{5.39}$$

Here $a$ is the radius of the resonator and $h$ is the height. If we express the radius in terms of the resonant wavelength $\lambda_0$ ($a = 1.2\lambda_0/\pi$), we obtain

$$Q = \frac{\pi(\sqrt{\mu/\epsilon}/R)(v/c)}{(1 + h/a)n} \tag{5.40}$$

Here $n$ is the number of resonators per wavelength (assuming the walls separating the resonators to be of negligible thickness); thus

$$n = h/\lambda = (h/\lambda_0)(c/v) \tag{5.41}$$

From (5.40) and (5.38) we obtain for a series of pill-box resonators

$$\text{db/wavelength} = 8.68(R/\sqrt{\mu/\epsilon})(c/v_g)(1 + h/a)n \tag{5.42}$$

In Appendix III an estimate of the $Q$ of an array of fine half-wave parallel wires is made by assuming conduction in one direction with a surface resistance $R$. On this basis, $Q$ is found to be

$$Q = (\sqrt{\mu/\epsilon}/R)(v/c) \tag{5.43}$$

and hence

$$\text{db/wavelength} = 27.3(R/\sqrt{\mu/\epsilon})(c/v_g) \tag{5.44}$$

For non-magnetic materials, surface resistance varies as the square root of the resistivity times the frequency. The table below gives $R$ for copper and db/wavelength for pill-box resonators for $h/a \ll 1$ (5.42) and for wires (5.44) for several frequencies

| f, mc | R, Ohms | (db/wavelength)/ $(c/v_g)$ | |
|---|---|---|---|
| | | Pill-box Resonators | Wires |
| 3,000 | .0142 | $3.3 \times 10^{-4}n$ | $10.3 \times 10^{-4}$ |
| 10,000 | .0260 | $6.0 \times 10^{-4}n$ | $18.1 \times 10^{-4}$ |
| 30,000 | .0450 | $10.4 \times 10^{-4}n$ | $32.6 \times 10^{-4}$ |

In Section 3.3b a circuit made up of resonators, with a group velocity .031 times the phase velocity, was discussed. Suppose such a circuit were

[2] Electromagnetic Waves, S. A. Schelkunoff, Van Nostrand, 1943. Page 269.

used at 1,000 volts ($c/v$ = 16.5), were 40 wavelengths long, and had three copper resonators per wavelength. The total attenuation in db is given below

| f, mc | Attenuation, db |
|---|---|
| 3,000 | 21 |
| 10,000 | 38 |
| 30,000 | 67 |

## PROBLEMS

1. A traveling-wave tube for operation at a wavelength of 10 cm has a helix of 0.15″ diameter, and a central beam of diameter 0.10″ and current density 0.1 amperes/cm² is used. The operating voltage is 1,000 volts. Calculate $C$ according to Chapter III and compare with the limiting value (5.23).

2. In a structure such as that shown in Fig. 4.10, there are 3 slots per wavelength along the structure, and the slots and fins are of equal thicknesses. What is the ratio of the stored energy for unit field for this structure and for (a) a similar structure with 3 extremely thin fins per wavelength (b) a similar structure with many extremely thin fins per wavelength (c) a structure with slots of the same width, but with one every 1.25 wavelengths?

# CHAPTER VI

# THE CIRCUIT DESCRIBED IN TERMS OF NORMAL MODES

## SYNOPSIS OF CHAPTER

IN CHAPTER II, the field produced by the current in the electron stream, which was assumed to vary as exp $(-\Gamma z)$, was deduced from a simple model in which the electron stream was assumed to be very close to an artificial line of susceptance $B$ and reactance $X$ per unit length. Following these assumptions, the voltage per unit length was found to be that of equation (2.10) and the field $E$ in the $z$ direction would accordingly be $\Gamma$ times this, or

$$E = \frac{\Gamma^2 \Gamma_1 K}{\Gamma_1^2 - \Gamma^2} i \qquad (6.1)$$

Here we will remember that $\Gamma_1$ is the natural propagation constant of the line, and $K$ is the characteristic impedance.

We further replaced $K$ by a quantity

$$E^2/\beta^2 P = 2K \qquad (6.2)$$

where $E$ is the field produced by a power flow $P$, and $\beta$ is the phase constant of the line. For a lossless line, $\Gamma_1$ is a pure imaginary and

$$\beta^2 = -\Gamma_1^2 \qquad (6.3)$$

From (6.1) and (6.2) we obtain

$$E = \frac{\Gamma^2 \Gamma_1 (E^2/\beta^2 P)}{2(\Gamma_1^2 - \Gamma^2)} i \qquad (6.4)$$

To the writer it seems intuitively clear that the derivation of Chapter II is correct for waves with a phase velocity small compared with the velocity of light, and that (6.4) correctly gives the part of the field associated with the excitation of the circuit. However, it is clear that there are other field components excited; a bunched electron stream will produce a field even in the absence of a circuit. Further, many legitimate questions can be raised. For instance, in Chapter II capacitive coupling only was considered. What about mutual inductance between the electron stream and the inductances of the line?

98

The best procedure seems to be to analyze the situation in a way we know to be valid, and then to make such approximations as seem reasonable. One approximation we can make is, for instance, that the phase velocity of the wave is quite small compared with the speed of light, so that

$$| \Gamma_1 |^2 \gg \beta_0^2 = (\omega/c)^2 \tag{6.5}$$

In this chapter we shall consider a lossless circuit which supports a group of transverse magnetic modes of wave propagation. The finned structure of Fig. 4.3 is such a circuit, and so are the circuits of Figs. 4.8 and 4.9 (assuming that the fins are so closely spaced that the circuit can be regarded as smooth). It is assumed that waves are excited in such a circuit by a current in the $z$ direction varying with distance as exp $(-\Gamma z)$ and distributed normal to the $z$ direction as a function of $x$ and $y$, $\hat{J}(x, y)$. Such a current might arise from the bunching at low signal levels of a broad beam of electrons confined by a strong magnetic field so as not to move appreciably normal to the $z$ direction.

The structure considered may support transverse electric waves, but these can be ignored because they will not be excited by the impressed current.

In the absence of an impressed current, any field distribution in the structure can be expressed as the sum of excitations of a number of pairs of normal modes of propagation. For one particular pair of modes, the field distribution normal to the $z$ direction can be expressed in terms of a function $\hat{\pi}_n(x, y)$ and the field components will vary in the $z$ direction as exp$(\pm\Gamma_n z)$. Here the $+$ sign gives one mode of the pair and the $-$ sign the other. If $\Gamma_n$ is real the mode is *passive*; the field decays exponentially with distance. If $\Gamma_n$ is imaginary the mode is *active*; the field pattern of the mode propagates without loss in the $z$ direction.

An impressed current which varies in the $z$ direction as exp$(-\Gamma z)$ will excite a field pattern which also varies in the $z$ direction as exp$(-\Gamma z)$, and as some function of $x$ and $y$ normal to the $z$ direction. We may, if we wish, regard the variation of the field normal to the $z$ direction as made up of a combination of the field patterns of the normal modes of propagation, the patterns specified by the functions $\hat{\pi}_n(x, y)$. Now, a pattern specified by $\hat{\pi}_n(x, y)$ coupled with a variation exp$(\pm\Gamma_n z)$ in the $z$ direction satisfies Maxwell's equations and the boundary conditions imposed by the circuit with *no* impressed current. If, however, we assume the same variation with $x$ and $y$ but a variation as exp$(-\Gamma z)$ with $z$, Maxwell's equations will be satisfied only if there is an impressed current having a distribution normal to the $z$ direction which also can be expressed by the function $\hat{\pi}_n(x, y)$.

Suppose we add up the various forced modes in such relative strength and phase that the total of the impressed currents associated with them is equal to the actual impressed current. Then, the sum of the fields of these modes is the actual field produced by the actual impressed current. The field is so expressed in (6.44) where the current components $J_n$ are defined by (6.36).

If it is assumed that there is only one mode of propagation, and if it is assumed that the field is constant over the electron flow, (6.44) can be put in the form shown in (6.47). For waves with a phase velocity small compared with the velocity of light, this reduces to (6.4), which was based on the simple circuit of Fig. 2.3.

Of course, actual circuits have, besides the one desired active mode, an infinity of passive modes and perhaps other active modes as well. In Chapter VII a way of taking these into account will be pointed out.

Actual circuits are certainly not lossless, and the fields of the helix, for instance, are not purely transverse magnetic fields. In such a case it is perhaps simplest to assume that the modes of propagation exist and to calculate the amount of excitation by energy transfer considerations. This has been done earlier[1], at first subject to the error of omitting a term which later[2] was added. In (6.55) of this chapter, (6.44) is reexpressed in a form suitable for comparison with this earlier work, and is found to agree.

Many circuits are not smooth in the $z$ direction. The writer believes that usually small error will result from ignoring this fact, at least at low signal levels.

## 6.1 Excitation of Transverse Magnetic Modes of Propagation by a Longitudinal Current

We will consider here a system in which the natural modes of propagation are transverse magnetic waves. The circuit of Fig. 4.3, in which a slow wave is produced by finned structures, is an example. We will remember that the modes of propagation derived in Section 4.1 of Chapter IV were of this type. We will consider here that any structure the circuit may have (fins, for instance) is fine enough so that the circuit may be regarded as smooth in the $z$ direction.

Any transverse electric modes which may exist in the structure will not be excited by longitudinal currents, and hence may be disregarded.

The analysis presented here will follow Chapter X of Schelkunoff's *Electromagnetic Waves*.

The divergence of the magnetic field $H$ is zero. As there is no $z$ component of field, we have

---

[1] J. R. Pierce, "Theory of the Beam-Type Traveling-Wave Tube," *Proc. I.R.E.*, Vol. 35, pp. 111–123, February, 1947.

[2] J. R. Pierce, "Effect of Passive Modes in Traveling-Wave Tubes," *Proc. I.R.E.*, Vol. 36, pp. 993–997, August, 1948.

$$\frac{\partial H_z}{\partial x} + \frac{\partial H_y}{\partial y} = 0 \tag{6.6}$$

This will be satisfied if we express the magnetic field in terms of a "stream function", $\pi$

$$H_x = \frac{\partial \pi}{\partial y} \tag{6.7}$$

$$H_y = -\frac{\partial \pi}{\partial x} \tag{6.8}$$

$\pi$ can be identified as the $z$ component of the vector potential (the vector potential has no other components).

We will assume $\pi$ to be of the form

$$\pi = \hat{\pi}\,(x, y)e^{-\Gamma z} \tag{6.9}$$

Here $\hat{\pi}\,(x, y)$ is a function of $x$ and $y$ only, which specifies the field distribution in any $x, y$ plane.

We can apply Maxwell's equations to obtain the electric fields

$$\frac{\partial H_z}{\partial y} - \frac{\partial H_y}{\partial z} = j\omega\epsilon E_x$$

Using (6.7) and (6.8), and replacing differentiation with respect to $z$ by multiplication by $-\Gamma$, we find

$$E_x = \frac{j\Gamma}{\omega\epsilon}\frac{\partial \pi}{\partial x} \tag{6.10}$$

Similarly

$$E_y = \frac{j\Gamma}{\omega\epsilon}\frac{\partial \pi}{\partial y} \tag{6.11}$$

We see that in an $x, y$ plane, a plane perpendicular to the direction of propagation, the field is given as the gradient of a scalar potential $V$

$$V = (-j\Gamma/\omega\epsilon)\pi \tag{6.12}$$

This is because we deal with transverse magnetic waves, that is, with waves which have no longitudinal or $z$ component of magnetic field. Thus, a closed path in an $x, y$ plane, which is normal to the direction of propagation, will link no magnetic flux, and the integral of the electric field around such a path will be zero.

We can apply the curl relation and obtain $E_z$

$$\frac{\partial H_y}{\partial x} - \frac{\partial H_x}{\partial y} = j\omega\epsilon E_z$$

$$E_z = \frac{j}{\omega\epsilon}\left(\frac{\partial^2 \pi}{\partial x^2} + \frac{\partial^2 \pi}{\partial y^2}\right) \tag{6.14}$$

Applying Maxwell's equations again, we have

$$\frac{\partial E_z}{\partial y} - \frac{\partial E_y}{\partial z} = j\omega\mu H_x$$

$$\frac{j}{\omega\epsilon}\frac{\partial}{\partial y}\left(\frac{\partial^2 \hat{\pi}}{\partial x^2} + \frac{\partial^2 \hat{\pi}}{\partial y^2}\right) + \frac{j\Gamma^2}{\omega\epsilon}\frac{\partial\hat{\pi}}{\partial y} = -j\omega\mu\frac{\partial\hat{\pi}}{\partial y}$$

(6.15)

This is certainly true if

$$\frac{\partial^2 \hat{\pi}}{\partial x^2} + \frac{\partial^2 \pi}{\partial y^2} = -(\Gamma^2 + \beta_0^2)\hat{\pi}$$

(6.16)

$$\beta_0 = \omega\sqrt{\mu\epsilon} = \omega/c$$

(6.17)

We find that this satisfies the other curl $E$ relations as well.

From (6.16) and (6.14) we see that

$$E_z = (-j/\omega\epsilon)(\Gamma^2 + \beta_0^2)\hat{\pi}(x, y)e^{-\Gamma z}$$

(6.18)

For a given physical circuit, it will be found that there are certain real functions $\hat{\pi}_n(x, y)$ which are zero over the conducting boundaries of the circuit, assuring zero tangential field at the surface of the conductor, and which satisfy (6.16) with some particular value of $\Gamma$, which we will call $\Gamma_n$. Thus, as a particular example, for a square waveguide of width $W$ some (but not all) of these functions are

$$\hat{\pi}_n(x, y) = \cos(n\pi y/W)\cos(n\pi x/W)$$

(6.19)

where $n$ is an integer. We see from (6.10), (6.11) and (6.18) that this makes $E_x$, $E_y$ and $E_z$ zero at the conducting walls $x = \pm W/2$, $y = \pm W/2$.

Each possible real function $\hat{\pi}_n(x, y)$ is associated with two values of $\Gamma_n$, one the negative of the other. The $\Gamma_n$'s are the natural propagation constants of the normal modes, and the $\hat{\pi}_n$'s are the functions giving their field distribution in the $x$, $y$ plane. The $\hat{\pi}_n$'s can be shown to be orthogonal, at least in typical cases. That is, integrating over the region in the $x$, $y$ plane in which there is field

$$\iint \hat{\pi}_n(x, y)\,\hat{\pi}_m(x, y)\,dx\,dy = 0$$

$$n \neq m$$

(6.20)

For a lossless circuit the various field distributions fall into two classes: those for which $\Gamma_n$ is imaginary, called active modes, which represent waves which propagate without attenuation; and those for which $\Gamma_n$ is real, which change exponentially with amplitude in the $z$ direction but do not change in phase. The latter can be used to represent the disturbance in a waveguide below cutoff frequency, for instance.

If $\Gamma_n$ is imaginary (an active mode) the power flow is real, while if $\Gamma_n$ is real (a passive mode) the power flow is imaginary (reactive or "wattless" power).

The spatial distribution functions $\hat{\pi}_n$ and the corresponding propagation constants $\Gamma_n$ are a means for specifying the electrical properties of a physical structure, just as are the physical dimensions which describe the physical structure and determine the various $\hat{\pi}_n$'s and $\Gamma_n$'s. In fact, if we know the various $\pi_n$'s and $\Gamma_n$'s, we can determine the response of the structure to an impressed current without direct reference to the physical dimensions.

In terms of the $\hat{\pi}_n$'s and $\Gamma_n$'s, we can represent any unforced disturbance in the circuit in the form

$$\sum_n \hat{\pi}_n(x, y)[A_n e^{-\Gamma_n z} + B_n e^{\Gamma_n z}] \tag{6.21}$$

Here $A_n$ is the complex amplitude of the wave of the $n$th spatial distribution traveling to the right, and $B_n$ the complex amplitude of the wave of the same spatial distribution traveling to the left.

It is of interest to consider the power flow in terms of the amplitude, $A_n$ or $B_n$. We can obtain the power flow $P$ by integrating the Poynting vector over the part of the $x$, $y$ plane within the conducting boundaries

$$P = \frac{1}{2} \int\int EXH^* \, ds$$

$$P = \frac{1}{2} \int\int (E_x H_y^* - E_y H_x^*) \, dx \, dy \tag{6.22}$$

By expressing the fields in terms of the stream function, we obtain

$$P = A_n A_n^* \left(\frac{-j\Gamma_n}{2\omega\epsilon}\right) \int\int \left[\left(\frac{\partial \hat{\pi}_n}{\partial x}\right)^2 + \left(\frac{\partial \hat{\pi}_n}{\partial y}\right)^2\right] dx \, dy \tag{6.23}$$

We can transform this by integrating by parts (essentially Green's theorem). Thus

$$\int_{x_1}^{x_2} \frac{\partial \hat{\pi}_n}{\partial x} \frac{\partial \hat{\pi}_n}{\partial x} \, dx = \hat{\pi}_n \frac{\partial \hat{\pi}_n}{\partial x}\Big|_{x_1}^{x_2} - \int_{x_1}^{x_2} \hat{\pi}_n \frac{\partial^2 \hat{\pi}_n}{\partial x^2} \, dx \tag{6.24}$$

Here $x_1$ and $x_2$, the limits of integration, lie on the conducting boundaries where $\hat{\pi}_n = 0$, and hence the first term on the right is zero. Doing the same for the second term in (6.23), we obtain

$$P_n = A_n A_n^* \left(\frac{-j\Gamma_n}{2\omega\epsilon}\right) \int\int \hat{\pi}_n \left(\frac{\partial^2 \hat{\pi}_n}{\partial x^2} + \frac{\partial^2 \hat{\pi}_n}{\partial y^2}\right) dx \, dy \tag{6.25}$$

By using (6.16), we obtain

$$P_n = A_n A_n^* \left(\frac{j\Gamma_n}{2\omega\epsilon}\right) (\Gamma_n^2 + \beta_0^2) \iint (\hat{\pi}_n)^2 \, dx \, dy \tag{6.26}$$

It is also of interest to express the $z$ component of the $n$th mode, $E_{zn}$, explicitly. For the wave traveling to the right we have, from (6.18),

$$E_{zn} = A_n \left(\frac{-j}{\omega\epsilon}\right) (\Gamma_n^2 + \beta_0^2)\hat{\pi}_n(x, y) \tag{6.27}$$

Let the field at some particular position, say, $x = y = 0$, be $E_{zn0}$. Then

$$A_n = \frac{j\omega\epsilon E_{zn0}}{(\Gamma_n^2 + \beta_0^2) \, \hat{\pi}_n(0, 0)} \tag{6.28}$$

and from (6.26)

$$P_n = (E_{zn0} E_{zn0}^*) \frac{-j\omega\epsilon\Gamma_n}{2\pi_n^2(0, 0)(\Gamma_n^2 + \beta_0^2)} \iint [\hat{\pi}_n(x, y)]^2 \, dx \, dy \tag{6.29}$$

We can rewrite this

$$\frac{E_{zn0} E_{zn0}^*}{(-\Gamma_n^2)P_n} = \frac{2\hat{\pi}_n^2(0, 0)(\Gamma_n^2 + \beta_0^2)}{-j\omega\epsilon\Gamma_n(-\Gamma_n^2) \iint [\hat{\pi}_n(x, y)]^2 \, dx \, dy} \tag{6.30}$$

For an active mode in a lossless circuit, $\Gamma_n$ is a pure imaginary, and the negative of its square is the square of the phase constant. Thus, for a particular mode of propagation we can identify (6.30) with the circuit parameter $E^2/\beta^2 P$ which we used in Chapter II.

Let us now imagine that there is an impressed current $J$ which flows in the $z$ direction and has the form

$$J = \hat{J}(x, y)e^{-\Gamma z} \tag{6.31}$$

According to Maxwell's equations we must have

$$\frac{\partial H_y}{\partial x} - \frac{\partial H_x}{\partial y} = j\omega\epsilon E_z + J \tag{6.32}$$

Now, we will assume that the fields are given by some overall stream function $\pi$ which varies with $x$ and $y$ and with $z$ as $\exp(-\Gamma z)$.

In terms of this function $\pi$, $H_x$, $H_y$ and $E_x$, $E_y$ will be given by relations (6.7), (6.8), (6.10), (6.11). However, the relation used in obtaining $E_z$ is not valid in the presence of the convection current. Instead of (6.16) we have

$$\frac{\partial H_y}{\partial x} - \frac{\partial H_x}{\partial y} = j\omega\epsilon E_z + J$$

$$E_z = \frac{j}{\omega\epsilon} \left(\frac{\partial^2 \pi}{\partial x^2} + \frac{\partial^2 \pi}{\partial y^2}\right) + \frac{j}{\omega\epsilon} J \tag{6.33}$$

Again applying the relation

$$\frac{\partial E_z}{\partial y} - \frac{\partial E_y}{\partial z} = -j\omega\mu H_x$$

we obtain

$$\frac{\partial^2 \pi}{\partial x^2} + \frac{\partial^2 \pi}{\partial y^2} = -(\Gamma^2 + \beta_0^2)\,\pi - J \qquad (6.34)$$

We will now divide both $\pi$ and $J$ into the spatial distributions characteristic of the normal unforced modes.
Let

$$\hat{J}(x, y) = \sum_n J_n \hat{\pi}_n(x, y) \qquad (6.35)$$

$$J_n = \frac{\displaystyle\iint \hat{J}(x, y)\hat{\pi}_n(x, y)\, dx\, dy}{\displaystyle\iint [\hat{\pi}_n(x, y)]^2\, dx\, dy} \qquad (6.36)$$

This expansion is possible because the $\pi_n$'s are orthogonal. Let

$$\hat{\pi} = e^{-\Gamma z} \sum_n C_n \hat{\pi}_n(x, y) \qquad (6.37)$$

Here there is no question of forward and backward waves; the forced excitation has the same $z$-distribution as the forcing current.

For the $n$th component, we have, from (6.16),

$$\frac{\partial^2 \hat{\pi}_n(x, y)}{\partial x^2} + \frac{\partial^2 \hat{\pi}_n(x, y)}{\partial y^2} = -(\Gamma_n^2 + \beta_0^2)\hat{\pi}_n(x, y) \qquad (6.38)$$

From (6.34) we must also have

$$C_n \left( \frac{\partial^2 \hat{\pi}_n(x, y)}{\partial x^2} + \frac{\partial^2 \hat{\pi}_n(x, y)}{\partial y^2} \right) \qquad (6.39)$$
$$= -C_n(\Gamma^2 + \beta_0^2)\hat{\pi}_n(x, y) - J_n \hat{\pi}_n(x, y)$$

Accordingly, we must have

$$C_n = \frac{J_n}{\Gamma_n^2 - \Gamma^2} \qquad (6.40)$$

The overall stream function is thus

$$\pi = e^{-\Gamma z} \sum_n \frac{\hat{\pi}_n(x, y) J_n}{\Gamma_n^2 - \Gamma^2} \qquad (6.41)$$

From (6.33) and (6.34) we see that

$$E_z = \frac{-j}{\omega\epsilon} (\Gamma^2 + \beta_0^2)\pi \qquad (6.42)$$

So

$$E_z = e^{-\Gamma z} \sum \frac{-j(\Gamma^2 + \beta_0^2)\hat{\pi}_n(x, y)J_n}{\omega\epsilon(\Gamma_n^2 - \Gamma^2)} \tag{6.43}$$

$$E_z = \frac{-j(\Gamma^2 + \beta_0^2)}{\omega\epsilon} e^{-\Gamma z} \sum \frac{\hat{\pi}_n(x, y)J_n}{\Gamma_n^2 - \Gamma^2} \tag{6.44}$$

## 6.2 COMPARISON WITH RESULTS OF CHAPTER II

Let us consider a case in which there is only one mode of propagation, characterized by $\hat{\pi}_1(x, y)$, $\Gamma_1$, and a case in which the current flows over a region in which $\hat{\pi}_1(x, y)$ has a constant value, say, $\hat{\pi}_1(0, 0)$. This corresponds to the case of the transmission line which was discussed in Chapter II.

We take only the term with the subscript 1 in (6.44) and (6.30). Combining these equations, we obtain for the field at 0, 0

$$E_z = \frac{(E^2/\beta^2 P)(\Gamma^2 + \beta_0^2)}{(\Gamma_1^2 + \beta_0^2)} \frac{\Gamma_1^3 J_1 \iint [\hat{\pi}_1(x, y)]^2 \, dx \, dy}{2\hat{\pi}_1(0, 0)} \tag{6.45}$$

We have from (6.36)

$$J_1 = \frac{\pi_1(0, 0)}{\iint [\hat{\pi}_1(x, y)]^2 \, dx \, dy} \tag{6.46}$$

From (6.45) and (6.46) we obtain

$$E_z = \frac{(\Gamma^2 + \beta_0^2)\Gamma_1^3(E^2/\beta^2 P)}{2(\Gamma_1^2 + \beta_0^2)(\Gamma_1^2 - \Gamma^2)} J e^{-\Gamma z} \tag{6.47}$$

Let us compare this with (6.4), which came from the transmission line analogy of Chapter II, identifying $E_z$ and $J$ with $E$ and $i$. We see that, for slow waves for which

$$\beta_0^2 \ll |\Gamma_1^2| \tag{6.48}$$

$$\beta_0^2 \ll |\Gamma^2| \tag{6.49}$$

(6.47) becomes the same as (6.4). It was, of course, under the assumption that the waves are slow that we obtained (2.10), which led to (6.4).

## 6.3 EXPANSION REWRITTEN IN ANOTHER FORM

Expression (6.44) can be rewritten so as to appear quite different. We can write

$$\Gamma^2 + \beta_0^2 = \Gamma^2 - \Gamma_n^2 + \Gamma_n^2 + \beta_0^2$$

Thus, we can rewrite the expression for $E_z$ as

$$E_z = e^{-\Gamma z} \left( (-j/\omega\epsilon) \sum_n \frac{(\Gamma_n^2 + \beta_0^2)\hat{\pi}_n(x, y)J_n}{\Gamma_n^2 - \Gamma^2} \right.$$
$$\left. + (j/\omega\epsilon) \sum_n \hat{\pi}_n(x, y)J_n \right) \tag{6.50}$$

The second term in the brackets is just $j/\omega\epsilon$ times the impressed current, as we can see from (6.35). The first term can be rearranged

$$(-i/\omega\epsilon)(\Gamma_n^2 + \beta_0^2)J_n$$

$$= \frac{(-j/\omega\epsilon)(\Gamma_n^2 + \beta_0^2) \iint \hat{\pi}_n(x, y)J(x, y)\, dx\, dy}{\iint [\hat{\pi}_n(x, y)]^2\, dx\, dy} \tag{6.51}$$

Referring back to (6.29), let $\Psi_n$ be twice the power $P_n$ carried by the unforced mode when the field strength is

$$| E_{zn0} | = 1 \tag{6.52}$$

Further, let us choose the $\hat{\pi}_n$'s so that, at some specified position, $x = y = 0$,

$$_n(0, 0) = 1 \tag{6.53}$$

Then

$$\Psi_n = \frac{-j\omega\epsilon\Gamma_n}{\Gamma_n^2 + \beta_0^2} \iint [\hat{\pi}_n(x, y)]^2\, dx\, dy \tag{6.54}$$

Using this in connection with (6.51), we obtain

$$E_z = e^{-\Gamma z} \left( - \sum_n \frac{\Gamma_n \hat{\pi}_n(x, y) \iint \hat{\pi}_n(x, y)\hat{J}(x, y)\, dx\, dy}{\Psi_n(\Gamma_n^2 - \Gamma^2)} \right.$$
$$\left. + (j/\omega\epsilon)\hat{J}(x, y) \right) \tag{6.55}$$

An expression for the forced field in terms of the parameters of the normal modes was given earlier[1,2]. In deriving this expression, the existence of a set of modes was assumed, and the field at a point was found as an integral over the disturbances induced in the circuit to the right and to the left and propagated to the point in question. Such a derivation applies for lossy and mixed waves, while that given here applies for lossless transverse-magnetic waves only.

The earlier derivation[1] leads to an expression identical with (6.55) except that $\Psi_n^*$ appears in place of $\Psi_n$. In this earlier derivation a sign was implicitly assigned to the direction of flow of reactive power (which really doesn't flow at all!) by saying that the reactive power flows in the direction in which the amplitude decreases. If we had assumed the reactive power to flow in the direction in which the amplitude increases, then, with the same definition of $\Psi_n$, for a passive mode $\Psi_n^*$ would have been replaced by $-\Psi_n^*$ which is equal to $\Psi_n$ (for a passive mode, $\Psi_n$ is imaginary).

In deriving (6.55), no such ambiguity arose, because the power flow was identified with the complex Poynting vector for the particular type of wave considered. In any practical sense, $\Psi$ is merely a parameter of the circuit, and it does not matter whether we call Im $\Psi$ reactive power flow to the right or to the left.

The existence of a derivation of (6.55) not limited in its application to lossless transverse magnetic waves is valuable in that practical circuits often have some loss and often (in the case of the helix, for instance) propagate mixed waves.

### 6.4 Iterated Structures

Many circuits, such as those discussed in Chapter IV, have structure in the $z$ direction. Expansions such as (6.55) do not strictly apply to such structures. We can make a plausible argument that they will be at least useful if all field components except one differ markedly in propagation constant from the impressed current. In this case we save the one component which is nearly in synchronism with the impressed current and hope for the best.

### Problems

1. Make a similar expansion including the effect of transverse currents.

# CHAPTER VII

# EQUATIONS FOR TRAVELING-WAVE TUBE

SYNOPSIS OF CHAPTER

IN CHAPTER VI we have expressed the properties of a circuit in terms of its normal modes of propagation rather than its physical dimensions. In this chapter we shall use this representation in justifying the circuit equation of Chapter II and in adding to it a term to take into account the local fields produced by a-c space charge. Then, a combined circuit and ballistical equation will be obtained, which will be used in the following chapters in deducing various properties of traveling-wave tubes.

In doing this, the first thing to observe is that when the propagation constant $\Gamma$ of the impressed current is near the propagation constant $\Gamma_1$ of a particular active mode, the excitation of that mode is great and the excitation varies rapidly as $\Gamma$ is changed, while, for passive modes or for active modes for which $\Gamma$ is not near to the propagation constant $\Gamma_n$, the excitation varies more slowly as $\Gamma$ is changed. It will be assumed that $\Gamma$ is nearly equal to the propagation constant $\Gamma_1$ of one active mode, is not near to the propagation constant of any other mode and varies over a small fractional range only. Then the sum of terms due to all other modes will be regarded as a constant over the range of $\Gamma$ considered. It will also be assumed that the phase velocities corresponding to $\Gamma$ and $\Gamma_1$ are small compared with the speed of light. Thus, (6.47) and (6.47a) are replaced by (7.1), where the first term represents the excitation of the $\Gamma_1$ mode and the second term represents the excitation of passive and "non-synchronous" modes. In another sense, this second term gives the field produced by the electrons in the absence of a wave propagating on the circuit, or, the field due to the "space charge" of the bunched electron stream. Equation (7.1) is the equation for the distributed circuit of Fig. 7.1. This is like the circuit of Fig. 2.3 save for the addition of the capacitances $C_1$ between the transmission circuit and the electron beam. We see that, because of the presence of these capacitances, the charge of a bunched electron beam will produce a field in addition to the field of a wave traveling down the circuit. This circuit is intuitively so appealing that it was originally thought of by guess and justified later.

Equation (7.1), or rather its alternative form, (7.7), which gives the voltage in terms of the impressed charge density, can be combined with the ballistical equation (2.22), which gives the charge density in terms of the voltage, to give (7.9), which is an equation for the propagation constant. The attenuation, the difference between the electron velocity and the phase velocity of the wave on the circuit in the absence of electrons and the difference between the propagation constant and that for a wave traveling with the electron speed are specified by means of the gain parameter $C$ and the parameters $d$, $b$ and $\delta$. It is then assumed that $d$, $b$ and $\delta$ are around unity or smaller and that $C$ is much smaller than unity. This makes it possible to neglect certain terms without serious error, and one obtains an equation (7.13) for $\delta$.

In connection with (7.7) and Fig. 7.1, it is important to distinguish between the *circuit voltage* $V_c$, corresponding to the first term of (7.7), and the total voltage $V$ acting on the electrons. These quantities are related by (7.14). The a-c velocity $v$ and the convection current $i$ are given within the approximation made ($C \ll 1$) by (7.15) and (7.16).

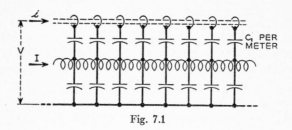

Fig. 7.1

## 7.1 Approximate Circuit Equation

From (6.47) we can write for a current $J = i$ and a summation over $n$ modes

$$E_z = (1/2)(\Gamma^2 + \beta_0^2)i \sum_n \frac{(E^2/\beta^2 P)_n \Gamma_n^3}{(\Gamma_n^2 + \beta_0^2)(\Gamma_n^2 - \Gamma^2)} \qquad (6.47a)$$

This has a number of poles at $\Gamma = \Gamma_n$. We shall be interested in cases in which $\Gamma$ is very near to a particular one of these, which we shall call $\Gamma_1$. Thus the term in the expansion involving $\Gamma_1$ will change rapidly with small variations in $\Gamma$. Moreover, even if $(E^2/\beta^2 P)_1$ and $\Gamma_1$ have very small real components, $\Gamma_1^2 - \Gamma^2$ can be almost or completely real for values of $\Gamma$ which have only small real components. Thus, one term of the expansion, that involving $\Gamma_1$, can go through a wide range of phase angles and magnitudes for very small fractional variations in $\Gamma$, fractional variations, as it turns out, which are of the order of $C$ over the range of interest.

The other modes are either passive modes, for which even in a lossy circuit $(E^2/\beta^2 P)_n$ is almost purely imaginary, and $\Gamma_n$ almost purely real, or they are active modes which are considerably out of synchronism with the electron velocity. Unless one of these other active modes has a propagation constant $\Gamma_n$ such that $|(\Gamma_1 - \Gamma_2)/\Gamma_1|$ is so small as to be of the order of $C$, the terms forming the summation will not vary very rapidly over the range of variation of $\Gamma$ which is of interest.

We will thus write the circuit equation in the approximate form

$$E = \left[\frac{\Gamma^2\Gamma_1(E^2/\beta^2 P)}{2(\Gamma_1^2 - \Gamma^2)} - \frac{j\Gamma^2}{\omega C_1}\right] i \qquad (7.1)$$

Here there has been a simplification of notation. $E$ is the $z$ component of electric field, as in Chapter II, and is assumed to vary as $\exp(-\Gamma z)$. $(E^2/\beta^2 P)$ is taken to mean the value for the $\Gamma_1$ mode. It has been assumed that $\beta_0^2$ is small compared with $|\Gamma_1^2|$ and $|\Gamma^2|$, and $\beta_0^2$ has been neglected in comparison with these quantities.

Further, it has been pointed out that for slightly lossy circuits, $(E^2/\beta^2 P)$ will have only a small imaginary component, and we will assume as a valid approximation that $(E^2/\beta^2 P)$ is purely real. We cannot, however, safely assume that $\Gamma_1$ is purely imaginary, for a small real component of $\Gamma_1$ can affect the value of $\Gamma_1^2 - \Gamma^2$ greatly when $\Gamma$ is nearly equal to $\Gamma_1$.

The first term on the right of (7.1) represents fields associated with the active mode of the circuit, which is nearly in synchronism with the electrons. We can think of these fields as summing up the effect of the electrons on the circuit over a long distance, propagated to the point under consideration.

The term $(-j\Gamma^2/\omega C_1)$ in (7.1) sums up the effect of all passive modes and of any active modes which are far out of synchronism with the electrons. It has been written in this form for a special purpose; the term will be regarded as constant over the range of $\Gamma$ considered, and $C_1$ will be given a simple physical meaning.

This second term represents the field resulting from the local charge density, as opposed to that of the circuit wave which travels to the region from remote points. Let us rewrite (7.1) in terms of voltage and charge density

$$E = -\frac{\partial V}{\partial z} = \Gamma V \qquad (7.2)$$

From the continuity equation

$$i = (j\omega/\Gamma)\rho \qquad (2.18)$$

$$V = \left[\frac{j\omega\Gamma_1(E^2/\beta^2 P)}{2(\Gamma_1^2 - \Gamma^2)} + \frac{1}{C_1}\right] \rho \qquad (7.3)$$

We see that $C_1$ has the form of a capacitance per unit length. We can, for instance, redraw the transmission-line analogue of Fig. 2.3 as shown in Fig. 7.1. Here, the current $I$ is still the line current; but the voltage $V$ acting on the beam is the line voltage plus the drop across a capacitance of $C_1$ farads per meter.

Consider as an illustration the case of unattenuated waves for which

$$\Gamma_1 = j\beta_1 \tag{7.5}$$

$$\Gamma = j\beta \tag{7.6}$$

where $\beta_1$ and $\beta$ are real. Then

$$V = \left[ \frac{\omega\beta_1(E^2/\beta^2 P)}{2(\beta_1^2 - \beta^2)} + \frac{1}{C_1} \right] \rho \tag{7.7}$$

In (7.7), the first term in the brackets represents the impedance presented to the beam by the "circuit"; that is, the ladder network of Figs. 2.3 and 7.1. The second term represents the additional impedance due to the capacitance $C_1$, which stands for the impedance of the nonsynchronous modes. We note that if $\beta < \beta_1$, that is, for a wave faster than the natural phase velocity of the circuit, the two terms on the right are of the same sign. This must mean that the "circuit" part of the impedance is capacitive. However, for $\beta > \beta_1$, that is, for a wave slower than the natural phase velocity, the first term is negative and the "circuit" part of the impedance is inductive. This is easily explained. For small values of $\beta$ the wavelength of the impressed current is long, so that it flows into and out of the circuit at widely separated points. Between such points the long section of series inductance has a higher impedance than the shunt capacitance to ground; the capacitive effect predominates and the circuit impedance is capacitive. However, for large values of $\beta$ the current flows into and out of the circuit at points close together. The short section of series inductance between such points provides a lower impedance path than does the shunt capacitance to ground; the inductive impedance predominates and the circuit impedance is inductive. Thus, for *fast* waves the circuit appears *capacitive* and for *slow* waves the circuit appears *inductive*.

Since we have justified the use of the methods of Chapter II within the limitations of certain assumptions, there is no reason why we should not proceed to use the same notation in the light of our fuller understanding. We can now, however, regard $V$ not as a potential but merely as a convenient variable related to the field by (7.2).

From (2.18) and (7.3) we obtain

$$V = \left[ \frac{\Gamma\Gamma_1(E^2/\beta^2 P)}{2(\Gamma_1^2 - \Gamma^2)} - \frac{j\Gamma}{\omega C_1} \right] i \tag{7.8}$$

We use this together with (2.22)

$$i = \frac{jI_0\beta_e\Gamma V}{2V_0(j\beta_e - \Gamma)^2} \qquad (2.22)$$

We obtain the overall equation

$$1 = \frac{jI_0\beta_e\Gamma}{2V_0(j\beta_e - \Gamma)}\left[\frac{\Gamma\Gamma_1(E^2/\beta^2 P)}{2(\Gamma_1 - \Gamma)} - \frac{j\Gamma}{\omega C_1}\right] \qquad (7.9)$$

In terms of the gain parameter $C$, which was defined in Chapter II,

$$C^3 = (E^2/\beta^2 P)(I_0/8V_0) \qquad (2.43)$$

we can rewrite (7.8)

$$(j\beta_e - \Gamma)^2 = \frac{j2\beta_e\Gamma^2\Gamma_1 C^3}{(\Gamma_1^2 - \Gamma^2)} + \frac{4\beta_e\Gamma^2 C^3}{\omega C_1(E^2/\beta^2 P)} \qquad (7.10)$$

We will be interested in cases in which $\Gamma$ and $\Gamma_1$ differ from $\beta_e$ by a small amount only. Accordingly, we will write

$$-\Gamma = -j\beta_e + \beta_e C \qquad (7.11)$$

$$-\Gamma_1 = -j\beta_e - j\beta_e Cb - \beta_e Cd \qquad (7.12)$$

The propagation constant $\Gamma$ describes propagation in the presence of electrons. A positive real value of $\delta$ means an increasing wave. A positive imaginary part means a wave traveling faster than the electrons.

The propagation constant $\Gamma_1$ refers to propagation in the circuit in the absence of electrons. A positive value of $b$ means the electrons go faster than the undisturbed wave. A positive value $d$ means that the wave is an attenuated wave which decreases as it travels.

If we use (7.11) and (7.12) in connection with (7.10) we obtain

$$\delta = \frac{[1 + C(2j\delta - C\delta^2)][1 + C(b - jd)]}{[-b + jd + j\delta + C(jbd - b^2/2 + d^2/2 + \delta^2/2)]}$$
$$- \frac{4\beta_e[(1 + C(2j\delta - C\delta^2)]C}{\omega C_1(E^2/\beta^2 P)} \qquad (7.13)$$

We will now assume that $|\delta|$ is of the order of unity, that $|b|$ and $|d|$ range from zero to unity or a little larger, and that $C \ll 1$. We will then neglect the parentheses multiplied by $C$, obtaining

$$\delta = \frac{1}{(-b + jd + j\delta)} - 4QC \qquad (7.14)$$

$$Q = \frac{\beta_e}{\omega C_1(E^2/\beta^2 P)} \qquad (7.15)$$

The quantity $\omega C_1$ has the dimensions of admittance per unit length, $\beta_e$ has the dimensions of (length)$^{-1}$ and $(E^2/\beta^2 P)$ has the dimensions of impedance. Thus, $Q$ is a dimensionless parameter (the space-charge parameter) which may be thought of as relating to the impedance parameter $(E^2/\beta^2 P)$ associated with the synchronous mode the impedance $(\beta_e/\omega C_1)$, attributable to all modes but the synchronous mode.

At this point it is important to remember that there are not only two impedances, but two voltage components as well. Thus, in (7.8), the first term in the brackets times the current represents the "circuit voltage", which we may call $V_c$. The second term in the brackets represents the voltage due to space charge, the voltage across the capacitances $C_1$. The two terms in the brackets are in the same ratio as the two terms on the right of (7.14), which came from them. Thus, we can express the circuit component of voltage $V_c$ in terms of the total voltage $V$ acting on the beam either from (7.8) as

$$V_c = \left[ 1 - \frac{j2(\Gamma_1^2 - \Gamma^2)}{\omega C_1 \Gamma_1 (E^2/\beta^2 P)} \right]^{-1} V \qquad (7.16)$$

or, alternatively, from (7.14) as

$$V_c = [1 - 4QC(-b + jd + j\delta)]^{-1} V \qquad (7.17)$$

From Chapter II we have relations for the electron velocity (2.15) and electron convection current (2.22). If we make the same approximations which were made in obtaining (7.14), we have

$$(ju_0 C/\eta)v = \frac{V}{\delta} \qquad (7.18)$$

$$(-2V_0 C^2/I)i = \frac{V}{\delta^2} \qquad (7.19)$$

We should remember also that the variation of all quantities with $z$ is as

$$e^{-j\beta_e z} e^{\beta_e C \delta z} \qquad (7.20)$$

The relations (7.18)–(7.19) together with (2.36), which tells us that the characteristic impedance of the circuit changes little in the presence of electrons if $C$ is small, sum up in terms of the more important parameters the linear operation of traveling-wave tubes in which $C$ is small. The parameters are: the gain parameter $C$, relative electron velocity parameter $b$, circuit attenuation parameter $d$ and space-charge parameter $Q$. In following chapters, the practical importance of these parameters in the operation of traveling-wave tubes will be discussed.

There are other effects not encompassed by these equations. The effect of transverse electron motions is small in most tubes because of the high focusing fields employed; it will be discussed in a later chapter. The differences between a field theory in which different fields act on different electrons and the theory leading to (7.14)–(7.20), which apply accurately only when all electrons at a given $z$-position are acted on by the same field, will also be discussed.

PROBLEMS

1. If all the rings connected to the $C_1$'s in Fig. 7.1 are connected together, is the phase velocity increased or decreased?

2. If Fig. 7.1 can really represent a helix, does connecting all the rings attached to the $C_1$'s to one another correspond to putting a conducting tube inside the helix? Why not?

3. What can be put in a helix at a given radius that will correspond to connecting the rings together?

# CHAPTER VIII

# THE NATURE OF THE WAVES

Synopsis of Chapter

IN THIS CHAPTER we shall discuss the effect of the various parameters on the rate of increase and velocity of propagation of the three forward waves. Problems involving boundary conditions will be deferred to later chapters.

The three parameters in which we are interested are those of (7.13), that is, $b$, the velocity parameter, $d$, the attenuation parameter and $QC$, the space-charge parameter. The fraction by which the electron velocity is greater than the phase velocity for the circuit in the absence of electrons is $bC$. The circuit attenuation is 54.6 $dC$ db/wavelength. $Q$ is a factor depending on the circuit impedance and geometry and on the beam diameter. For a helically conducting sheet of radius $a$ and a hollow beam of radius $a_1$, $Q$ can be obtained from Fig. 8.12.

The three forward waves vary with distance as

$$e^{-j\beta_e(1-yC)z}e^{\beta_e xCz}$$

$$\beta_e = \frac{\omega}{u_0}$$

Thus, a positive value of $y$ means a wave which travels faster than the electrons, and a positive value of $x$ means an increasing wave. The gain in db per wavelength of the increasing waves is $BC$, and $B$ is defined by (8.9).

Figure 8.1 shows $x$ and $y$ for the three forward waves for a lossless circuit ($d = 0$). The increasing wave is described by $x_1$, $y_1$. The gain is a maximum when the electron velocity is equal to the velocity of the undisturbed wave, or, when $b = 0$. For large positive values of $b$ (electrons much faster than undisturbed wave), there is no increasing wave. However, there is an increasing wave for all negative values of $b$ (all low velocities). For the increasing wave, $y_1$ is negative; thus, the increasing wave travels more slowly than the electrons, *even when the electrons travel more slowly than the circuit wave in the absence of electrons.* For the range of $b$ for which there is an increasing wave, there is also an attenuated wave, described by $x_2 = -x_1$ and $y_2 = y_1$. There is also an unattenuated wave described by $y_3(x_3 = 0)$.

For very large positive and negative values of $b$, the velocity of two of the waves approaches the electron velocity ($y$ approaches zero) and the velocity of the third wave approaches the velocity of the circuit wave in the absence of electrons ($y$ approaches minus $b$). For large negative values of $b$, $x_1$, $y_1$ and $x_2$, $y_2$ become the "electron" waves and $y_3$ becomes the "circuit" wave. For large values of $b$, $y_1$ and $y_3$ become the "electron" waves and $y_2$ becomes the "circuit" wave. The "circuit" wave is essentially the wave in the absence of electrons, modified slightly by the presence of a non-synchronous electron stream. The "electron waves" represent the motion of "bunches" along the electron stream, slightly affected by the presence of the circuit.

Figures 8.2 and 8.3 indicate the effect of loss. Loss decreases the gain of the increasing wave, adds to the attenuation of the decreasing wave and adds attenuation to the wave which was unattenuated in the lossless case. For large positive and negative values of $b$, the attenuation of the circuit wave (given by $x_3$ for negative values of $b$ and $x_2$ for positive values of $b$) approaches the attenuation in the absence of electrons.

Figure 8.4 shows $B$, the gain of the increasing wave in db per wavelength per unit $C$. Figure 8.5 shows, for $b = 0$, how $B$ varies with $d$. The dashed line shows a common approximation: that the gain of the increasing wave is reduced by $\frac{1}{3}$ of the circuit loss. Figure 8.6 shows how, for $b = 0$, $x_1$, $x_2$ and $x_3$ vary with $d$. We see that, for large values of $d$, the wave described by $x_2$ has almost the same attenuation as the wave on the circuit in the absence of electrons.

Figures 8.7–8.9 show $x$, $y$ for the three waves with no loss ($d = 0$) but with a-c space charge taken into account ($QC \neq 0$). The immediately striking feature is that there is now a minimum value of $b$ below which there is no increasing wave.

We further note that, for large negative and positive values of $b$, $y$ for the electron waves approaches $\pm 2 \sqrt{QC}$. In these ranges of $b$ the electron waves are dependent on the electron inertia and the field produced by a-c space charge, and have nothing to do with the active mode of the circuit.

As $QC$ is made larger, the value of $b$ for which the gain of the increasing wave is a maximum increases. Now, $C$ is proportional to the cube root of current. Thus, as current is increased, the voltage for maximum gain of the increasing wave increases. An increase in optimum operating voltage with an increase in current is observed in some tubes, and this is at least partly explained by these curves.* There is also some decrease in the maximum value of $x_1$ and hence of $B$ as $QC$ is increased. This is shown more clearly in Fig. 8.10.

If $x$ and $B$ remained constant when the current is varied, then the gain per wavelength would rise as $C$, or, as the $\frac{1}{3}$ power of current. However,

---

* Other factors include a possible lowering of electron speed because of d-c space charge, and boundary condition effects.

we see from Fig. 8.10 that $B$ falls as $QC$ is increased. The gain per wavelength varies as $BC$ and, because $Q$ is constant for a given tube, it varies as $BQC$. In Fig. 8.11, $BQC$, which is proportional to the gain per wavelength of the increasing wave, is plotted vs $QC$, which is proportional to the $\frac{1}{3}$ power of current. For very small values of current (small values of $QC$), the gain per wavelength is proportional to the $\frac{1}{3}$ power of current. For larger values of $QC$, the gain per wavelength becomes proportional to the $\frac{1}{4}$ power of current.

It would be difficult to present curves covering the simultaneous effect of loss $(d)$ and space charge $(QC)$. As a sort of substitute, Figs. 8.13 and 8.14 show $\partial x_1/\partial d$ for $d = 0$ and $b$ chosen to maximize $x_1$, and $\partial x_1/\partial (QC)$ for $QC = 0$ and $b = 0$. We see from 8.13 that, while for small values of $QC$ the gain of the increasing wave is reduced by $\frac{1}{3}$ of the circuit loss, for large values of $QC$ the gain of the increasing wave is reduced by $\frac{1}{2}$ of the circuit loss.

## 8.1 Effect of Varying the Electron Velocity

Consider equation (7.13) in case $d = 0$ (no attenuation) and $Q = 0$ (neglect of space-charge). We then have

$$\delta^2(\delta + jb) = -j \tag{8.1}$$

Here we will remember that

$$\beta_e = \omega/u_0 \tag{8.2}$$

$$-\Gamma_1 = -j\beta_e(1 + Cb) = -j\omega/v_1 \tag{8.3}$$

Here $v_1$ is the phase velocity of the wave in the absence of electrons, and $u_0$ is the electron speed. We see that

$$u_0 = (1 + Cb)v_1 \tag{8.4}$$

Thus, $(1 + Cb)$ is the ratio of the electron velocity to the velocity of the *undisturbed wave*, that is, the wave in the absence of electrons. Hence, $b$ is a measure of velocity difference between electrons and undisturbed wave. For $b > 0$, the electrons go faster than the undisturbed wave; for $b < 0$ the electrons go slower than the undisturbed wave. For $b = 0$ the electrons have the same speed as the undisturbed wave.

If $b = 0$, (8.1) becomes

$$\delta^3 = -j \tag{8.5}$$

which we obtained in Chapter II.

In dealing with (8.1), let

$$\delta = x + jy$$

The meaning of this will be clear when we remember that, in the presence of electrons, quantities vary with $z$ as (from (7.10))

$$e^{-j\beta_e(1+jC\delta)z}$$

$$= e^{-j\beta_e(1-Cy)z} e^{\beta_e Cxz} \tag{8.6}$$

If $v$ is the phase velocity in the presence of electrons, we have

$$\omega/v = (\omega/u_0)(1 - Cy) \tag{8.7}$$

If $Cy \ll 1$, very nearly

$$v = u_0(1 + Cy) \tag{8.8}$$

In other words, if $y > 0$, the wave travels faster than the electrons; if $y < 0$ the wave travels more slowly than the electrons.

From (8.6) we see that, if $x > 0$, the wave increases as it travels and if $x < 0$ the wave decreases as it travels. In Chapter II we expressed the gain of the increasing wave as

$$BCN \text{ db}$$

where $N$ is the number of wavelengths. We see that

$$B = 20(2\pi)(\log_{10}e)x$$

$$B = 54.5x \tag{8.9}$$

In terms of $x$ and $y$, (8.1) becomes

$$(x^2 - y^2)(y + b) + 2x^2y + 1 = 0 \tag{8.10}$$

$$x(x^2 - 3y^2 - 2yb) = 0 \tag{8.11}$$

We see that (8.11) yields two kinds of roots: those corresponding to unattenuated waves, for which $x = 0$ and those for which

$$x^2 = 3y^2 + 2yb \tag{8.12}$$

If $x = 0$, from (8.10)

$$y^2(y + b) = 1$$

$$b = -y + 1/y^2 \tag{8.13}$$

If we assume values of $y$ ranging from perhaps $+4$ to $-4$ we can find the corresponding values of $b$ from (8.13), and plot out $y$ vs $b$ for these unattenuated waves.

For the other waves, we substitute (8.12) into (8.10) and obtain

$$2yb^2 + 8y^2b + 8y^3 + 1 = 0 \tag{8.14}$$

This equation is a quadratic in $b$, and, by assigning various values of $y$, we can solve for $b$. We can then obtain $x$ from (8.12).

In this fashion we can construct curves of $x$ and $y$ vs $b$. Such curves are shown in Fig. 8.1.

We see that for

$$b < (3/2)(2)^{1/3}$$

there are two waves for which $x \neq 0$ and one unattenuated wave. The increasing and decreasing waves ($x \neq 0$) have equal and opposite values of $x$, and since for them $y < 1$, they travel more slowly than the electrons, *even when the electrons travel more slowly than the undisturbed wave.* It can be

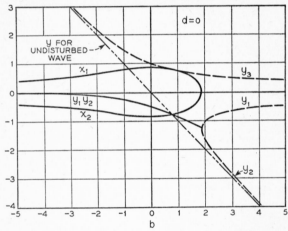

Fig. 8.1—The three waves vary with distance as $\exp\ (-j\beta_e + j\beta_e Cy + \beta_e Cx)z$. Here the $x$'s and $y$'s for the three waves are shown vs the velocity parameter $b$ for no attenuation ($d = 0$) and no space charge ($QC = 0$).

shown that the electrons must travel faster than the increasing wave in order to give energy to it.

For $b > (3/2)(2)^{1/3}$, there are 3 unattenuated waves: two travel faster than the electrons and one more slowly.

For large positive or negative values of $b$, two waves have nearly the electron speed ($|y|$ small) and one wave travels with the speed of the undisturbed wave. We measure velocity with respect to electron velocity. Thus, if we assigned a parameter $y$ to describe the velocity of the undisturbed wave relative to the electron velocity, it would vary as the $45°$ line in Fig. 8.1.

The data expressed in Fig. 8.1 give the variation of gain per wavelength of the undisturbed wave with electron velocity, and are also useful in fitting boundary conditions; for this we need to know the three $x$'s and the three $y$'s.

In a tube in which the total gain is large, a change in $b$ of $\pm 1$ about $b = 0$ can make a change of several db in gain. Such a change means a difference between phase velocity of the undisturbed wave, $v_1$, and electron velocity $u_0$ by a fraction approximately $\pm C$. Hence, the allowable difference between phase velocity $v_1$ of the undisturbed wave, which is a function of frequency, and electron velocity, which is not, is of the order of $C$.

## 8.2 EFFECT OF ATTENUATION

If we say that $d \neq 0$ but has some small positive value, we mean that the circuit is lossy, and in the absence of electrons the voltage decays with distance as

$$e^{-\beta_e Cd}$$

Hence, the loss $L$ in db/wavelength is

$$L = 20(2\pi)(\log_{10}e)Cd$$
$$L = 54.5Cd \text{ db/wavelength} \tag{8.15}$$

or

$$d = .01836 \ (L/C) \tag{8.16}$$

For instance, for $C = .025$, $d = 1$ means a loss of 1.36 db/wavelength.

If we assume $d \neq 0$ we obtain the equations

$$(x^2 - y^2)(y + b) + 2xy(x + d) + 1 = 0 \tag{8.17}$$

$$(x^2 - y^2)(x + d) - 2xy(y + b) = 0 \tag{8.18}$$

The equations have been solved numerically for $d = .5$ and $d = 1$, and the curves which were obtained are shown in Figs. 8.2 and 8.3. We see that for a circuit with attenuation there is an increasing wave for all values of $b$ (electron velocity). The velocity parameters $y_1$ and $y_2$ are now distinct for all values of $b$.

We see that the maximum value of $x_1$ decreases as loss is increased. This can be brought out more clearly by showing $x_1$ vs $b$ on an expanded scale. It is perhaps more convenient to plot $B$, the db gain per wavelength per unit $C$, vs $b$, and this has been done for various values of $d$ in Fig. 8.4.

We see that for small values of $d$ the maximum value of $x_1$ occurs very near to $b = 0$. If we let $b = 0$ in (8.17) and (8.18) we obtain

$$y(x^2 - y^2) + 2xy(x + d) + 1 = 0 \tag{8.19}$$

$$(x^2 - y^2)(x + d) - 2xy^2 = 0 \qquad (8.20)$$

We can rewrite (8.20) in the form

$$y = \pm x \left(\frac{1 + d/x}{3 + d/x}\right)^{1/2} \qquad (8.21)$$

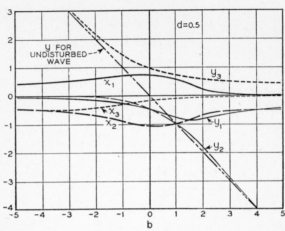

Fig. 8.2—The $x$'s and $y$'s for a circuit with attenuation ($d = .5$).

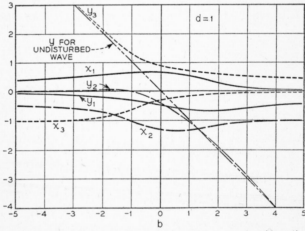

Fig. 8 3—The $x$'s and $y$'s for a circuit with attenuation ($d = 1$).

If we substitute this into (8.19) we can solve for $x$ in terms of the parameter $d/x$

$$x = \mp \left[\frac{\left(\dfrac{3 + d/x}{1 + d/x}\right)^{1/2}}{2\left(\dfrac{1}{3 + d/x} + 1 + d/x\right)}\right]^{1/3} \qquad (8.22)$$

Here we take both upper signs or both lower signs in (8.21) and (8.22). If we assume $d/x \ll 1$ and expand, keeping no powers of $d/x$ higher than the first, we obtain

$$x = \mp (\sqrt{3}/2)(1 - (1/3(d/x))) \qquad (8.23)$$

The plus sign will give $x_1$, which is the $x$ for the increasing wave. Let $x_{10}$ be the value of $x_1$ for $d = 0$ (no loss).

$$x_{10} = \sqrt{3}/2 \qquad (8.24)$$

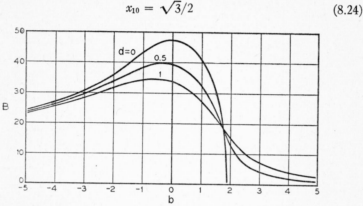

Fig. 8.4—The gain of the increasing wave is $BCN$ db, where $N$ is the number of wavelengths.

Then for small values of $d$

$$x_1 = x_{10}(1 - (1/3)(d/x_{10}))$$

$$(8.25)$$

$$x_1 = x_{10} - 1/3d$$

This says that, for small losses, the reduction of gain *of the increasing wave* from the gain in db for zero loss is $\frac{1}{3}$ of the circuit attenuation in db. The reduction of *net gain*, which will be greater, can be obtained only by matching boundary conditions in the presence of loss (see Chapter IX).

In Fig. 8.5, $B = 54.6 \, x_1$ has been plotted vs $d$ from (8.22). The straight line is for $x_{10} = d/3$.

In Fig. 8.6, $-x_1$, $x_2$ and $x_3$ have been plotted vs $d$ for a large range in $d$. As the circuit is made very lossy, the waves which for no loss are unattenuated and increasing turn into a pair of waves with equal and opposite small attenuations. These waves will be essentially disturbances in the electron stream, or space-charge waves. The original decreasing wave turns into a wave which has the attenuation of the circuit, and is accompanied by small disturbances in the electron stream.

8.3 SPACE-CHARGE EFFECTS

Suppose that we let $d$, the attenuation parameter, be zero, but consider cases in which the space-charge parameter $QC$ is not zero. We then obtain

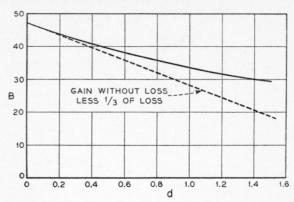

Fig. 8.5—For $b = 0$, that is, for electrons with a velocity equal to the circuit phase velocity, the gain factor $B$ falls as the attenuation parameter $d$ is increased. For small values of $d$, the gain is reduced by $\frac{1}{3}$ of the circuit loss.

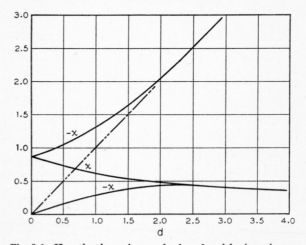

Fig. 8.6—How the three $x$'s vary for $b = 0$ and for large losses.

the equations

$$(x^2 - y^2)(b + y) + 2x^2 y + 4QC(b + y) + 1 = 0 \qquad (8.26)$$

$$x[(x^2 - y^2) - 2y(y + b) + QC] = 0 \qquad (8.27)$$

Solutions of this have been found by numerical methods for $QC = .25$, .5 and 1; these are shown in Figs. 8.7–8.9.

We see at once that the electron velocity for maximum gain shifts markedly as $QC$ is increased. Hence, the region around $b = 0$ is not in this case worthy of a separate investigation.

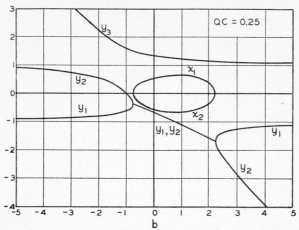

Fig. 8.7—The $x$'s and $y$'s for the three waves with zero loss ($d = 0$) but with space charge ($QC = .25$).

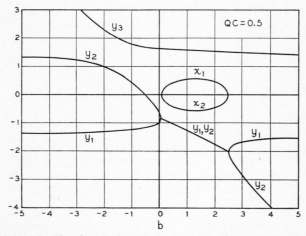

Fig. 8.8—The $x$'s and $y$'s with greater space charge ($QC = .5$).

It is interesting to plot the maximum value of $x_1$ vs. the parameter $QC$. This has, in effect, been done in Fig. 8.10, which shows $B$, the gain in db per wavelength per unit $C$, vs. $QC$.

We can obtain a curve proportional to db per wavelength by plotting $BQC$ vs. $QC$. ($Q$ is independent of current.) This has been done in Fig. 8.11. For $QC < 0.025$, the gain in db per wavelength varies linearly with

*QC*. Chu and Rydbeck found that under certain conditions gain varies approximately as the $\frac{1}{4}$ power of the current. This would mean a slope of $\frac{3}{4}$ on Fig. 8.11. A $\frac{3}{4}$ power dashed line is shown in Fig. 8.11; it fits the upper part of the curve approximately.

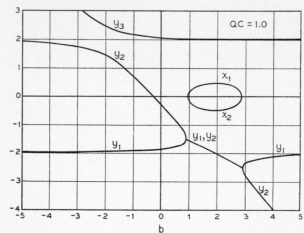

Fig. 8.9—The *x*'s and *y*'s with still greater space charge ($QC = 1$).

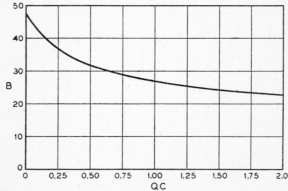

Fig. 8.10—How the gain factor *B* decreases as *QC* is increased, for the value of *b* which gives a maximum value of $x_1$.

If we examine Figs. 8.7–8.9 we find that for large and small values of *b* there are, as in other cases, a circuit wave, for which *y* is nearly equal to $-b$, and two space-charge waves. For these, however, *y* does not approach zero.

Let us consider equation (7.13). If *b* is large, the first term on the right becomes small, and we have approximately

$$\delta = \pm j2\sqrt{QC} \tag{8.28}$$

These waves correspond to the space-charge waves of Hahn and Ramo, and are quite independent of the circuit impedance, which appears in (8.28) merely as an arbitrary parameter defining the units in which $\delta$ is measured. Equation (8.28) also describes the disturbance we would get if we shorted out the circuit by some means, as by adding excessive loss.

Practically, we need an estimate of the value of $Q$ for some typical circuit. In Appendix IV an estimate is made on the following basis: The helix

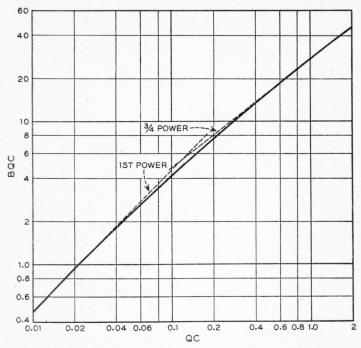

Fig. 8.11—The variation of a quantity proportional to the cube of the gain of the increasing wave (ordinate) with a quantity proportional to current (abscissa). For very small currents, the gain of the increasing wave is proportional to the ⅓ power of current, for large currents to the ¼ power of current.

of radius $a$ is replaced by a conducting cylinder of the same radius, a thin cylinder of convection current of radius $a_1$ and current of $i \exp(-j\beta z)$ is assumed, and the field is calculated and identified with the second term on the right of (7.1). R. C. Fletcher has obtained a more accurate value of $Q$ by a rigorous method. His work is reproduced in Appendix VI, and in Fig. 1 of that appendix, Fletcher's value of $Q$ is compared with the approximate value of Appendix IV.

In Fig. 8.12, the value $Q(\beta/\gamma)^2$ of Appendix IV is plotted vs. $\gamma a$ for $a_1/a = .9, .8, .7$. For $a_1/a = 1$, $Q = 0$. In a typical 4,000 mc traveling-wave tube, $\gamma a = 2.8$ and $C$ is about .025. Thus, if we take the effective beam radius as .5 times the helix radius, $Q = 5.6$ and $QC = .14$.

We note from (7.14) that $Q$ is the ratio of a capacitive impedance to $(E^2/\beta^2 P)$. In obtaining the curves of Fig. 8.12, the value of $(E^2/\beta^2 P)$ for a helically conducting sheet was assumed. This is given by (3.8) and (3.9). If $(E^2/\beta^2 P)$ is different for the circuit actually used, and it is somewhat different, even for an actual helix, $Q$ from Fig. 8.12 should be multiplied by $(E^2/\beta^2 P)$ for the helically conducting sheet, from (3.8) and (3.9), and divided by the value of $(E^2/\beta^2 P)$ for the circuit used.

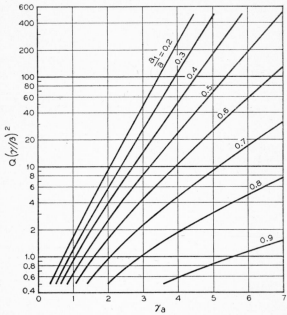

Fig. 8.12—Curves for obtaining $Q$ for a helically conducting sheet and a hollow beam. The radius of the helically conducting sheet is $a$ and that of the beam is $a_1$.

## 8.4 DIFFERENTIAL RELATIONS

It would be onerous to construct curves giving $\delta$ as a function of $b$ for many values of attenuation and space charge. In some cases, however, useful information may be obtained by considering the effect of adding a small amount of attenuation when $QC$ is large, or of seeing the effect of space charge when $QC$ is small but the attenuation is large. We start with (7.13)

$$\delta^2 = \frac{1}{(-b + jd + j\delta)} - 4QC \qquad (7.13)$$

Let us first differentiate (7.13) with respect to $\delta$ and $d$

$$2\delta \, d\delta = \frac{-j \, dd - j \, d\delta}{(-b + j \, d + j\delta)^2} \tag{8.29}$$

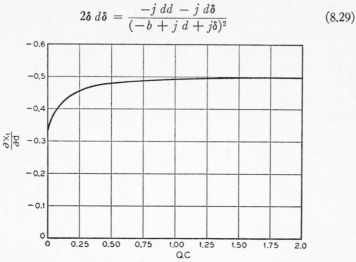

Fig. 8.13—A curve giving the rate of change of $x_1$ with attenuation parameter $d$ for $d = 0$ and for various values of the space-charge parameter $QC$. For small values of $QC$ the gain of the increasing wave is reduced by $\frac{1}{3}$ of the circuit loss; for large values of $QC$ the gain of the increasing wave is reduced by $\frac{1}{2}$ of the circuit loss.

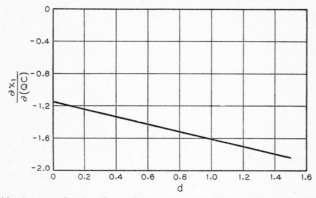

Fig. 8.14—A curve showing the variation of $x_1$ with $QC$ for $QC = 0$ and for various values of the attenuation parameter $d$.

By using (7.13) we obtain

$$d\delta = \left(\frac{-j2\delta}{(\delta^2 + 4QC)^2} - 1\right)^{-1} dd \tag{8.30}$$

If we allow $d$ to be small, we can use the values of $\delta$ of Figs. 8.7–8.9 to plot the quantity

$$\mathrm{Re}(d\delta_1/dd) = dx_1/dd \tag{8.31}$$

vs. $QC$. In Fig. 8.13, this has been done for $b$ chosen to make $x_1$ a maximum. We see that a small loss $dd$ causes more reduction of gain as $QC$ is increased (more space charge).

Let us now differentiate (7.13) with respect to $QC$

$$2\delta \, d\delta = \frac{-j \, d\delta}{(-b + j \, d + j\delta)^2} - 4 \, d(QC) \qquad (8.32)$$

By using (7.13) with $QC = 0$ we obtain

$$d\delta = \left( \frac{-4}{2\delta + j\delta^4} \right) d(QC) \qquad (8.33)$$

In Fig. 8.14, $dx/d(QC)$ has been plotted vs. $d$ for $b = 0$.

We see that the reduction of gain for a small amount of space charge becomes greater, the greater the loss is increased ($d$ increased).

Both Fig. 8.13 and Fig. 8.14 indicate that for large values of $QC$ or $d$ the gain will be overestimated if space charge ($QC$) and loss ($d$) are considered separately.

PROBLEMS

1. A helix for a 1,600 volt traveling-wave tube for 10 cm operation has a diameter of 0.15″. The solid beam has a diameter of 0.10″. The beam current is 0.10 ma. Calculate $C$ according to impedance of Chapter III. Assuming $b = d = Q = 0$, what is the gain of the increasing wave in 20 wavelengths?

2. For the tube of Problem 1, obtain values of $C$ and $Q$ from Appendix VI (with the help of Appendix VII, if needed). Assuming $b = d = 0$, what is the gain in 40 wavelengths? Compare with the results of Problem 1? How much of the difference is due to change in $C$ and how much to the fact that $Q \neq 0$?

3. Keeping $b = 0$ for 10 cm, calculate the gain as in Problem 2 for 6 cm, 8 cm, 12 cm, 14 cm.

4. Make the calculation of Problem 2 assuming 40 db uniformly distributed loss in 20 wavelengths instead of $d = 0$.

# CHAPTER IX
# DISCONTINUITIES

W\E WANT TO KNOW the overall gain of traveling-wave tubes. So far, we have evaluated only the gain of the increasing wave, and we must find out how strong an increasing wave is set up when a voltage is applied to the circuit.

Beyond this, we may wish for some reason to break the circuit up into several sections having different parameters. For instance, it is desirable that a traveling-wave tube have more loss in the backward direction than it has gain in the forward direction. If this is not so, small mismatches will result either in oscillation or at least in the gain fluctuating violently with frequency. We have already seen in Chapter VIII the effect of a uniform loss in reducing the gain of the increasing wave. We need to know also the overall effect of short sections of loss in order to know how loss may best be introduced.

Such problems are treated in this chapter by matching boundary conditions at the points of discontinuity. It is assumed that there is no reflected wave at the discontinuity. This will be very nearly so, because the characteristic impedances of the waves differ little over the range of loss and velocity considered. Thus, the total voltages, a-c convection currents and the a-c velocities on the two sides of the point of discontinuity are set equal.

For instance, at the beginning of the circuit, where the unmodulated electron stream enters, the total a-c velocity and the total a-c convection current—that is, the sums of the convection currents and the velocities for the three waves—are set equal to zero, and the sum of the voltages for the three waves is set equal to the applied voltage.

For the case of no loss ($d = 0$) and an electron velocity equal to circuit phase velocity ($b = 0$) we find that the three waves are set up with equal voltages, each $\frac{1}{3}$ of the applied voltage. The voltage along the circuit will then be the sum of the voltages of the three waves, and the way in which the magnitude of this sum varies with distance along the circuit is shown in Fig. 9.1. Here $CN$ measures distance from the beginning of the circuit and the amplitude relative to the applied voltage is measured in db.

The dashed curve represents the voltage of the increasing wave alone.

For large values of $CN$ corresponding to large gains, the increasing wave predominates and we can neglect the effect of the other waves. This leads to the gain expression

$$G = A + BCN \text{ db}$$

Here $BCN$ is the gain in db of the increasing wave and $A$ measures its initial level with respect to the applied voltage.

In Fig. 9.2, $A$ is plotted vs. $b$ for several values of the loss parameter $d$. The fact that $A$ goes to $\infty$ for $d = 0$ as $b$ approaches $(3/2) (2)^{1/3}$ does not imply an infinite gain for, at this value of $b$, the gain of the increasing wave approaches zero and the voltage of the decreasing wave approaches the negative of that for the increasing wave.

Figure 9.3 shows how $A$ varies with $d$ for $b = 0$. Figure 9.4 shows how $A$ varies with $QC$ for $d = 0$ and for $b$ chosen to give a maximum value of $B$ (the greatest gain of the increasing wave).

Suppose that for $b = QC = 0$ the loss parameter is suddenly changed from zero to some finite value $d$. Suppose also that the increasing wave is very large compared with the other waves reaching the discontinuity. We can then calculate the ratio of the increasing wave just beyond the discontinuity to the increasing wave reaching the discontinuity. The solid line of Fig. 9.5 shows this ratio expressed in decibels. We see that the voltage of the increasing wave excited in the lossy section is less than the voltage of the incident increasing wave.

Now, suppose the waves travel on in the lossy section until the increasing wave again predominates. If the circuit is then made suddenly lossless, we find that the increasing wave excited in this lossless section will have a greater voltage than the increasing wave incident from the lossy section, as shown by the dashed curve of Fig. 9.5. This increase is almost as great as the loss in entering the lossy section. Imagine a tube with a long lossless section, a long lossy section and another long lossless section. We see that the gain of this tube will be less than that of a lossless tube of the same total length by about the reduction of the gain of the increasing wave in lossy section.

Suppose that the electromagnetic energy of the circuit is suddenly absorbed at a distance beyond the input measured by $CN$. This might be done by severing a helix and terminating the ends. The a-c velocity and convection current will be unaffected in passing the discontinuity, but the circuit voltage drops to zero. For $d = b = QC = 0$, Fig. 9.6 shows the ratio of $V_1$, the amplitude of the increasing wave beyond the break, to $V$, the amplitude the increasing wave would have had if there were no break. We see that for $CN$ greater than about 0.2 the loss due to the break is not serious. For *CN* large (the break far from the input) the loss approaches 3.52 db.

Beyond such a break, the total voltage increases with *CN* as shown in Fig. 9.7, and from *CN* = 0.2 the circuit voltage is very nearly equal to the voltage of the increasing wave.

Often, for practical reasons loss is introduced over a considerable distance, sometimes by putting lossy material near to a helix. Suppose we use *CN* computed as if for a lossless section of circuit as a measure of length of the lossy section, and assume that the loss is great enough so that the circuit voltage (as opposed to that produced by space charge) can be taken as zero. Such a lossy section acts as a drift space. Suppose that an increasing wave only reaches this lossy section. The amplitude of the increasing wave excited beyond the lossy section in db with respect to the amplitude of the increasing wave reaching the lossy section is shown vs. *CN*, which measures the length of the lossy section, in Fig. 9.8.

### 9.1 GENERAL BOUNDARY CONDITIONS

We have already assumed that $C$ is small, and when this is so the characteristic impedance of the various waves is near to the circuit characteristic impedance $K$. We will neglect any reflections caused by differences among the characteristic impedances of the various waves.

We will consider cases in which the circuit is terminated in the $+z$ direction, so as to give no backward wave. We will then be concerned with the 3 forward waves, for which $\delta$ has the values $\delta_1$, $\delta_2$, $\delta_3$ and the waves represented by these values of $\delta$ have voltages $V_1$, $V_2$, $V_3$, electron velocities $v_1$, $v_2$, $v_3$ and convection currents $i_1$, $i_2$, $i_3$.

Let $V$, $v$, $i$ be the total voltage, velocity and convection current at $z = 0$. Then we have

$$V_1 + V_2 + V_3 = V \qquad (9.1)$$

and from (7.15) and (7.16),

$$\frac{V_1}{\delta_1} + \frac{V_2}{\delta_2} + \frac{V_3}{\delta_3} = (ju_0C/\eta)v \qquad (9.2)$$

$$\frac{V_1}{\delta_1^2} + \frac{V_2}{\delta_2^2} + \frac{V_3}{\delta_3^2} = (-2V_0C^2/I_0)i \qquad (9.3)$$

These equations yield, when solved,

$$V_1 = [V - (\delta_2 + \delta_3)(ju_0C/\eta)v + \delta_2\delta_3(-2V_0C^2/I_0)i]$$
$$[(1 - \delta_2/\delta_1)(1 - \delta_3/\delta_1)]^{-1} \qquad (9.4)$$

We can obtain the corresponding expressions for $V_2$ and $V_3$ simply by interchanging subscripts; to obtain $V_2$, for instance, we substitute subscript 2 for 1 and subscript 1 for 2 in (9.4).

## 9.2 LOSSLESS HELIX, SYNCHRONOUS VELOCITY, NO SPACE CHANGE

Suppose we consider the case in which $b = d = Q = 0$, so that we have the values of $\delta$ obtained in Chapter II

$$\delta_1 = e^{-j\pi/6} = \sqrt{3}/2 - j1/2$$

$$\delta_2 = e^{-j5\pi/6} = - \sqrt{3}/2 - j1/2 \qquad (9.5)$$

$$\delta_3 = e^{j\pi/2} = j$$

Suppose we inject an unmodulated electron stream into the helix and apply a voltage $V$. The obvious thing is to say that, at $z = 0$, $v = i = 0$. It is not quite clear, however, that $v = 0$ at $z = 0$ (the beginning of the circuit). Whether or not there is a stray field, which will give an initial velocity modulation, depends on the type of circuit. Two things are true, however. For the small values of $C$ usually encountered such a velocity modulation constitutes a small effect. Also, the fields of the first part of the helix act essentially to velocity modulate the electron stream, and hence a neglect of any small initial velocity modulation will be about equivalent to a small displacement of the origin.

If, then, we let $v = i = 0$ and use (9.4) we obtain

$$V_1 = V[(1 - \delta_2/\delta_1)(1 - \delta_3/\delta_1)]^{-1} \qquad (9.6)$$

$$V_1 = V/3 \qquad (9.7)$$

Similarly, we find that

$$V_2 = V_3 = V/3 \qquad (9.8)$$

We have used $V$ to denote the voltage at $z = 0$. Let $V_z$ be the voltage at $z$. We have

$$V_z = (V/3)e^{-j\beta_e z}(e^{j(1/2)\beta_e Cz+(\sqrt{3}/2)\beta_e Cz} + e^{j(1/2)\beta_e Cz-(\sqrt{3}/2)\beta_e Cz} + e^{j\beta_e Cz})$$

$$V_z = (V/3)e^{-j\beta_e(1-C)z} (1 + 2 \cosh ((\sqrt{3}/2)\beta eCz)e^{-j(3/2)\beta_e Cz}) \qquad (9.9)$$

From this we obtain

$$|V_z/V|^2 = (1/9)[1 + 4 \cosh^2(\sqrt{3}/2)\beta_e Cz$$
$$+ 4 \cos (3/2)\beta_e Cz \cosh (\sqrt{3}/2)\beta_e Cz] \qquad (9.10)$$

We can express gain in db as $10 \log_{10} |V_z/V|^2$, and, in Fig. 9.1, gain in db is plotted vs $CN$, where $N$ is the number of cycles.

We see that initially the voltage does not change with distance. This is natural, because the electron stream initially has no convection current, and hence cannot act on the circuit until it becomes bunched. Finally, of course, the increasing wave must predominate over the other two, and the slope of the line must be

$$B = 47.3/CN \qquad (9.11)$$

The dashed line represents the increasing wave, which starts at $V_z/V = \frac{1}{3}$ ($-9.54$ db) and has the slope specified by (9.11). Thus, if we write for the increasing wave that gain $G$ is

$$G = A + BCN \text{ db} \qquad (9.12)$$

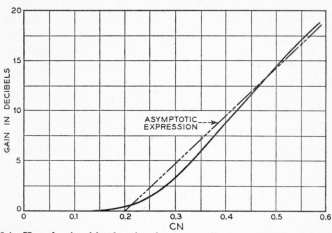

Fig. 9.1—How the signal level varies along a traveling-wave tube for the special case of zero loss and space charge and an electron velocity equal to the circuit phase velocity (solid curve). The dashed curve is the level of the increasing wave alone, which starts off with $\frac{1}{3}$ of the applied voltage, or at $-9.54$ *db*.

This is an asymptotic expression for the total voltage at large values of $z$, where $|V_1| \gg |V_2|$, $|V_3|$, and for $b = d = Q = 0$

$$A = -9.54 \text{ db}$$
$$B = 47.3 \qquad (9.13)$$

We see that (9.11) is pretty good for $CN > .4$, and not too bad for $CN > .2$.

9.3 LOSS IN HELIX

In Chapter VIII, curves were given for $\delta_1$, $\delta_2$, $\delta_3$ vs. $b$ for $QC = 0$ and for $d$, the loss parameter, equal to 0, 0.5 and 1. From the data from which these curves were derived one can calculate the initial loss parameter by means of (9.6)

$$A = 20 \log_{10} |V_1/V| \qquad (9.14)$$

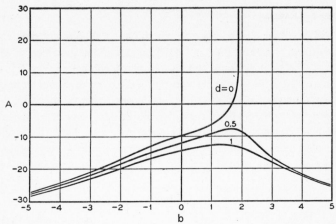

Fig. 9.2—When the gain is large we need consider the increasing wave only. Using this approximation, the gain in db is $A + BCN$ db. Here $A$ is shown vs the velocity parameter $b$ several values of the attenuation parameter $d$, for no space charge ($QC = 0$).

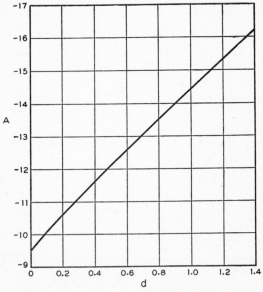

Fig. 9.3—$A$ vs $d$ for $b = 0$ and $QC = 0$.

In Fig. 9.2, $A$ is plotted vs $b$ for these three values of $d$.

It is perhaps of some interest to plot $A$ vs $d$ for $b = 0$ (the electron velocity equal to the phase velocity of the undisturbed wave). Such a plot is shown in Fig. 9.3.

## 9.4. SPACE CHARGE

We will now consider the case in which $QC \neq 0$. We will deal with this case only for $d = 0$, and for $b$ adjusted for maximum gain per wavelength.

There is a peculiarity about this case in that a certain voltage $V$ is applied to the *circuit* at $z = 0$, and we want to evaluate the *circuit* voltage associated with the increasing wave, $V_{c1}$, in order to know the gain.

At $z = 0$, $i = 0$. Now, the term which multiplies $i$ to give the space-charge component of voltage (the second term on the right in (7.11)) is the same for all three waves and hence at $z = 0$ the circuit voltage is the total voltage. Thus, (9.1)–(9.3) hold. However, after $V_1$ has been obtained from (9.4), with

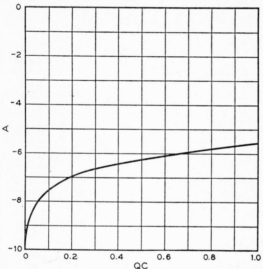

Fig. 9.4—$A$ vs $QC$ for $d = 0$ and $b$ chosen for maximum gain of the increasing wave.

$V = V_1$, $v = i = 0$, then the circuit voltage $V_{c1}$ must be obtained through the use of (7.14), and the initial loss parameter is

$$A = 20 \log_{10} | V_{c1}/V | \qquad (9.15)$$

By using the appropriate values of $\delta$, the same used in plotting Figs. 8.1 and 8.7–8.9, the loss parameter A was obtained from (9.15) and plotted vs $QC$ in Fig. 9.4.

## 9.5 CHANGE IN LOSS

We might think it undesirable in introducing loss to make the whole length of the helix lossy. For instance, we might expect the power output to be higher if the last part of the helix had low loss. Also, from Figs. 8.2

and 8.3 we see that the initial loss A becomes higher as $d$ is increased. This is natural, because the electron stream can act to cause gain only after it is bunched, and if the initial section of the circuit is lossy, the signal decays before the stream becomes strongly bunched.

Let us consider a section of a lossless helix which is far enough from the input so that the increasing wave predominates and the total voltage $V$ can be taken as that corresponding to the increasing wave

$$V = V_1 \tag{9.16}$$

Then, at this point

$$(ju_0C/\eta)v = V_1/\delta_1 \tag{9.17}$$

$$(-2V_0C^2/I_0)i = V_1/\delta_1^2 . \tag{9.18}$$

Here $\delta_1$ is the value for $d = 0$ (and, we assume, $b = 0$). If we substitute the values from (9.16) in (9.4), and use in (9.4) the values of $\delta$ corresponding to $b = Q = 0$, $d \neq 0$, and call the value of $V_1$ we obtain $V_1'$, we obtain the ratio of the initial amplitude of the increasing wave in the lossy section to the value of the increasing wave just to the left of the lossy section. Thus, the loss in the amplitude of the increasing wave in going from a lossless to a lossy section is $20 \log_{10} | V_1'/V_1 |$. This loss is plotted vs $d$ in Fig. 8.5.

This loss is accounted for by the fact that $| i_1/V_1 |$ becomes larger as the loss parameter $d$ is increased. Thus, the convection current injected into the lossy section is insufficient to go with the voltage, and the voltage must fall.

If we go from a lossy section $(d \neq 0, b = 0)$ to a lossless section $(d = 0, b = 0)$ we start with an excess of convection current and $| V_1' |$, the initial amplitude of the increasing wave to the right of the discontinuity is greater than the amplitude $| V_1 |$ of the increasing wave to the left. In Fig. 9.5, $20 \log_{10} | V_1'/V_1 |$ is plotted vs $d$ for this case also.

We see that if we go from a lossless section to a lossy section, and if the lossy section is long enough so that the increasing wave predominates at the end of it, and if we go back to a lossless section at the end of it, the net loss and gain at the discontinuities almost compensate, and even for $d = 3$ the net discontinuity loss is less than 1 db. This does not consider the reduction of gain of the increasing wave in the lossy section.

## 9.6 Severed Helix

If the loss introduced is distributed over the length of the helix, the gain will decrease as the loss is increased (Fig. 8.5). If, however, the loss is distributed over a very short section, we easily see that as the loss is increased more and more, the gain must approach a constant value. The circuit will be in effect severed as far as the electromagnetic wave is concerned, and any excitation in the output will be due to the a-c velocity and convection current of the electron stream which crosses the lossy section.

We will first idealize the situation and assume that the helix is severed and by some means terminated looking in each direction, so that the voltage falls from a value $V$ to a value 0 in zero distance, while $v$ and $i$ remain unchanged.

We will consider a case in which $b = d = Q = 0$, and in which a voltage

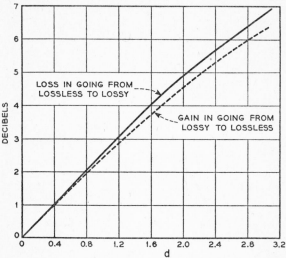

Fig. 9.5—Suppose that the circuit loss parameter changes suddenly with distance from 0 to $d$ or from $d$ to 0. Suppose there is an increasing wave only incident at the point of change. How large will the increasing wave beyond the point of change be? These curves tell ($b = QC = 0$).

$V$ is applied to the helix $N$ wavelengths before the cut. Then, just before the cut,

$$V_1 = (V/3)e^{-j2\pi N}e^{2\pi NC\delta_1}$$
$$V_2 = (V/3)e^{-j2\pi N}e^{2\pi NC\delta_2} \quad (9.19)$$
$$V_3 = (V/3)e^{-j2\pi N}e^{2\pi NC\delta_3}$$

and

$$(ju_0C/\eta)v_1 = V_1/\delta_1$$
$$(-2V_0C^3/I_0)i_1 = V_1/\delta_1^2 \quad (9.20)$$

etc.

Whence, just beyond the break which makes $V = 0$, $V$, $v$ and $i$ are

$$V = 0$$

$$(ju_0C/\eta)v = V_1/\delta_1 + V_2/\delta_2 + V_3/\delta_3 \qquad (9.21)$$

$$(-2V_0C^2/I_0)i = V_1/\delta_1^2 + V_2/\delta_2^2 + V_3/\delta_3^2$$

Putting these values in (9.4), we can find $V_1'$, the value of the increasing wave to the right of the break. The ratio of the magnitude of the increasing wave to the magnitude it would have if it were not for the break is then $| V_1'/V_1 |$, and this ratio is plotted vs $CN$ in Fig. 9.6, where $N$ is the number of wavelengths in the first section.

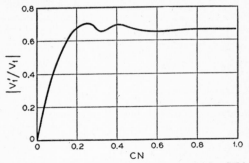

Fig. 9.6—Suppose the circuit is severed a distance measured by $CN$ beyond the input, so that the voltage just beyond the break is zero. The ordinate is the ratio of the amplitude of the increasing wave beyond the break to that it would have had with an unbroken circuit ($b = QC = 0$).

We see that there will be least loss in severing the helix for $CN$ equal to approximately $\frac{1}{4}$. From Fig. 9.1, we see that at $CN = \frac{1}{4}$ the voltage is just beginning to rise. In a typical 4,000 megacycle traveling-wave tube, $CN$ is approximately unity for a 10 inch helix, so the loss should be put at least 2.5″ beyond the input. Putting the loss further on changes things little; asymptotically, $| V_1'/V |$ approaches $\frac{2}{3}$, or 3.52 db loss, for large values of $CN$ (loss for from input).

It is of some interest to know how the voltage rises to the right of the cut. It was assumed that the cut was far from the point of excitation, so that only increasing wave of magnitude $V_1$ was present just to the left of the cut. The initial amplitudes of the three waves, $V_1'$, $V_2'$, $V_3'$ to the right of the cut were computed and the magnitude of their sum plotted vs $CN$ as it varies with distance to the right of the cut. The resulting curve, expressed in db with respect to the magnitude of the increasing wave $V_1$ just to the left of the cut, is shown in Fig. 9.7. Again, we see that at a distance $CN = \frac{1}{4}$ to the right of the cut the increasing wave (dashed straight line) predominates.

## 9.7 SEVERED HELIX WITH DRIFT SPACE

In actually putting concentrated loss in a helix, the loss cannot be concentrated in a section of zero length for two reasons. In the first place, this is physically difficult if not impossible; in the second place it is desirable that the two halves of the helix be terminated in a reflectionless manner at the cut, and it is easiest to do this by tapering the loss. For instance, if the loss is put in by spraying aquadag (graphite in water) on ceramic rods supporting the helix, it is desirable to taper the loss coating at the ends of the lossy section.

Perhaps the best reasonably simple approximation we can make to such a lossy section is one in which the section starts far enough from the input

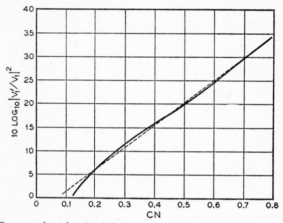

Fig. 9.7—Suppose that the circuit is severed and an increasing wave only is incident at the break. How does the signal build up beyond the break? The solid curve shows $(b = QC = 0)$. 0 db is the level of the incident increasing wave.

so that at the beginning of the lossy section only an increasing wave is present. In the lossy section $CN$ long we will consider that the loss completely shorts out the circuit, so that (8.28) holds. Thus, in the lossy section we will have only two values of $\delta$, which we will call $\delta_I$ and $\delta_{II}$.

$$\delta_I = jk \tag{9.21}$$

$$\delta_{II} = -jk \tag{9.22}$$

$$k = 2\sqrt{QC} \tag{9.23}$$

Let $V_I$ and $V_{II}$ be the voltages of the waves corresponding to $\delta_I$ and $\delta_{II}$ at the beginning of the lossy section. Let $\delta_1$, $\delta_2$, $\delta_3$ be the values of $\delta$ to the left and right of the lossy section. Let $V_1$ be the amplitude of the increasing wave just to the left of the lossy section. Then, by equating velocities and convection currents at the start of the lossy section, we obtain

$$V_1/\delta_1 = V_I/\delta_I + V_{II}/\delta_{II} \tag{9.24}$$

and, from (9.21) and (9.22)

$$V_1/\delta_1 = (-j/k)(V_I - V_{II}) \tag{9.25}$$

Similarly

$$V_1/\delta_1^2 = V_I/\delta_{II}^2 + V_{II}\,\delta_{II}^2$$
$$V_1/\delta_1^2 = -(1/k^2)(V_I + V_{II}) \tag{9.26}$$

So that

$$V_I = j(V_1/2)(k/\delta_1)(jk/\delta_1 + 1) \tag{9.27}$$

$$V_{II} = j(V_1/2)(k/\delta_1)(jk/\delta_1 - 1) \tag{9.28}$$

At the output of the lossy section we have the voltages $V_I'$ and $V_{II}'$

$$V_I' = V_I e^{-j2\pi N} e^{-j2\pi k C N} \tag{9.29}$$

$$V_{II}' = V_{II} e^{-j2\pi N} e^{-j2\pi k C N} \tag{9.30}$$

Thus, at the end of the lossy section we have

$$V = V_I' + V_{II}' \tag{9.31}$$

$$(ju_0C/\eta)v = V_I'/\delta_I + V_{II}'/\delta_{II}$$
$$(ju_0C/\eta)v = (-j/k)(V_I' - V_{II}') \tag{9.32}$$

and similarly

$$(-2V_0C^2/I_0)i = (-1/k^2)(V_I' + V_{II}') \tag{9.33}$$

From (9.27) and (9.28) we see that

$$V_I' + V_{II}' = -(k/\delta_1)[+(k/\delta_1)\cos 2\pi k C N + \sin 2\pi k C N]V_1 e^{-j2\pi N} \tag{9.34}$$

$$V_I' - V_{II}' = j(k/\delta_1)[-(k/\delta_1)\sin 2\pi k C N + \cos 2\pi k C N]V_1 e^{-j2\pi N} \tag{9.35}$$

Whence

$$V = -(k/\delta_1)[+(k/\delta_1)\cos 2\pi k C N + \sin 2\pi k C N]V_1 e^{-j2\pi N} \tag{9.36}$$

$$(ju_0C/\eta)v = (1/\delta_1)[-(k/\delta_1)\sin 2\pi k C N + \cos 2\pi k C N]V_1 e^{-j2\pi N} \tag{9.37}$$

$$(-2V_0C^2/I_0)i = (1/\delta_1)[(1/\delta_1)\cos 2\pi k C N + (1/k)\sin 2\pi k C N]V_1 e^{-j2\pi N} \tag{9.38}$$

These can be used in connection with (9.4) in obtaining $V_1'$, the value of $V_1$ just beyond the lossy section; that is, the amplitude of the component of increasing wave just beyond the lossy section.

In typical traveling-wave tubes the lossy section usually has a length such that $CN$ is $\frac{1}{4}$ or less. In Fig. 9.8 the loss in db in going through the lossy section, 20 $\log_{10} | V_1'/V_1 |$, has been plotted vs. $CN$ for $QC = 0$, .25, .5 for the range $CN = 0$ to $CN = .5$.

We see that, for low space charge, increasing the length of a drift space increases the loss. For higher space charge it may either increase or decrease the loss. It is not clear that the periodic behavior characteristic of the curves for $QC = 0.5$ and 1, for instance, will obtain for a drift space with tapered loss at each end. The calculations may also be considerably in error for broad electron beams ($\gamma a$ large). The electric field pattern in the helix differs

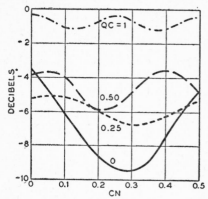

Fig. 9.8—Suppose that we break the circuit and insert a drift tube of length measured by $CN$ in terms of the traveling-wave tube $C$ and $N$. Assume an increasing wave only before the drift tube. The increasing wave beyond the drift tube will have a level with respect to the incident increasing wave as shown by the ordinate. Here $d = 0$ and $b$ is chosen to maximize $x_1$.

from that in the drift space. In the case of broad electron beams this may result in the excitation in the drift space of several different space charge waves having different field patterns and different propagation constants.

A suggestion has been made that the introduction of loss itself has a bad effect. The only thing that affects the electrons is an electric field. Unpublished measurements made by Cutler mode by moving a probe along a helix indicate that in typical short high-loss sections the electric field of the helix is essentially zero. Hence, except for a short distance at the ends, such lossy sections should act simply as drift spaces.

## 9.8 OVERALL BEHAVIOR OF TUBES

The material of Chapters VIII and IX is useful in designing traveling-wave tubes. Prediction of the performance of a given tube over a wide range of voltage and current is quite a different matter. For instance, in order to predict gain for voltage or current ranges for which the gain is small, the three waves must be taken into account. As current is varied, the loss parameter $d$ varies, and this means different $x$'s and $y$'s must be computed for different currents. Finally, at high currents, the space-charge parameter $Q$ must be taken into account. In all, a computation of tube behavior under a variety of conditions is an extensive job.

Fortunately, for useful tubes operating as intended, the gain is high. When this is so, the gain can be calculated quite accurately by asymptotic relations. Such an overall calculation of the gain of a helix-type tube with distributed loss is summarized in Appendix VII.

PROBLEMS

1. Calculate the overall or net gain in Problems 1–4 of Chapter VIII.

2. Instead of a uniformly distributed loss, the tube of Problem 4 of Chapter VIII has a very lossy central section 4 wavelengths long, leaving 8 active wavelengths of helix before and after the lossy section. Calculate the gain at 10 cm, $b = 0$.

3. How close to the input might the lossy section of Problem 2 start: In wavelengths? In inches?

# CHAPTER X

# NOISE FIGURE

**B**ECAUSE THERE IS no treatment of the behavior at high frequencies of an electron flow with a Maxwellian distribution of velocities, one might think there could be no very satisfactory calculation of the noise figure of traveling-wave tubes. Various approximate calculations can be made, and two of these will be discussed here. Experience indicates that the second and more elaborate of these is fairly well founded. In each case, an approximation is made in which the actual multi-velocity electron current is replaced by a current of electrons having a single velocity at a given point but having a mean square fluctuation of velocity or current equal to a mean square fluctuation characteristic of the multi-velocity flow.

In one sort of calculation, it is assumed that the noise is due to a current fluctuation equal to that of shot noise (equation (10.1)) in the current entering the circuit. For zero loss, an electron velocity equal to the phase velocity of the circuit and no space charge, this leads to an expression for noise figure (10.5), which contains a term proportional to beam voltage $V_0$ times the gain parameter $C$. One can, if he wishes, add a space-charge noise reduction factor multiplying the term $80\, V_0 C$. This approach indicates that the voltage and the gain per wavelength should be reduced in order to improve the noise figure.

In another approach, equations applying to single-valued-velocity flow between parallel planes are assumed to apply from the cathode to the circuit, and the fluctuations in the actual multi-velocity stream are represented by fluctuations in current and velocity at the cathode surface. It is found that for space-charge-limited emission the current fluctuation has no effect, and so all the noise can be expressed in terms of fluctuations in the velocity of emission of electrons.

For a special case, that of a gun with an anode at circuit potential $V_0$, a cathode-anode transit angle $\theta_1$, and an anode-circuit transit angle $\theta_2$, an expression for noise figure (10.28) is obtained. This expression can be rewritten in terms of a parameter $L$ which is a function of $P$

$$F = 1 + (\tfrac{1}{2})(4 - \pi)(T_c/T)(1/C)L$$

$$P = (\theta_1 - \theta_2)C$$

Formally, $F$ can be minimized by choosing the proper value of $P$. In Fig. 10.3, the minimum value of $L$, $L_m$, is plotted vs. the velocity parameter $b$ for zero loss and zero space charge $(d = QC = 0)$. The corresponding value of $P$, $P_m$, is also shown.

$P$ is a function of the cathode-anode transit angle $\theta_1$, which cannot be varied without changing the current density and hence $C$, and of anode-circuit transit angle $\theta_2$, which can be given any value. Thus, $P$ can be made very small if one wishes, but it cannot be made indefinitely large, and it is not clear that $P$ can always be made equal to $P_m$. On the other hand, these expressions have been worked out for a rather limited case: an anode potential equal to circuit potential, and no a-c space charge. It is possible that an optimization with respect to gun anode potential and space charge parameter $QC$ would predict even lower noise figures, and perhaps at attainable values of the parameters.

In an actual tube there are, of course, sources of noise which have been neglected. Experimental work indicates that partition noise is very important and must be taken into account.

## 10.1 Shot Noise in the Injected Current

A stream of electrons emitted from a temperature-limited cathode has a mean square fluctuation in convection current $\overline{i_s^2}$

$$\overline{i_s^2} = 2eI_0B_0 \tag{10.1}$$

Here $e$ is the charge on an electron, $I_0$ is the average or d-c current and $B$ is the bandwidth in which the frequencies of the current components whose mean square value is $\overline{i_s^2}$ lie. Suppose this fluctuation in the beam current of a traveling-wave tube were the sole cause of an increasing wave $(V = v = 0)$. Then, from (9.4) the mean square value of that increasing wave,, $\overline{V_{1s}^2}$, would be

$$\overline{V_{1s}^2} = (8eBV_0^2C^4/I_0) \mid \delta_2\delta_3 \mid^2 \mid (1 - \delta_2/\delta_1)(1 - \delta_3/\delta_1) \mid^{-2} \tag{10.2}$$

Now, suppose we have an additional noise source: thermal noise voltage applied to the circuit. If the helix is matched to a source of temperature $T$, the thermal noise power $P_t$ drawn from the source is

$$P_t = kTB \tag{10.3}$$

Here $k$ is Boltzman's constant, $T$ is temperature in degrees Kelvin and, as before, $B$ is bandwidth in cycles. If $K_t$ is the longitudinal impedance of the circuit the mean square noise voltage $\overline{V_t^2}$ associated with the circuit will be

$$\overline{V_t^2} = kTBK_t \tag{10.4}$$

and the component of increasing wave excited by this voltage, $\overline{V_{1\iota}^2}$, will be, from (9.4),

$$\overline{V_{1\iota}^2} = kTBK_{\iota} \mid (1 - \delta_2/\delta_1)(1 - \delta_3/\delta_1) \mid^{-2} \tag{10.5}$$

The noise figure of an amplifier is defined as the ratio of the total noise output power to the noise output power attributable to thermal noise at the input alone. We will regard the mean-square value of the initial voltage $V_1$ of the increasing wave as a measure of noise output. This will be substantially true if the signal becomes large prior to the introduction of further noise. For example, it will be substantially true in a tube with a severed helix if the helix is cut at a point where the increasing wave has grown large compared with the original fluctuations in the electron stream which set it up.

Under these circumstances, the noise figure $F$ will be given by

$$F = (\overline{V_{1s}^2} + \overline{V_{1\iota}^2})/(\overline{V_{1\iota}^2})$$

$$F = 1 + (e/kT)(8V_0^2C^4/I_0K_{\iota}) \mid \delta_2\delta_3 \mid^2 \tag{10.3}$$

Now we have from Chapter II that

$$C^3 = I_0K_{\iota}/4V_0$$

whence

$$F = 1 + 2(eV_0/kT)C \mid \delta_2\delta_3 \mid^2 \tag{10.4}$$

The standard reference temperature is $290°K$. Let us assume $b = d = QC = 0$. For this case we have found $\mid \delta_2 \mid = \mid \delta_3 \mid = 1$. Thus, for these assumptions we find

$$F = 1 + 80V_0C \tag{10.5}$$

A typical value of $V_0$ is 1,600 volts; a typical value of $C$ is .025. For these values

$$F = 3{,}201$$

In db this is a noise of 35 db.

This is not far from the noise figure of traveling-wave tubes when the cathode temperature is lowered so as to give temperature-limited emission. The noise figure of traveling-wave tubes in which the cathode is at normal operating temperature and is active, so that emission is limited by space-charge, can be considerably lower. In endeavoring to calculate the noise figure for space-charge-limited electron flow from the cathode we must proceed in a somewhat different manner.

## 10.2 The Diode Equations

Llewellyn and Peterson[1] have published a set of equations governing the behavior of parallel plane diodes with a single-valued electron velocity. They sum up the behavior of such a diode in terms of nine coefficients $A^*$–$I^*$, in the following equations

$$V_b - V_a = A^* I + B^* q_a + C^* v_a \tag{10.6}$$

$$q_b = D^* I + E^* q_a + F^* v_a \tag{10.7}$$

$$v_b = G^* I + H^* q_a + I^* v_a \tag{10.8}$$

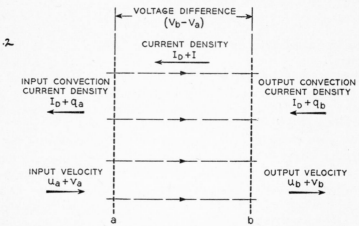

Fig. 10.1—Parallel electron flow between two planes $a$ and $b$ normal to the flow, showing the currents, velocities and voltages.

These equations and the values of the various coefficients in terms of current, electron velocity and transit angle are given in Appendix V. The diode structure to which they apply is indicated in Fig. 10.1. Electrons enter normal to the left plane and pass out at the right plane. The various quantities involved are transit angle between the two planes and:

$I_0$     d-c current density to left

$I$     a-c current density to left

$q_a$     a-c convection current density to left at input plane $a$

$q_b$     a-c convection current density to left at output plane $b$

$u_a$     d-c velocity to right at plane $a$

$u_b$     d-c velocity to right at plane $b$

$v_a$     a-c velocity to right at plane $a$

$v_b$     a-c velocity to right at plane $b$

$V_b$-$V_a$    a-c potential difference between plane $b$ and plane $a$

[1] F. B. Llewellyn and L. C. Peterson, "Vacuum Tube Networks," *Proc. I.R.E.*, Vol. 32, pp. 144–166, March, 1944.

We will notice that $I$ and the $q$'s are current *densities* and that, contrary to the convention we have used, they are taken as positive to the left. Thus, if the area is $\sigma$, we would write the output convection current; as

$$i = -\sigma q_b$$

where $q_b$ is the convection current density used in (10.6)–(10.8).

Peterson has used (10.6)–(10.8) in calculating noise figure by replacing the actual multi-velocity flow from the cathode by a single-velocity flow with the same mean square fluctuation in velocity, namely,[2]

$$\overline{v_t^2} = (4 - \pi)\eta \ (kT_c/I_0)B \qquad (10.9)$$

Here $T_c$ is the cathode temperature in degrees Kelvin and $I_0$ is the cathode current.

Whatever the justification for such a procedure, Rack[3] has shown that it gives a satisfactory result at low frequencies, and unpublished work by Cutler and Quate indicates surprisingly good quantitative agreement under conditions of long transit angle at 4,000 mc.

We must remember, however, that the available values of the coefficients of (10.6)–(10.8) are for a broad electron beam in which there are a-c fields in the $z$ direction only. Now, the electron beam in the gun of a traveling-wave tube is ordinarily rather narrow. While the a-c fields may be substantially in the $z$-direction near the cathode, this is certainly not true throughout the whole cathode-anode space. Thus, the coefficients used in (10.6)–(10.8) are certainly somewhat in error when applied to traveling-wave tube guns.

Various plausible efforts can be made to amend this situation, as, by saying that the latter part of the beam in the gun acts as a drift region in which the electron velocities are not changed by space-charge fields. However, when one starts such patching, he does not know where to stop. In the light of available knowledge, it seems best to use the coefficients as they stand for the cathode-anode region of the gun.

Let us then consider the electron gun of the traveling-wave tube to form a space-charge limited diode which is short-circuited at high frequencies.

If we assume complete space charge (space-charge limited emission) and take the electron velocity at the cathode to be zero, we find that the quantities multiplying $q_a$ in (10.6)–(10.8) are zero.

$$B^* = E^* = H^* = 0^* \qquad (10.10)$$

[2] L. C. Peterson, "Space-Charge and Transit-Time Effects on Signal and Noise in Microwave Tetrodes," *Proc. I.R.E.*, Vol. 35, pp. 1264–1272, November, 1947.

[3] A. J. Rack, "Effect of Space Charge and Transit Time on the Shot Noise in Diodes," *Bell System Technical Journal*, Vol. 17, pp. 592–619, October, 1938.

Accordingly, the magnitude of the noise convection current at the cathode does not matter. If we assume that the gun is a short-circuited diode as far as r-f goes

$$V_b - V_a = 0 \tag{10.11}$$

Then from (10.6), (10.10) and (10.11) we obtain

$$I = -\frac{C^*}{A^*}\, v_a \tag{10.12}$$

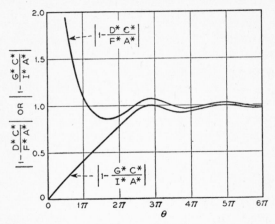

Fig. 10.2—Some expressions useful in noise calculations, showing how they approach unity at large transit angles.

Accordingly, from (10.7) and (10.8) we obtain

$$q_b = \left(1 - \frac{D^*C^*}{F^*A^*}\right) F^* v_a \tag{10.13}$$

$$v_b = \left(1 - \frac{G^*C^*}{I^*A^*}\right) I^* v_a \tag{10.14}$$

In Fig. 10.2, $|\,1 - D^*C^*/F^*A^*\,|$ and $|\,1 - G^*C^*/I^*A^*\,|$ are plotted vs $\theta$, the transit angle. We see that for transit angles greater than about $3\pi$ these quantities differ negligibly from unity, and we may write

$$q_b = F^* v_a \tag{10.15}$$

$$v_b = I^* v_a \tag{10.16}$$

More specifically, we find

$$q_b = \frac{v_a I_0 \beta_1 e^{-\beta_1}}{u_b} \tag{10.17}$$

$$v_b = -v_a e^{-\beta_1} \tag{10.18}$$

Here $\beta_1$ is $j$ times the transit angle in radians from cathode to anode. For $v_a$ we use a velocity fluctuation with the mean-square value given by (10.9).

Suppose now that there is a constant-potential drift space following the diode anode, of length $\beta_2/j$ in radians. If we apply (10.6)–(10.8) and assume that the space-charge is small and the transit angle long, we find that $q_b'$, the value of $q_b$ at the end of this drift space, is given in terms of $q_a'$ and $v_a'$, the values at the beginning of this drift space, by

$$q_b' = (q_a' + (I_0/u_b)\beta_2 v_a')e^{-\beta_2} \qquad (10.19)$$

The case of $v_b'$, the velocity at the end of this drift space, is a little different. The first term on the right of (10.8) can be shown to be negligible for long transit angles and small space charge. The last term on the right represents the purely kinematic bunching. For the assumption of small space charge the middle term gives not zero but a first approximation of a space-charge effect, assuming that all the space-charge field acts longitudinally. Thus, this middle term gives an overestimate of the effect of space-charge in a narrow, high-velocity beam. If we include both terms, we obtain

$$v_b' = H_2^* q_a' + e^{-\beta_2} v_a' \qquad (10.20)$$

Here the term on the right is the purely kinematic term.*

Now, the current from the gun is assumed to go into the drift space, so that $q_a'$ is $q_b$ from (10.17) and $v_a'$ is $v_a$ from (10.18). The d-c velocity at the gun anode and throughout the drift space are both given by $u_b$. If we make these substitutions in (10.19) and (10.20) we obtain

$$q_b' = (I_0/u_b)(\beta_1 - \beta_2)e^{-(\beta_1+\beta_2)}v_a \qquad (10.21)$$

$$v_b' = -\left(2\frac{\beta_1}{\beta_2} + 1\right)e^{-(\beta_1+\beta_2)}v_a \qquad (10.22)$$

The term $2\beta_1/\beta_2$ in (10.22) is the "space-charge" term. We will in the following analysis omit this, making the same sort of error we do in neglecting space charge in the traveling-wave section of the tube. If space charge in the drift space is to be taken into account, it is much better to proceed as in 9.7.

From the drift-space the current goes into the helix. It is now necessary to change to the notation we have used in connection with the traveling-wave tube. The chief difference is that we have taken currents as positive to the right, but allowed $I_0$ to be the d-c current to the left. If $i$ and $v$ are

---

* The first term has been written as shown because it is easiest to use the small space-charge value of $H^*$ for the drift region ($H_2^*$) in connection with the space-charge limited value of $F^*$ for the cathode-anode region rather than in connection with (10.17).

our a-c convection current and velocity at the beginning of the helix, and $I_0$ and $u_0$ the d-c beam current and velocity, and $\sigma$ the area of the beam,

$$i = -\sigma q_b'$$

$$v = v_b$$

$$I_0 = \sigma I_0 \tag{10.23}$$

$$u_0 = u_0$$

In addition, we will use transit angles $\theta_1$ and $\theta_2$ in place of $\beta_1$ and $\beta_2$

$$\beta_1 = j\theta_1$$

$$\beta_2 = j\theta_2 \tag{10.24}$$

We then obtain from (10.21) and (10.22)

$$q = -j(I_0/u_0)(\theta_1 - \theta_2)e^{-j(\theta_1+\theta_2)}v_a \tag{10.25}$$

$$v = -e^{-j(\theta_1+\theta_2)}v_a \tag{10.26}$$

## 10.3 OVERALL NOISE FIGURE

We are now in a position to use (9.4) in obtaining the overall noise figure. We have already assumed that the space-charge is small in the drift space between the gun anode and the helix ($QC = 0$). If we continue to assume this in connection with (9.4), the only voltage is the helix voltage and for the noise caused by the velocity fluctuation at the cathode, $v_a$, $V = 0$ at the beginning of the helix. Thus, the mean square initial noise voltage of the increasing wave, $\overline{V_{1s}^2}$, will be, from (10.21), (10.22), (9.4) and (10.9),

$$\overline{V_{1s}^2} = (2(4 - \pi)kT_cCBV_0/I_0)| \delta_2\delta_3(\theta_1 - \theta_2)C + (\delta_2 + \delta_3) |^2$$
$$| (1 - \delta_2/\delta_1)(1 - \delta_3/\delta_1) |^{-2} \tag{10.27}$$

As before, we have, from the thermal noise input to the helix

$$\overline{V_{1t}^2} = kTBK_t| (1 - \delta_2/\delta_1)(1 - \delta_3/\delta_1) |^{-2} \tag{10.5}$$

and the noise figure becomes

$$F = 1 + \overline{V_{1s}^2}/\overline{V_{1t}^2}$$

$$F = 1 + (1/2)(4 - \pi)(T_c/T)(1/C)| \delta_2\delta_3(\theta_1 - \theta_2)C + (\delta_2 + \delta_3) |^2 \tag{10.28}$$

Here use has been made of the fact that

$$C = K_tI/4V_0$$

Let us investigate this for the case $b = d = 0$ (we have already assumed $QC = 0$). In this case

$$\delta_2 = \sqrt{3}/2 - j1/2$$

$$\delta_3 = j$$

and we obtain

$$F = 1 + (1/2)(4 - \pi)(T_c/T)(1/C)|\, (P/2 - \sqrt{3}/2)$$
$$- j(\sqrt{3}P/2 - 1/2)\,|^2 \qquad (10.29)$$

$$P = (\theta_1 - \theta_2)C \qquad (10.30)$$

For a given gun transit-angle $\theta_1$, the parameter $P$ can be given values ranging from $\theta_1 C$ to large negative values by increasing the drift angle $\theta_2$ between the gun anode and the beginning of the helix.

We see that

$$F = 1 + (1/2)(4 - \pi)(T_c/T)(1/C)(P^2 - \sqrt{3}P + 1) \quad (10.31)$$

The minimum value of $(P^2 - \sqrt{3}P + 1)$ occurs when

$$P = \sqrt{3}/2 \qquad (10.32)$$

if the product of the gun transit angle and $C$ is large enough, this can be attained. The corresponding value of $(P^2 - \sqrt{3}P + 1)$ is $\frac{1}{4}$, and the corresponding noise figure is

$$F = 1 + (1/2)(1 - \pi/4)(T_c/T)(1/C) \qquad (10.33)$$

A typical value for $T_c$ is $1020°K$, and for a reference temperature of $290°K$,

$$T_c/T = 3.5$$

A typical value of $C$ is .025. For these values

$$F = 17$$

or a noise figure of 12 db.

Let us consider cases for no attenuation or space-charge but for other electron velocities. In this case we write, as before

$$\delta_2 = x_2 + jy_2$$

$$\delta_3 = x_3 + jy_3$$

Let us write, for convenience,

$$L = |\, \delta_2 \delta_3 P + \delta_1 + \delta_2 \,|^2 \qquad (10.34)$$

Then we find that

$$L = [(x_2x_3)^2 + (y_2y_3)^2 + (x_2y_3)^2 + (x_3y_2)^2]P^2$$
$$+ 2[x_3(y_2^2 + x_2^2) + x_2(x_3^2 + y_3^2)]P \qquad (10.35)$$
$$+ (x_2 + x_3)^2 + (y_2 + y_3)^2$$

This has a minimum value for $P = P_m$

$$P_m = \frac{-[x_3(x_2^2 + y_2^2) + x_2(x_3^2 + y_3^2)]}{(x_2x_3)^2 + (y_2y_3)^2 + (x_2y_3)^2 + (x_3y_2)^2} \qquad (10.36)$$

We note that, as we are not dealing with the increasing wave, $x_2$ and $x_3$

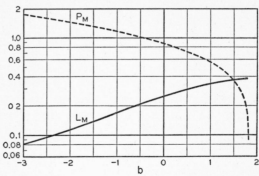

Fig. 10.3—According to the theory presented, the overall noise figure of a tube with a lossless helix and no space charge is proportional to $L$. Here we have a minimum value of $L_m$, minimized with respect to $P$, which is dependent on gun transit angle, and also the corresponding value of $P$, $P_m$. According to this curve, the optimum noise figure should be lowest for low electron velocities (low values of $b$). It may, however, be impossible to make $P$ equal to $P_m$.

must be either negative or zero, and hence $P_m$ is always positive. For no space-charge and no attenuation, $x_3$ is zero for all values of $b$ and

$$P_m = \frac{-x_2}{y_2^2 + x_2^2} \qquad (10.37)$$

From (10.36) and (10.35), the minimum value of $L$, $L_m$, is

$$L_m = (x_2 + x_3)^2 + (y_2 + y_3)^2$$
$$- \frac{[x_3(y_2^2 + x_2^2) + x_2(x_3^2 + y_3^2)]^2}{(x_2x_3)^2 + (y_2y_3)^2 + (x_2y_3)^2 + (x_3y_2)^2} \qquad (10.38)$$

When $x_3 = 0$, as in (10.37)

$$L_m = x_2^2 + y_2^2 + 2y_2y_3 + \frac{y_2^2 y_3^2}{x_2^2 + y_2^2} \qquad (10.39)$$

In Fig. 10.3, $P_m$ and $L_m$ are plotted vs $b$ for no attenuation ($d = 0$). We see that $P_m$ becomes very small as $b$ approaches $(3/2)2^{1/3}$, the value at which the increasing wave disappears.

If space charge is to be taken into account, it should be taken into account both in the drift space between anode and helix and in the helix itself. In the helix we can express the effect of space-charge by means of the parameter QC and boundary conditions can be fitted as in Chapter IX. The drift space can be dealt with as in Section 9.7 of Chapter IX. The inclusion of the effect of space-charge by this means will of course considerably complicate the analysis, especially if $b \neq 0$.

While working with Field at Stanford, Dr. C. F. Quate extended the theory presented here to include the effect of all three waves in the case of low gain, and to include the effect of a fractional component of beam current having pure shot noise, which might arise through failure of space-charge reduction of noise toward the edge of the cathode. His extended theory agreed to an encouraging extent with his experimental results. Subsequent unpublished work carried out at these Laboratories by Cutler and Quate indicates a surprisingly good agreement between calculations of this sort and observed noise current, and emphasizes the importance of properly including both partition noise and space charge in predicting noise figure.

10.4 OTHER NOISE CONSIDERATIONS

Space-charge reduction of noise is a cooperative phenomenon of the whole electron beam. If some electrons are eliminated, as by a grid, additional "partition" noise is introduced. Peterson shows how to take this into account.[2]

An electron may be ineffective in a traveling-wave tube not only by being lost but by entering the circuit near the axis where the r-f field is weak rather than near the edge where the r-f field is high. Partition noise arises because sidewise components of thermal velocity cause a fluctuation in the amount of current striking a grid or other intercepting circuit. If such sidewise components of velocity appreciably alter electron position in the helix, a noise analogous to partition noise may arise even if no electrons actually strike the helix. Such a noise will also occur if the "counteracting pulses" of low-charge density which are assumed to smooth out the electron flow are broad transverse to the beam.

These considerations lead to some maxims in connection with low-noise traveling-wave tubes: (1) do not allow electrons to be intercepted by various electrodes (2) if practical, make sure that $I_0(\beta r)$ is reasonably constant over the beam, and/or (3) provide a very strong magnetic focusing field, so that electrons cannot move appreciably transversely.

## 10.5 Noise in Transverse-Field Tubes

Traveling-wave tubes can be made in which there is no longitudinal field component at the nominal beam position. One can argue that, if a narrow, well-collimated beam is used in such a tube, the noise current in the beam can induce little noise signal in the circuit (none at all for a beam of zero thickness with no sidewise motion). Thus, the idea of using a transverse-field tube as a low-noise tube is attractive. So far, no experimental results on such tubes have been announced.

A brief analysis of transverse-field tubes is given in Chapter XIII.

Problems

1. Using the conditions of Problem 2 of Chapter VIII, calculate the optimum noise figure for $b = 0$.

2. Extend the calculations of Problem 1 and plot optimum noise figure vs. $b$.

3. For $b = 0$, find the expression for noise figure corresponding to (10.29) but based on the assumption that there is an additional component of noise current at the beginning of the helix.

$$\overline{i^2} = \alpha(2eI_0B)$$

(where $I_0$ is the total beam current and $\alpha$ is the fraction intercepted).

# CHAPTER XI

# BACKWARD WAVES

W E NOTED IN CHAPTER IV that, in filter-type circuits, there is an infinite number of spatial harmonics which travel in both directions. Usually, in a tube which is designed to make use of a given forward component the velocity of other forward components is enough different from that of the component chosen to avoid any appreciable interaction with the electron stream. It may well be, however, that a backward-traveling component has almost the same speed as a forward-traveling component.

Suppose, for instance, that a tube is designed to make use of a given forward-traveling component of a forward wave. Suppose that there is a forward-traveling component of a backward wave, and this forward-traveling component is also near synchronism with the electrons. Does this mean that under these circumstances both the backward-traveling and the forward-traveling waves will be amplified?

The question is essentially that of the interaction of an electron stream with a circuit in which the phase velocity is in step with the electrons but the group velocity and the energy flow are in a direction contrary to that of electron motion.

We can most easily evaluate such a situation by considering a distributed circuit for which this is true. Such a circuit is shown in Fig. 11.1. Here the series reactance $X$ per unit length is negative as compared with the more usual circuit of Fig. 11.2. In the circuit of Fig. 11.2, the phase shift is $0°$ per section at zero frequency and assumes positive values as the frequency is increased. In the circuit of Fig. 11.1 the phase shift is $-180°$ per section at a lower cutoff frequency and approaches $0°$ per section as the frequency approaches infinity.

Suppose we consider the equations of Chapter II. In (2.9) we chose the sign of $X$ in such a manner as to make the series reactance positive, as in Fig. 11.2, rather than negative, as in Fig. 11.1. All the other equations apply equally well to either circuit. Thus, for the circuit of Fig. 11.1, we have, instead of (2.10),

$$V = \frac{+\Gamma\Gamma_1 i}{(\Gamma^2 - \Gamma_1^2)} \tag{11.1}$$

The sign is changed in the circuit equation relating the convection current and the voltage. Similarly, we can modify the equations of Chapter VII,

(7.9) and (7.12), by changing the sign of the left-hand side. From Chapter VIII, the equation for a lossless circuit with no space charge is

$$\delta^2(\delta + jb) = -j \qquad (8.1)$$

The corresponding modification is to change the sign preceding $\delta^2$, giving

$$\delta^2(\delta + jb) = +j \qquad (11.2)$$

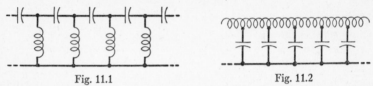

Fig. 11.1                                      Fig. 11.2

Fig. 11.1—A circuit with a negative phase velocity. The electrons can be in synchronism with the field only if they travel in a direction opposite to that of electromagnetic energy flow.

Fig. 11.2—A circuit with a positive phase velocity.

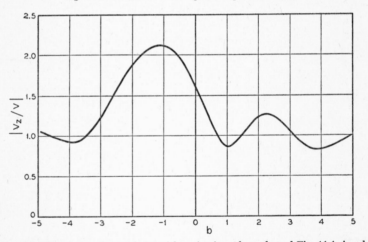

Fig. 11.3—Suppose we have a tube with a circuit such as that of Fig. 11.1, in which the circuit energy is really flowing in the opposite direction from the electron motion. Here, for $QC = d = 0$, we have the ratio of the magnitude of the voltage $V_z$ a distance $z$ from the point of injection of electrons to the magnitude of the voltage $V$ at the point of injection of electrons. $V_z$ is really the input voltage, and there will be gain at values of $b$ for which $|V_z/V| < 1$.

In (11.2), $b$ and $\delta$ have the usual meaning in terms of electron velocity and propagation constant.

Now consider the equation

$$\delta^2(\delta - jk) = j \qquad (11.3)$$

Equations (11.2) and (8.1) apply to different systems. We have solutions of (8.1) and we want solutions of (11.2). We see that a solution of (11.2) is a solution of (11.3) for $k = -b$. We see that a solution of (11.3) is the conjugate of a solution of (8.1) if we put $b$ in (8.1) equal to $k$ in (11.3). Thus, a solution of (11.2) is the conjugate of a solution of (8.1) in which $b$ in (8.1) is made the negative of the value of $b$ for which it is desired to solve (11.2).

We can use the solutions of Fig. 8.1 in connection with the circuit of Fig. 11.1 in the following way: wherever in Fig. 8.1 we see $b$, we write in instead $-b$, and wherever we see $y_1$, $y_2$ or $y_3$ we write in instead $-y_1$, $-y_2$ or $-y_3$.

Thus, for synchronous velocity, we have

$$\delta_1 = \sqrt{3}/2 + j\frac{1}{2}$$

$$\delta_2 = -\sqrt{3}/2 + j\frac{1}{2}$$

$$\delta_3 = -j$$

We can determine what will happen in a physical case only by fitting boundary conditions so that at $z = 0$ the electron stream, as it must, enters unmodulated.

Let us, for convenience, write $\Phi$ for the quantity $\beta Cz$

$$\beta Cz = \Phi \tag{11.4}$$

We will have for the total voltage $V_z$ at $z$ in terms of the voltage $V$ at $z = 0$

$$V_z = Ve^{-j\beta z}([(1 - \delta_2/\delta_1)(1 - \delta_3/\delta_1)]^{-1}e^{-j\Phi y_1}e^{\Phi x_1}$$

$$+ [(1 - \delta_3/\delta_2)(1 - \delta_1/\delta_2)]^{-1}e^{-j\Phi y_2}e^{\Phi x_2} \tag{11.5}$$

$$+ [(1 - \delta_1/\delta_3)(1 - \delta_2/\delta_3)]^{-1}e^{-j\Phi y_3}e^{\Phi x_3})$$

We must remember that in using values from an unaltered Fig. 8.1 we use in the $\delta$'s and as the $y$'s the negative of the $y$'s shown in the figure (the sign of the $x$'s is unchanged), and for a given value of $b$ we enter Fig. 8.1 at $-b$.

In Fig. 11.3, $|V_z/V|$ has been plotted vs $b$ for $\Phi = 2$. We see that, for several values of $b$, $|V_z|$ (the input voltage) is less than $|V|$ (the output voltage) and hence there can be "backward" gain.

We note that as $\Phi$ is made very large, the wave which increases with increasing $\Phi$ will eventually predominate, and $|V_z|$ will be greater than $|V|$. "Backward gain" occurs not through a "growing wave" but rather through a sort of interference between wave components, as exhibited in Fig. 11.3.

Fig. 11.3 is for a lossless circuit; the presence of circuit attenuation would alter the situation somewhat.

# CHAPTER XII

# POWER OUTPUT

A THEORETICAL EVALUATION of the power output of a traveling-wave tube requires a theory of the non-linear behavior of the tube. In this book we have dealt with a linearized theory only. No attempt will be made to develop a non-linear theory. Some results of non-linear theory will be quoted, and some conclusions drawn from experimental work will be presented.

One thing appears clear both from theory and from experiment: the gain parameter $C$ is very important in determining efficiency. This is perhaps demonstrated most clearly in some unpublished work of A. T. Nordsieck.

Nordsieck assumed:

(1) The same a-c field acts on all electrons.

(2) The only fields present are those associated with the circuit ("neglect of space charge").

(3) Field components of harmonic frequency are neglected.

(4) Backward-traveling energy in the circuit is neglected.

(5) A lossless circuit is assumed.

(6) $C$ is small (it always is).

Nordsieck obtained numerical solutions for such cases for several electron velocities. He found the maximum efficiency to be proportonal to $C$ by a factor we may call $k$. Thus, the power output $P$ is

$$P = kCI_0V_0 \tag{12.1}$$

In Fig. 12.1, the factor $k$ is plotted vs. the velocity parameter $b$. For an electron velocity equal to that of the unperturbed wave the fractional efficiency obtained is $3C$; for a faster electron velocity the efficiency rises to $7C$. For instance, if $C = .025$, $3C$ is $7.5\%$ and $7C$ is $15\%$. For 1,600 volts 15 ma this means 1.8 or 3.6 watts. If, however, $C = 0.1$, which is attainable, the indicated efficiency is $30\%$ to $70\%$.

Experimental efficiencies often fall very far below such figures, although some efficiencies which have been attained lie in this range. There are three apparent reasons for these lower efficiencies. First, small non-uniformities in wave propagation set up new wave components which abstract energy from the increasing wave, and which may subtract from the normal output. Second, when the a-c field varies across the electron flow, not all electrons are acted on equally favorably. Third, most tubes have a central lossy section followed by a relatively short output section. Such tubes may overload so severely in the lossy section that a high level in the output section is never attained. There is not enough length of loss-free circuit to provide sufficient gain in the output circuit so that the signal can build up to maximum amplitude from a low level increasing wave. Other tubes with distributed loss suffer because the loss cuts down the efficiency.

Some power-series non-linear calculations made by L. R. Walker show that for fast velocities of injection the first non-linear effect should be an expansion, not a compression. Nordsieck's numerical solutions agree with this. A power series approach is inadequate in dealing with truly large-signal be-

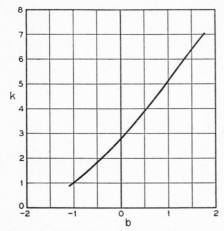

Fig. 12.1—The calculated efficiency is expressed as $kC$, where $k$ is a function of the velocity parameter $b$. This curve shows $k$ as given by Nordsieck's high-level calculations

havior. In fact, Nordsieck's work shows that the power-series attack, if based on an assumption that there is no overtaking of electrons by electrons emitted later, must fail at levels much below the maximum output.

Further work by Nordsieck indicates that the output may be appreciably reduced by variation of the a-c field across the beam.

It is unfortunate that Nordsieck's calculations do not cover a wider range of conditions. Fortunately, unlikely as it might seem, the linear theory can tell us a little about what limitation of power we might expect. For instance, from (7.15) we have

$$\frac{v}{u_0} = -j\,\frac{\eta V}{u_0^2\,\delta C}$$

$$\frac{v}{u_0} = -j\left(\frac{V}{2V_0}\right)\left(\frac{1}{\delta C}\right) \qquad (12.2)$$

while from (7.16) we have

$$\frac{i}{I_0} = -\left(\frac{V}{2V_0}\right)\left(\frac{1}{\delta C}\right)^2 \tag{12.3}$$

We expect non-linear effects to become important when an a-c quantity is no longer small compared with a d-c quantity. We see that because $(1/\delta C)$ is large, $|i/I_0|$ will be larger than $|v/u_0|$.

The important non-linearity is a sort of over-bunching or limit to bunching. For instance, suppose we were successful in bunching the electron flow into very short pulses of electrons, as shown in Fig. 12.2 As the pulses approach zero length, the ratio of the peak value of the fundamental component of convection current to the average or d-c current $I_0$ approaches 2. We may, then, get some hint as to the variation of power output as various parameters are varied by letting $|i| = 2I_0$ and finding the variation of power in the circuit for an a-c convection current as we vary various parameters.

Fig. 12.2—If the electron beam were bunched into pulses short compared with a cycle, the peak value of the component of fundamental frequency would be twice the d-c current $I_0$.

Deductions made in this way cannot be more than educated guesses, but in the absence of non-linear calculations they are all we have.

From (7.1) we have for the *circuit field* associated with the *active mode* (neglecting the field due to space charge)

$$E = \frac{\Gamma^2 \Gamma_1 (E^2/\beta^2 P)}{2(\Gamma_1^2 - \Gamma^2)} \tag{12.4}$$

This relation is, of course, valid only for an electron convection current $i$ which varies with distance as $\exp(-\Gamma z)$. For the power to be large for a given magnitude of current, $E$ should be large. For a given value of $i$, $E$ will be large if $\Gamma$ is very nearly equal to $\Gamma_1$. This is natural. If $\Gamma$ were equal to $\Gamma_1$, the natural propagation constant of the circuit, the contribution to the field by the current $i$ in every elementary distance would have such phase as to add in phase with every other contribution.

Actually, $\Gamma_1$ and $\Gamma$ cannot be quite equal. We have from (7.10) and (7.11)

$$-\Gamma_1 = \beta_e(-j - jCb - Cd) \tag{12.5}$$

$$-\Gamma = \beta_e(-j + jCy_1 + Cx_1) \tag{12.6}$$

For a physical circuit the attenuation parameter $d$ must be positive while, for an increasing wave, $x$ must be positive. We see that we may expect $E$ to be greatest for a given current when $d$ and $x$ are small, and when $y$ is nearly equal to the velocity parameter $b$.

Suppose we use (12.4) in expressing the power

$$P = \frac{E^2}{\beta^2(E^2/\beta^2 P)} = \left| \frac{\Gamma^4 \Gamma_1^2 (E^2/\beta^2 P)}{4\beta^2(\Gamma_1^2 - \Gamma^2)^2} i^2 \right|. \tag{12.7}$$

Here we identify $\beta$ with $-j\Gamma_1$. Further, we use (2.43), (12.5) and (12.6), and assuming $C$ to be small, neglect terms involving $C$ compared with unity. We will further let $i$ have a value

$$i = 2I_0 \tag{12.8}$$

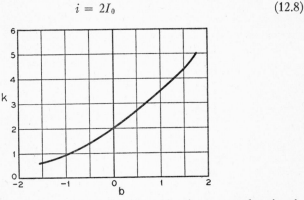

Fig. 12.3—An efficiency parameter $k$ calculated by taking the power as that given by near theory for an r-f beam current with a peak value twice the d-c beam current.

We obtain
i
1

$$P = kCI_0V_0 \tag{12.9}$$

$$k = \frac{2}{(b + y)^2 + (x + d)^2} \tag{12.10}$$

We will now investigate several cases. Let us consider first the case of a lossless circuit ($d = 0$) and no space charge ($QC = 0$) and plot the efficiency factor $k$ vs. $b$. The values of $x$ and $y$ are those of Fig. 8.1. Such a plot is shown in Fig. 12.3.

If we compare the curve of Fig. 12.3 with the correct curve of Nordsieck, we see that there is a striking qualitative agreement and, indeed, fair quantitative agreement. We might have expected on the one hand that the electron stream would never become completely bunched ($i = 2I_0$) and that, as it approached complete bunching, behavior would already be non-linear. This would tend to make (12.10) optimistic. On the other hand, even after $i$

attains its maximum value and starts to fall, power can still be transferred to the circuit, though the increase of field with distance will no longer be exponential. This makes it possible that the value of $k$ given by (12.10) will be exceeded. Actually, the true $k$ calculated by Nordsieck is a little higher than that given by (12.10).

Let us now consider the effect of loss. Figure 12.4 shows $k$ from (12.10) vs. $d$ for $b = QC = 0$. We see that, as might be expected, the efficiency falls as the loss is increased. C. C. Cutler has shown experimentally through un-published work that the power actually falls off much more rapidly with $d$.

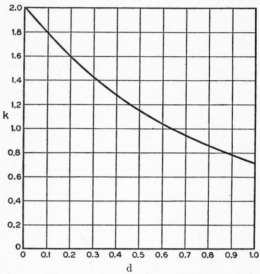

Fig. 12.4—The efficiency parameter $k$ calculated as in Fig. 12.3 but for $b = 0$ (an elec-tron velocity equal to the circuit phase velocity) and for various values of the attenuation parameter $d$. Experimentally, the efficiency falls off more rapidly as $d$ is increased.

Finally, Fig. 12.5 shows $k$ from (12.10) vs. $QC$, with $d = 0$ and $b$ chosen to make $x_1$ a maximum. We see that there is a pronounced rise in efficiency as the space-charge parameter $QC$ is increased.

J. C. Slater has suggested in Microwave Electronics a way of looking at energy production essentially based on observing the motions of electrons while traveling along with the speed of the wave. He suggests that the elec-trons might eventually be trapped and oscillate in the troughs of the sinu-soidal field. If so, and if they initially have an average velocity $\Delta v$ greater than that of the wave, they cannot emerge with a velocity lower than the velocity of the wave less $\Delta v$. Such considerations are complicated by the fact that the phase velocity of the wave in the large-signal region will not be the same as its phase velocity in the small-signal region. It is interesting, however, to see what limiting efficiencies this leads to.

The initial electron velocity for the increasing wave is approximately

$$v_a = v_c(1 - y_1 C) \tag{12.11}$$

where $v_c$ is the phase velocity of the wave in the absence of electrons. The quantity $y_1$ is negative. According to Slater's reckoning, the final electron velocity cannot be less than

$$v_b = v_c(1 + y_1 C) \tag{12.12}$$

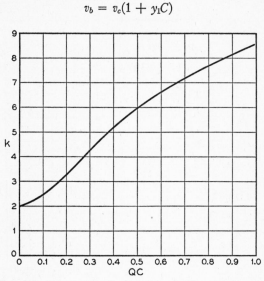

Fig. 12.5—The efficiency parameter $k$ calculated as in Fig. 12.3, for zero loss and for an electron velocity which makes the gain of the increasing wave greatest, vs the space-charge parameter $QC$.

The limiting efficiency $\eta$ accordingly will be, from considerations of kinetic energy

$$\eta = \frac{v_a^2 - v_b^2}{v_a^2}$$

$$\eta = \frac{4y_1 C}{(1 - y_1 C)^2}.$$

If $y_1 C \ll 1$, very nearly

$$\eta = 4 y_1 C \tag{12.13}$$

We see that this also indicates an efficiency proportional to $C$. In Fig. 12.6 $4y_1$ is plotted vs. $b$ for $QC = d = 0$. We see that this quantity ranges from 2 for $b = 0$ up to 5 for larger values of $b$. It is surprising how well this agrees with corresponding values of 3 and 7 from Nordsieck's work. Moreover (12.13) predicts an increase in efficiency with increasing $QC$.

Thus, we may expect the efficiency to vary with $C$ from several points of view.

It is interesting to consider what happens if at a given frequency we change the current. By changing the current while holding the voltage constant we increase both the input power and the efficiency, for $C$ varies as $I_0^{1/3}$. Thus, in changing the current alone we would expect the power to vary as the 4/3 power of $I_0$

$$P \approx I_0^{4/3} \tag{12.14}$$

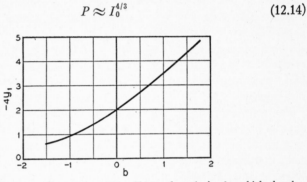

Fig. 12.6—According to a suggestion made by Slater, the velocity by which the electrons are slowed down cannot be greater than twice the difference between the electron velocity and the wave velocity. If we use the velocity difference given by the linear theory, for zero loss ($d = 0$) this would make the efficiency parameter $k$ equal to $-4y_1$. Here $-4y_1$ is plotted vs $b$ for $QC = 0$.

Here space charge has been neglected, and actually power may increase more rapidly with current than (12.14) indicates.

A variety of other cases can be considered. At a given voltage and current, $C$ and the efficiency rise as the helix diameter is made smaller. However, as the helix diameter is made smaller it may be necessary to decrease the current, and the optimum gain will come at higher frequencies. For a given beam diameter, the magnetic focusing field required to overcome space-charge repulsion is constant if $I_0/V_0^{1/2}$ is held constant, and hence we might consider increasing the current as the 1/2 power of the voltage, and thus increasing the power input as the 3/2 power of the voltage. On the other hand, the magnetic focusing field required to correct initial angular deflections of electrons increases as the voltage is raised.

There is no theoretical reason why electrons should strike the circuit. Thus, it is theoretically possible to use a very high beam power in connection with a very fragile helix. Practically, an appreciable fraction of the beam current is intercepted by the helix, and this seems unavoidable for wave lengths around a centimeter or shorter, for accurate focusing becomes more difficult as tubes are made physically smaller. Thus, in getting very high powers at ordinary wavelengths or even moderate powers at shorter wavelengths, filter type circuits which provide heat dissipation by thermal conduction may be necessary. We have seen that the impedance of such circuits is lower than that of a helix for the broadband condition (group velocity equal to phase velocity). However, high impedances and hence large values of $C$ can be attained at the expense of bandwidth by lowering the group velocity. This tends to raise the efficiency, as do the high currents which are allowable because of good heat dissipation. However, lowering group velocity increases attenuation, and this will tend to reduce efficiency somewhat.

It has been suggested that the power can be increased by reducing the phase velocity of the circuit near the output end of the tube, so that the electrons which have lost energy do not fall behind the waves. This is a complicated but attractive possibility. It has also been suggested that the electrode which collects electrons be operated at a voltage lower than that of the helix.

The general picture of what governs and limits power output is fairly clear as long as $C$ is very small. If attenuation near the output of the tube is kept small, and the circuit is constructed so as to approximate the requirement that nearly the same field acts on all electrons, efficiencies as large as 40% are indicated within the limitations of the present theory. With larger values of $C$ it is not clear what the power limitation will be.

The usual traveling-wave tube would seem to have a serious competitor for power applications in the traveling-wave magnetron amplifier, which is discussed briefly in a later chapter.

### PROBLEMS

1. Obtain expression similar to (12.19) assuming (a) a beam of constant current density filling the helix (b) a thin beam of constant current at the surface of the helix. Compare the variation of power with $V_0$ in these two cases with that in (12.18).

2. Suppose that one can attain a constant current density, regardless of beam diameter. What helix diameter should give most power output? Highest efficiency?

3. Suppose that one could attain a constant current regardless of helix diameter. What would be the best helix diameter?

# CHAPTER XIII

# TRANSVERSE MOTION OF ELECTRONS

## SYNOPSIS OF CHAPTER

SO FAR WE HAVE taken into account only longitudinal motions of electrons. This is sufficient if the transverse fields are small compared to the longitudinal fields (as, near the axis of an axially symmetrical circuit) or, if a strong magnetic focusing field is used, so that transverse motions are inhibited. It is possible, however, to obtain traveling-wave gain in a tube in which the longitudinal field is zero at the mean position of the electron beam. For a slow wave, the electric field is purely transverse only along a plane. The transverse field in this plane forces electrons away from the plane and preferentially throws them into regions of retarding field, where they give up energy to the circuit. This mechanism is not dissimilar to that in the longitudinal field case, in which the electrons are moved longitudinally from their unperturbed positions, preferentially into regions of more retarding field.

Whatever may be said about tubes utilizing transverse fields, it is certainly true that they have been less worked on than longitudinal-field tubes. In view of this, we shall present only a simple analysis of their operation along the lines of Chapter II. In this analysis we take cognizance of the fact that the charge induced in the circuit by a narrow stream of electrons is a function not only of the charge per unit length of the beam, but of the distance between the beam and the circuit as well.

The factor of proportionality between distance and induced charge can be related to the field produced by the circuit. Thus, if the variation of $V$ in the $x, y$ plane (normal to the direction of propagation) is expressed by a function $\Phi$, as in (13.3), the effective charge $\rho_E$ is expressed by (13.8) and, if $y$ is the displacement of the beam normal to the $z$ axis, by (13.9) where $\Phi'$ is the derivative of $\Phi$ with respect to $y$.

The equations of motion used must include displacements normal to the $z$ direction; they are worked out including a constant longitudinal magnetic focusing field. Finally, a combined equation (13.23) is arrived at. This is rewritten in terms of dimensionless parameters, neglecting some small terms, as (13.26)

$$j\delta - b = \frac{1}{\delta^2} + \frac{\alpha^2}{(\delta^2 + f^2)}.$$

Here $\delta$ and $b$ have their usual meanings; $\alpha$ is the ratio between the transverse and longitudinal field strengths, and $f$ is proportional to the strength of the magnetic focusing field.

In case of a purely transverse field, a new gain parameter $D$ is defined. $D$ is the same as $C$ except that the longitudinal a-c field is replaced by the transverse a-c field. In terms of $D$, $b$ and $\delta$ are redefined by (13.36) and (13.37), and the final equation is (13.38). Figures 13.5–13.10 show how the $x$'s and $y$'s vary with $b$ for various values of $f$ (various magnetic fields) and Fig. 13.11 shows how $x_1$, which is proportional to the gain of the increasing wave in db per wavelength, decreases as magnetic field is increased. A numerical example shows that, assuming reasonable circuit impedance, a magnetic field which would provide a considerable focusing action would still allow a reasonable gain.

The curves of Figs. 13.6–13.10 resemble very much the curves of Figs. 8.7–8.9 of Chapter VIII, which show the effect of space charge in terms of the parameter $QC$. This is not unnatural; in one case space charge forces tend to return electrons which are accelerated longitudinally to their undisturbed positions. In the other case, magnetic forces tend to return electrons which are accelerated transversely to their undisturbed positions. In each case the circuit field acts on an electron stream which can itself sustain oscillations. In one case, the oscillations are of a plasma type, and the restoring force is caused by space charge of the bunched electron stream; in the other case the electrons can oscillate transversely in the magnetic field with cyclotron frequency.

Let us, for instance, compare (7.13), which applies to purely longitudinal displacements with space charge, with (13.38), which applies to purely transverse fields with a longitudinal magnetic field. For zero loss ($d = 0$), (7.13) becomes

$$1 = (j\delta - b)(\delta^2 + 4QC)$$

While

$$1 = (j\delta - b)(\delta^2 + f^2) \tag{13.38}$$

describes the transverse case. Thus, if we let

$$4QC = f^2$$

the equations are identical.

When there is both a longitudinal and a transverse electric field, the equation for $\delta$ is of the fifth degree. Thus, there are five forward waves. For an electron velocity equal to the circuit phase velocity ($b = 0$) and for no attenuation, the two new waves are unattenuated.

If there is no magnetic field, the presence of a transverse field component merely adds to the gain of the increasing wave. If a small magnetic field is imposed in the presence of a transverse field component, this gain is somewhat reduced.

## 13.1 CIRCUIT EQUATION

Consider a tubular electrode connected to ground through a wire, shown in Fig. 13.1. Suppose we bring a charge $Q$ into the tube from $\infty$. A charge $Q$ will flow to ground through the wire. This is the situation assumed in the analysis of Chapter II. In Fig. 2.3 it is assumed that all the lines of force from the charge in the electron beam terminate on the circuit, so that the whole charge may be considered as impressed on the circuit.

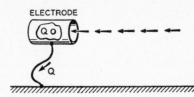

Fig. 13.1—When a charge $Q$ approaches a grounded conductor from infinity and in the end all the lines of force from the charge end on the conductor, a charge $Q$ flows in the grounding lead.

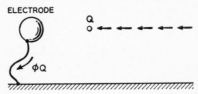

Fig. 13.2—If a charge $Q$ approaches a conductor from infinity but in the end only part of the lines of force from the charge end on the conductor, a charge $\Phi Q$ flows in the grounding lead, where $\Phi < 1$.

Now consider another case, shown in Fig. 13.2, in which a charge $Q$ is brought from $\infty$ to the vicinity of a grounded electrode. In this case, not all of the lines of force from the charge terminate on the electrode, and a charge $\Phi Q$ which is smaller than $Q$ flows through the wire to ground.

We can represent the situation of Fig. 13.2 by the circuit shown in Fig. 13.3. Here $C_2$ is the capacitance between the charge and the electrode and $C_1$ is the capacitance between the charge and ground. We see that the charge $\Phi Q$ which flows to ground when a charge $Q$ is brought to $a$ is

$$\Phi Q = Q C_2 / (C_1 + C_2) \tag{13.1}$$

Now suppose we take the charge $Q$ away and hold the electrode at a potential $V$ with respect to ground, as shown in Fig. 13.4. What is the potential $V_a$ at $a$? We see that it is

$$V_a = [C_2 / (C_1 + C_2)] V = \Phi V \tag{13.2}$$

Thus, the same factor $\Phi$ relates the actual charge to the "effective charge" acting on the circuit and the actual circuit voltage to the voltage produced at the location of the charge.

We will not consider in this section the "space charge" voltage produced by the charge itself (the voltage at point $a$ in Fig. 13.4).

The circuit voltage $V$ we consider as varying as $\exp(-\Gamma z)$ in the direction of propagation. The voltage in the vicinity of the circuit is given by

$$V(x, y) = \Phi V \tag{13.3}$$

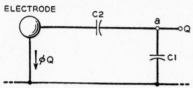

Fig. 13.3—The situation of Fig. 13.2 results in the same charge flow as if the charge were put on terminal $a$ of the circuit shown, which consists of two capacitors of capacitances $C_1$ and $C_2$.

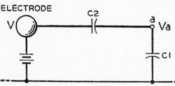

Fig. 13.4—A voltage $V$ inserted in the ground lead divides across the condensers so that $V_a = \Phi V$, where $\Phi$ is the same factor which relates the charge flowing in the ground lead to the charge $Q$ applied at $a$ in Figs. 13.2 and 13.3.

Here $x$ and $y$ refer to coordinates normal to $z$ and $\Phi$ is a function of $x$ and $y$. We will choose $x$ and $y$ so

$$\partial\Phi/\partial x = 0 \tag{13.4}$$

Then

$$E_y = -V\partial\Phi/\partial y = -\Phi'V \tag{13.5}$$

$$\Phi' = \partial\Phi/\partial y \tag{13.6}$$

In (13.3), $\Phi$ will vary somewhat with $\Gamma$, but, as we are concerned with a small range only in $\Gamma$, we will consider $\Phi$ a function of $y$ only.

From Chapter II we have

$$V = \frac{-\Gamma\Gamma_1 Ki}{(\Gamma^2 - \Gamma_1^2)} \tag{2.10}$$

and

$$\rho = \frac{-j\Gamma i}{\omega}. \tag{2.18}$$

So that

$$V = \frac{-j\omega\Gamma_1 K\rho}{(\Gamma^2 - \Gamma_1^2)}. \tag{13.7}$$

In (13.7), it is assumed that $\Phi = 1$. If $\Phi \neq 1$, we should replace $\rho$ in (13.7) by the a-c component of effective charge. The total effective charge $\rho_E$ is

$$\rho_E = \Phi(\rho + \rho_0) \tag{13.8}$$

The term $\rho_0$ is included because $\Phi$ will vary if the $y$-position of the charge varies. To the first order, the a-c component $\rho_E$ of the effective charge is,

$$\rho_E = \Phi\rho + \rho_0\Phi'y \tag{13.9}$$

$$\rho_E = \Phi\rho - (I_0/u_0)\Phi'y \tag{13.9}$$

Here $y$ is the a-c variation in position along the $y$ coordinate. Thus, if $\Phi \neq 0$, we have instead of (13.7)

$$V = \frac{-j\omega\Gamma_1 K(\Phi\rho - (I_0/u_0)\Phi' y)}{(\Gamma^2 - \Gamma_1^2)}. \tag{13.10}$$

This is the circuit equation we shall use.

## 13.2 Ballistic Equations

We will assume an unperturbed motion of velocity $u_0$ in the $z$ direction, parallel to a uniform magnetic focusing field of strength $B$. As in Chapter II, products of a-c quantities will be neglected.

In the $x$ direction, perpendicular to the $y$ and $z$ directions

$$d\dot{x}/dt = -\eta B\dot{y} \tag{13.11}$$

Assume that $\dot{x} = 0$ at $y = 0$. Then

$$\dot{x} = \eta By \tag{13.12}$$

In the $y$ direction we have

$$d\dot{y}/dt = \eta(B\dot{x} - E_y) \tag{13.13}$$

From (13.5) this is

$$d\dot{y}/dt = \eta(B\dot{x} + \Phi'V) \tag{13.14}$$

$$d\dot{y}/dt = \partial\dot{y}/\partial t + (\partial\dot{y}/\partial z)(dz/dt) \tag{13.15}$$

$$(d\dot{y}/dt) = u_0(j\beta_e - \Gamma)\dot{y} \tag{13.16}$$

We obtain from (13.16), (13.14) and (13.12)

$$(j\beta_e - \Gamma)y = -u_0\beta_m^2 y + \eta\Phi'V/u_0 \tag{13.17}$$

$$\beta_m = \eta B/u_0 \tag{13.18}$$

Here $\eta B$ is the cyclotron radian frequency and $\beta_m$ is a corresponding propagation constant.

Now

$$\dot{y} = \partial y/\partial t - (\partial y/\partial z)(\partial z/\partial t) \qquad (13.19)$$

$$\dot{y} = u_0(j\beta_e - \Gamma)y \qquad (13.20)$$

From (13.20) and (13.17) we obtain

$$y = \frac{\Phi' V}{2V_0[(j\beta_e - \Gamma)^2 + \beta_m^2]}. \qquad (13.21)$$

It is easily shown that the equation for $\rho$ can be obtained exactly as in Chapter II. From (2.22) and (2.18) we have

$$\rho = \frac{I_0 \Gamma^2 \Phi V}{2u_0 V_0(j\beta_e - \Gamma)^2}. \qquad (13.22)$$

### 13.3 COMBINED EQUATION

From the circuit equation (13.10) and the ballistical equations (13.21) and (13.22) we obtain

$$1 = \frac{-j\beta_e \Gamma_1 \Gamma^2 \Phi^2 K I_0}{2V_0(\Gamma^2 - \Gamma_1^2)} \left[ \frac{1}{(j\beta_e - \Gamma)^2} - \frac{(\Phi'/\Phi)^2}{\Gamma^2[(j\beta_e - \Gamma)^2 + \beta_m^2]} \right]. \qquad (13.23)$$

The voltage at the beam is $\Phi$ times the circuit voltage, so the effective impedance of the circuit at the beam is $\Phi^2$ times the circuit impedance. Thus

$$C^3 = \Phi^2 K I_0/4V_0 \qquad (13.24)$$

It will be convenient to define a dimensionless parameter $f$ specifying $\beta_m$ and hence the magnetic field

$$f = \beta_m/\beta_e C \qquad (13.25)$$

We will also use $\delta$ and $b$ as defined earlier

$$-\Gamma = -j\beta_e + \beta_e C\delta$$

$$-\Gamma_1 = -j\beta_e - j\beta_e Cb$$

After the usual approximations, (13.23) yields

$$j\delta - b = \frac{1}{\delta^2} + \frac{\alpha^2}{(\delta^2 + f^2)} \qquad (13.26)$$

$$\alpha^2 = (\Phi'/\beta_e\Phi)^2 \qquad (13.27)$$

It is interesting to consider the quantity $(\Phi'/\beta_e\Phi)^2$ for typical fields. For instance, in the two-dimensional electrostatic field in which the potential $V$ is given by

$$V = Ae^{-\beta_e y}e^{-j\beta_e z} \tag{13.28}$$

$$\partial V/\partial y = -\beta_e V \tag{13.29}$$

and everywhere

$$\alpha^2 = (\Phi'/\beta_e\Phi)^2 = 1. \tag{13.30}$$

Relation (13.30) is approximately true far from the axis in an axially symmetrical field.

Consider a potential giving a purely transverse field at $y = 0$

$$V = Ae^{-j\beta_e z} \sinh \beta_e y \tag{13.31}$$

$$\frac{\partial V}{\partial y} = \beta Ae^{-j\beta_e z} \cosh \beta_e y. \tag{13.32}$$

In this case, at $y = 0$

$$\alpha^2 = (\Phi'/\beta_e\Phi)^2 = \infty \tag{13.33}$$

In the case of a purely transverse field we let

$$D^3 = \frac{I_0 \Phi'^2 K}{4V_0 \beta_e^2} \tag{13.34}$$

$$D^3 = (E_y^2/\beta^2 P)(I_0/8V_0) \tag{13.35}$$

In (13.35), $E_y$ is the magnitude of the $y$ component of field for a power flow $P$, and $\beta$ is the phase constant.

We then redefine $\delta$ and $b$ in terms of $D$ rather than $C$

$$-\Gamma = -j\beta_e + \beta_e D\delta \tag{13.36}$$

$$-\Gamma_1 = -j\beta_e - j\beta_e Db \tag{13.37}$$

and our equation for a purely transverse field becomes

$$1 = (j\delta - b)(\delta^2 + f^2) \tag{13.38}$$

In (13.38), $\delta$ and $b$ are of course not the same as in (13.26) but are defined by (13.36) and (13.37).

### 13.4 Purely Transverse Fields

The case of purely transverse fields is of interest chiefly because, as was mentioned in Chapter X, it has been suggested that such tubes should have low noise.

In terms of $x$ and $y$ as usually defined

$$\delta = x + jy$$

equation (13.38) becomes

$$x[(x^2 - y^2 + f^2) - 2y(y + b)] = 0 \qquad (13.39)$$

$$(y + b)(x^2 - y^2 + f^2) + 2x^2 y + 1 = 0 \qquad (13.40)$$

From the $x = 0$ solution of (13.39) we obtain

$$x = 0 \qquad (13.41)$$

$$b = \frac{1}{y^2 - f^2} - y. \qquad (13.42)$$

It is found that this solution obtains for large and small values of $b$. For very large and very small values of $b$, either

$$y \doteq -b \qquad (13.43)$$

or

$$y \doteq \pm f \qquad (13.44)$$

The wave given by (13.43) is a circuit wave; that given by (13.44) represents electrons traveling down the tube and oscillating with the cyclotron frequency in the magnetic field.

In an intermediate range of $b$, we have from (13.39)

$$x = \pm \sqrt{2y(y + b) - (f^2 - y^2)} \qquad (13.45)$$

and

$$b = -2y \pm \sqrt{f^2 - 1/2y}. \qquad (13.46)$$

For a given value of $f^2$ we can assume values of $y$ and obtain values of $b$. Then, $x$ can be obtained from (13.45). In Figs. 13.5–13.10, $x$ and $y$ are plotted vs. $b$ for $f^2 = 0, .5, 1, 4$ and 10. It should be noted that $x_1$, the parameter expressing the rate of increase of the increasing wave, has a maximum at larger values of $b$ as $f$ is increased (as the magnetic focusing field is increased). Thus, for higher magnetic focusing fields the electrons must be shot into the circuit faster to get optimum results than for low fields. In Fig. 13.11, the maximum positive value of $x$ is plotted vs. $f$. The plot serves to illustrate the effect on gain of increasing the magnetic field.

Let us consider an example. Suppose

$$\lambda = 7.5 \text{ cm}$$

$$D = .03$$

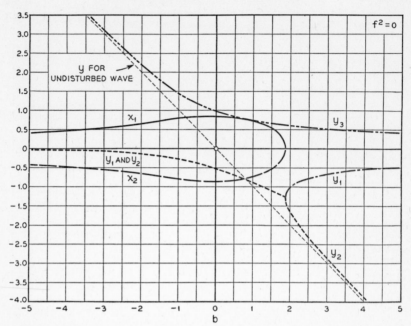

Fig. 13.5—The $x$'s and $y$'s for the three forward waves when the circuit field is purely transverse at the thin electron stream, for zero magnetic focusing field ($f^2 = 0$).

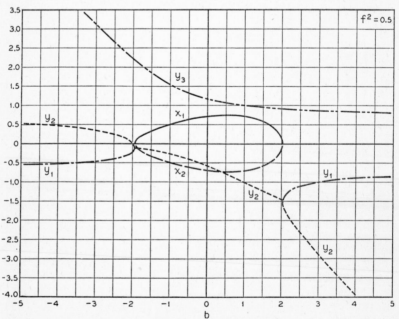

Fig. 13.6—Curves similar to those of Fig. 13.5 for a parameter $f^2 = 1$. The parameter $f$ is proportional to the strength of the magnetic focusing field.

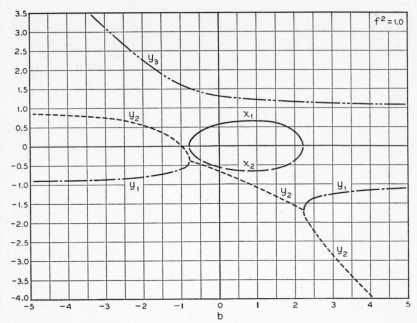

Fig. 13.7—The $x$'s and $y$'s for $f^2 = 1.0$.

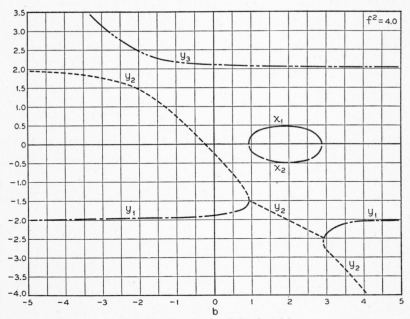

Fig. 13.8—The $x$'s and $y$'s for $f^2 = 2.0$.

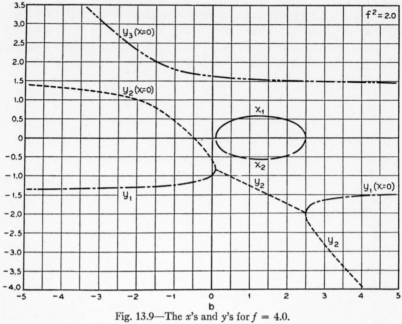

Fig. 13.9—The x's and y's for f = 4.0.

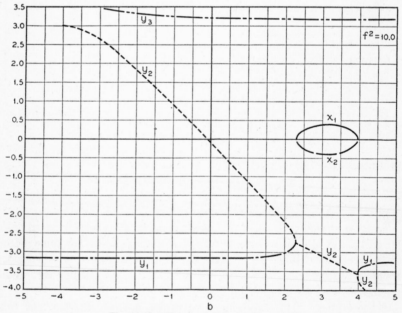

Fig. 13.10—The x's and y's for $f^2 = 10.0$.

These values are chosen because there is a longitudinal field tube which operates at 7.5 cm with a value of $C$ (which corresponds to $D$) of about .03. The table below shows the ratio of the maximum value of $x_1$ to the maximum value of $x_1$ for no magnetic focusing field.

| Magnestic Field in Gauss | $f$ | $x_1/x_{10}$ |
|---|---|---|
| 0 | 0 | 1 |
| 50 | 1.17 | .71 |
| 100 | 2.34 | .50 |

A field of 50 to 100 gauss should be sufficient to give useful focusing action. Thus, it may be desirable to use magnetic focusing fields in transverse-

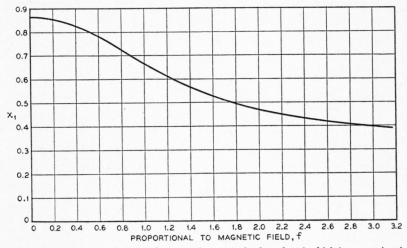

Fig. 13.11—Here $x_1$ , the $x$ for the increasing wave, is plotted vs $f$, which is proportional to the strength of the focusing field. The velocity parameter $b$ has been chosen to maximize $x_1$ . The ordinate $x_1$ is proportional to gain per wavelength.

field traveling-wave tubes. This will be more especially true in low-voltage tubes, for which $D$ may be expected to be higher than .03.

## 13.5 MIXED FIELDS

In tubes designed for use with longitudinal fields, the transverse fields far off the axis approach in strength the longitudinal fields. The same is true of transverse field tubes far off the axis. Thus, it is of interest to consider equation (13.26) for cases in which $\alpha$ is neither very small nor very large, but rather is of the order of unity.

If the magnetic field is very intense so that $f^2$ is large, then the term containing $\alpha^2$, which represents the effect of transverse fields, will be very small and the tube will behave much as if the transverse fields were absent.

Consideration of both terms presents considerable difficulty as (13.26) leads to five waves (5 values of $\delta$) instead of three. The writer has attacked the problem only for the special case of $b = 0$. In this case we obtain from (13.26)

$$\delta = -j\left[\frac{1}{\delta^2} + \frac{\alpha^2}{\delta^2 + f^2}\right] \tag{13.47}$$

MacColl has shown[1] that the two "new" waves (waves introduced when $\alpha = 0$) are unattenuated and thus unimportant and uninteresting (unless, as an off-chance, they have some drastic effect in fitting the boundary conditions).

Proceeding from this information, we will find the change in $\delta$ as $f^2$ is increased from zero. From (13.47) we obtain

$$d\delta = j\left[\frac{2d\delta}{\delta^3} + \frac{2\alpha^2 \delta d\delta}{(\delta^2 + f^2)^2} + \frac{\alpha^2 df^2}{(\delta^2 + f^2)^2}\right] \tag{13.48}$$

Now, if $f = 0$

$$\delta^3 = -j(1 + \alpha^2) \tag{13.49}$$

If we use this in connection with (13.48) we obtain

$$d\delta = -\frac{\alpha^2}{3\delta} df^2 \tag{13.50}$$

For an increasing wave

$$\delta_1 = (1 + (\Phi'/\beta_e\Phi)^2)(\sqrt{3}/2 - j/2) \tag{13.51}$$

Hence, for the increasing wave

$$d\delta_1 = \frac{\alpha^2(-\sqrt{3}/2 - j/2)}{3(1 + \alpha^2)} df^2 \tag{13.52}$$

This shows that applying a small magnetic field tends to decrease the gain. This does not mean, however, that the gain with a longitudinal and transverse field and a magnetic field is less than the gain with the longitudinal field alone. To see this we assume that not $f^2$ but $(\Phi'/\beta_e\Phi)^2$ is small. Differentiating, we obtain

$$d\delta = -j\left[-\frac{2d\delta}{\delta^3} - \frac{2\alpha^2 \delta d\delta}{(\delta^2 + f^2)^2} + \frac{d\alpha^2}{\delta^2 + f^2}\right] \tag{13.53}$$

If $\alpha = 0$

$$\delta^3 = -j \tag{13.54}$$

[1] J. R. Pierce, "Transverse Fields in Traveling-Wave Tubes," *Bell System Technical Journal*, Vol. 27, pp. 732–746.

and we obtain

$$d\delta = \frac{1}{3} \frac{\delta^3}{(\delta^2 + f^2)} \, d\alpha^2 \tag{13.55}$$

$$d\delta = \frac{-j}{3(\delta^2 + f^2)} \, d\alpha^2 \tag{13.56}$$

If we have a very large magnetic field $(f^2 \gg |\delta^2|)$, then

$$d\delta = \frac{-j}{3f^2} \, d\alpha^2 \tag{13.57}$$

and the change in $\delta$ is purely reactive. If $f = 0$ (no magnetic field), from (13.55)

$$d\delta = \frac{\delta}{3} \, d\alpha^2 \tag{13.58}$$

Adding a transverse field component increases the magnitude of $\delta$ without changing the phase angle.

PROBLEMS

1. The energy in the circuit comes from the energy represented by the longitudinal velocity of the injected electrons. If the electric field is transverse, how is the energy transferred from the electrons to the field?

2. Draw vectors showing the phase relation of the fields, electron velocities and the displacement $y$ for purely transverse operation with $b = f = 0$.

3. For $b = f = 0$ and purely transverse operation (as, (13.54)), fit the boundary conditions for an unmodulated stream of electrons entering the circuit and evaluate the initial loss parameter $A$.

# CHAPTER XIV

# FIELD SOLUTIONS

SO FAR, it has been assumed that the same a-c field acts on all electrons. This has been very useful in getting results, but we wonder if we are overlooking anything by this simplification.

The more complicated situation in which the variation of field over the electron stream is taken into account cannot be investigated with the same generality we have achieved in the case of "thin" electron streams. The chief importance we will attach to the work of this chapter is not that of producing numerical results useful in designing tubes. Rather, the chapter relates the appropriate field solutions to those we have been using and exhibits and evaluates features of the "broad beam" case which are not found in the "thin beam" case.

To this end we shall examine with care the simplest system which can reasonably be expected to exhibit new features. The writer believes that this will show qualitatively the general features of most or all "broad beam" cases.

The case is that of an electron stream of constant current density completely filling the opening of a double finned circuit structure, as shown in Fig. 14.1. The susceptance looking into the slots between the fins is a function of frequency only and not of propagation constant. Thus, at a given frequency, we can merely replace the slotted circuit members by susceptance sheets relating the magnetic field to the electric field, as shown in Fig. 14.2. The analysis is carried out with this susceptance as a parameter. Only the mode of propagation with a symmetrical field pattern is considered.

First, the case for zero current density is considered. The natural mode of propagation will have a phase constant $\beta$ such that $H_x/E_z$ for the central region is the same as $H_x/E_z$ for the finned circuit. The solid curve of Fig. 14.3 shows a quantity proportional to $H_x/E_z$ for the central space vs $\theta = \beta d$ ($d$ defined by Fig. 14.1), a quantity proportional to $\beta$. The dashed line $P$ represents $H_x/E_z$ for a given finned structure. The intersections specify values of $\theta$ for the natural active modes of propagation to the left and to the right, and, hence, values of the natural phase constants.

The structure also has passive modes of propagation. If we assume fields which vary in the $z$ direction as $\exp{(\Phi/d)z}$, $H_x/E_z$ for the central

182

opening varies with $\Phi$ as shown in part in Fig. 14.4. A horizontal line representing a given susceptance of the finned structure will intersect the curve at an infinite number of points. Each intersection represents a passive mode which decays at a particular rate in the $z$ direction and varies sinusoidally with a particular period in the $y$ direction.

If the effect of the electrons in the central space is included, $H_x/E_z$ for the central space no longer varies as shown in Fig. 14.3, but as shown in Fig. 14.5 instead. The curve goes off to $+\infty$ near a value of $\theta$ corresponding to a phase velocity near to the electron velocity. The nature of the modes depends on the susceptance of the finned structure. If this is represented by $P_1$, there are four unattenuated waves; for $P_3$ there are two unattenuated waves and an increasing and a decreasing wave. $P_2$ represents a transitional case.

Not the whole of the curve for the central space is shown on Fig. 14.5. In Fig. 14.6 we see on an expanded scale part of the region about $\theta = 1$, between the points where the curve goes through 0. The curve goes to $+\infty$ and repeatedly from $-\infty$ to $+\infty$, crossing the axis an infinite number of times as $\theta$ approaches unity. For any susceptance of the finned structure, this leads to an infinite number of unattenuated modes, which are space-charge waves; for these the amplitude varies sinusoidally with different periods across the beam. Not all of them have any physical meaning, for near $\theta = 1$ the period of cyclic variation across the beam will become small even compared to the space between electrons.

Returning to Fig. 14.1, we may consider a case in which the central space between the finned structures is very narrow ($d$ very small). This will have the effect of pushing the solid curve of Fig. 14.5 up toward the horizontal axis, so that for a reasonable value of $P$ (say, $P_1$, $P_2$ or $P_3$ of Fig. 14.5) there is no intersection. That is, the circuit does not propagate any unattenuated waves. In this case there are still an increasing and a decreasing wave. The behavior is like that of a multi-resonator klystron carried to the extreme of an infinite number of resonators. If we add resonator loss, the behavior of gain per wavelength with frequency near the resonant frequency of the slots is as shown in Fig. 14.7.

One purpose of this treatment of a broad electron stream is to compare its results with those of the previous chapters. There, the treatment considered two aspects separately: the circuit and the effect of the electrons.

Suppose that at $y = d$ in Fig. 14.1 we evaluate not $H_x$ for the finned structure and for the central space separately, but, rather, the difference or discontinuity in $H_x$. This can be thought of as giving the driving current necessary to establish the field $E_z$ with a specified phase constant. In Fig. 14.8, $y_1$ is proportional to this $H_x$ or driving current divided by $E_z$. The dashed curve $y_2$ is the variation of driving current with $\theta$ or $\beta$ which we have used in earlier chapters, fitted to the true curve in slope and magnitude at $y = 0$. Over the range of $\theta$ of interest in connection with increasing waves, the fit is good.

The difference between $H_x/E_z$ for the central space without electrons (Fig. 14.3) and $H_x/E_z$ for the central space with electrons (Fig. 14.5) can be taken as representing the driving effect of the electrons. The solid curve of Fig. 14.9 is proportional to this difference, and hence represents the true effect of the electrons. The dashed curve is from the ballistical equation used in previous chapters. This has been fitted by adjusting the space-charge parameter $Q$ only; the leading term is evaluated directly in terms of current density, beam width, $\beta$, and variation of field over the beam, which is assumed to be the same as in the absence of electrons.

Figure 14.10 shows a circuit curve (as, of Fig. 14.8) and an electronic curve (as, of Fig. 14.10). These curves contain the same information as the curves (including one of the dashed horizontal lines) of Fig. 14.5, but differently distributed. The intersections represent the modes of propagation.

If such curves were the approximate (dashed) curves of Figs. 14.8 and 14.9, the values of $\theta$ for the modes would be quite accurate for real intersections. It is not clear that "intersections" for complex values of $\theta$ would be accurately given unless they were for near misses of the curves. In addition, the complicated behavior near $\theta = 1$ (Fig. 14.6) is quite absent from the approximate electronic curve. Thus, the approximate electronic curve does not predict the multitude of unattenuated space-charge waves near $\theta = 1$. Further, the approximate expressions predict a lower limiting electron velocity below which there is no gain. This is not true for the exact equations when the electron flow fills the space between the finned structures completely.

It is of some interest to consider complex intersections in the case of near misses by using curves of simple form (parabolas), as in Fig. 14.11. Such an analysis shows that high gain is to be expected in the case of curves such as those of Fig. 14.10, for instance, when the circuit curve is not steep and when the curvature of the electronic curve is small. In terms of physical parameters, this means a high impedance circuit and a large current density.

## 14.1 THE SYSTEM AND THE EQUATIONS

The system examined is a two-dimensional one closely analogous to that of Fig. 4.4. It is shown in Fig. 14.1. It consists of a central space extending from $y = -d$ to $y = +d$, and arrays of thin fins separated by slots extending for a distance $h$ beyond the central opening and short-circuited at the outer ends. An electron flow of current density $J_0$ amperes/$m^2$ fills the open space. It is assumed that the electrons are constrained by a strong magnetic field so that they can move in the $z$ direction only.

We can simplify the picture a little. The open edges of the slots merely form impedance sheets.

From 4.12 we see that at $y = -d$

$$\frac{H_x}{E_z} = \frac{j\omega\epsilon}{\beta_0} \cot \beta_0 h \qquad (14.1)$$

$$\frac{H_x}{E_z} = -jB \qquad (14.2)$$

$$B = - \sqrt{\epsilon/\mu} \cot \beta_0 h \qquad (14.3)$$

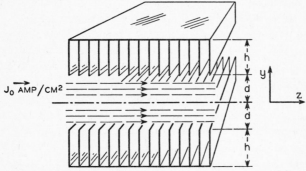

Fig. 14.1—Electron flow completely fills the open space between two finned structures. A strong axial magnetic field prevents transverse motions.

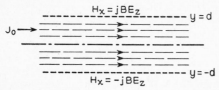

Fig. 14.2—In analyzing the structure of Fig. 14.1, the finned members are regarded as susceptance sheets.

for

$$\beta_0/\omega\epsilon = 1/c\epsilon = \sqrt{\mu/\epsilon} = 377 \text{ ohms} \qquad (14.4)$$

Similarly, at $y = +d$,

$$\frac{H_x}{E_z} = jB \qquad (14.5)$$

We can use $B$ as a parameter rather than $h$. Thus, we obtain the picture of Fig. 14.2. This picture is really more general than Fig. 14.1, for it applies for any transverse-magnetic circuit outside of the beam.

Inside of the beam the effect of the electrons is to change the effective dielectric constant in the $z$ direction. Thus, from (2.22) we have for the electron convection current

$$i = \frac{jJ_0\beta_e\Gamma V}{2V_0(j\beta_e - \Gamma)^2} \tag{2.22}$$

Now

$$E_z = -\frac{\partial V}{\partial z} = \Gamma V \tag{14.6}$$

so that

$$i = \frac{jJ_0\beta_e E_z}{2V_0(j\beta_e - \Gamma)^2} \tag{14.7}$$

The appearance of a voltage $V$ in (2.22) and (14.6) does not mean that these relations are invalid for fast waves. In (2.22) the only meaning which need be given to $V$ is that defined by (14.6), as it is the electric field as specified by (14.6) that was assumed to act on the electrons in deriving (2.22).

Let us say that the total a-c current density in the $z$ direction, $J_z$, is

$$J_z = j\omega\epsilon_1 E_z \tag{14.8}$$

This current consists of a displacement current $j\omega\epsilon E_z$ and the current $i$, so that

$$J_z = j\omega\epsilon_1 E_z = j\omega\epsilon E_z\left(1 + \frac{J_0\beta_e}{2\epsilon\omega V_0(j\beta_e - \Gamma)^2}\right) \tag{14.9}$$

Hence

$$\epsilon_1/\epsilon = \left(1 + \frac{J_0\beta_e}{2\epsilon\omega V_0(j\beta_e - \Gamma)^2}\right) \tag{14.10}$$

This gives the ratio of the effective dielectric constant in the $z$ direction to the actual dielectric constant. We will proceed to put this in a form which in the long run will prove more convenient.

Let us define a quanity $\beta$

$$\Gamma = j\beta \tag{14.11}$$

and a quantity $A$

$$A = \frac{J_0 d^2}{2\epsilon u_0 V_0} \tag{14.12}$$

And quantities $\theta$ and $\theta_e$

$$\theta_e = \beta_e d = (\omega/u_0)d \tag{14.13}$$

$$\theta = \beta d \tag{14.14}$$

We recognize $d$ as the half-width of the opening filled by electrons. Then

$$\epsilon_1/\epsilon = 1 - \frac{A}{(\theta_e - \theta)^2} \qquad (14.15)$$

We can say something about the quantity $A$. From purely d-c considerations, the electron flow will cause a fall in d-c potential toward the center of the beam. Indeed, this is so severe for large currents that it sets a limit to the current density which can be transmitted. If we take $V_0$ and $u_0$ as values at $y = \pm d$ (the wall), the maximum value of $A$ as defined by (14.12) is 2/3, and at this maximum value the potential at $y = 0$ is $V_0/4$. This is inconsistent with the analysis, in which $V_0$ and $u_0$ are assumed to be constant across the electron flow. Thus, for the current densities for which the analysis is valid, which are the current densities such as are usually used in traveling-wave tubes

$$A \ll 1 \qquad (14.16)$$

In the a-c analysis we will deal here only with the symmetrical type of wave in which $E_z(+y) = E_z(-y)$. The work can easily be extended to cover cases for which $E_z(+y) = -E_z(-y)$. We assume

$$H_x = H_0 \sinh \gamma y e^{-j\beta z} \qquad (14.17)$$

From Maxwell's equations

$$j\omega\epsilon E_y = \frac{\partial H_x}{\partial z} = -j\beta H_0(\sinh \gamma y)e^{-j\beta z}$$

$$E_y = -\frac{\beta}{\omega\epsilon} H_0(\sinh \lambda y)e^{-j\beta z} \qquad (14.18)$$

Similarly

$$j\omega\epsilon_1 E_z = -\frac{\partial H_x}{\partial y} = -\gamma H_0(\cosh \gamma y)e^{-j\beta z}$$

$$E_z = \frac{j\gamma}{\omega\epsilon_1} H_0(\cosh \gamma y)e^{-j\beta z} \qquad (14.19)$$

We must also have

$$-j\omega\mu H_x = \frac{\partial E_z}{\partial y} - \frac{\partial E_y}{\partial z}$$

$$-j\omega\mu H_0 e^{-j\beta z} \sinh \gamma y = \frac{j\gamma^2}{\omega\epsilon_1} H_0 e^{-j\beta z} \cosh \gamma y - \frac{j\beta^2}{\omega\epsilon} H_0 e^{-j\beta z} \sinh \gamma y$$

$$\gamma^2 = (\epsilon_1/\epsilon)(\beta^2 - \beta_0^2) \qquad (14.20)$$

$$\beta_0^2 = \omega^2\mu\epsilon = \omega^2/c^2 \qquad (14.21)$$

Now, from (14.17), (14.19) and (14.20)

$$\frac{H_x}{E_z} = \frac{-j\omega\epsilon(\epsilon_1/\epsilon)\tanh\ [(\epsilon_1/\epsilon)^{1/2}(\beta^2 - \beta_0^2)^{1/2}\ y]}{(\epsilon_1/\epsilon)^{1/2}(\beta^2 - \beta_0^2)^{1/2}} \qquad (14.22)$$

But

$$\omega\epsilon = (\omega/c)(c\epsilon) = \beta_0\sqrt{\epsilon/\mu} \qquad (14.23)$$

Hence

$$\frac{H_x}{E_z} = \frac{-j\sqrt{\epsilon/\mu}(\epsilon_1/\epsilon)^{1/2}\beta_0\tanh\ [(\epsilon_1/\epsilon)^{1/2}(\beta^2 - \beta_0^2)^{1/2}y]}{(\beta^2 - \beta_0^2)^{1/2}} \qquad (14.24)$$

At $y = d$, (14.5) must apply. From (14.24) we can write

$$P = -\frac{(\epsilon_1/\epsilon)^{1/2}\tanh\ [(\epsilon_1/\epsilon)^{1/2}(\theta^2 - \theta_0^2)^{1/2}]}{(\theta^2 - \theta_0^2)^{1/2}} \qquad (14.25)$$

Here $\theta$ is given by (14.14)

$$\theta_0 = \beta_0 d = (\omega/c)d \qquad (14.26)$$

and $P$ is given by

$$P = B/\beta_0 d\sqrt{\epsilon/\mu} = B/\theta_0\sqrt{\epsilon/\mu} \qquad (14.27)$$

Thus, $\theta_0$ expresses $d$ in radians at free-space wavelength and $P$ is a measure of the wall reactance, the susceptance rising as $B$ rises.

## 14.2 Waves in the Absence of Electrons

In this section we will consider (14.25) in the case in which there are no electrons and $\epsilon_1/\epsilon = 1$. In this case (14.25) becomes

$$P = -\frac{\tanh\ (\theta^2 - \theta_0^2)^{1/2}}{(\theta^2 - \theta_0^2)^{1/2}} \qquad (14.28)$$

Suppose we plot the right-hand side of (14.28) vs $\theta$ for real values of $\theta_1$ corresponding to unattenuated waves. In Fig. 14.3 this has been done for $\theta_0 = 1/10$. For $\theta_0 > \pi/2$ the behavior near the origin is different, but in cases corresponding to actual traveling wave tubes $\theta_0 < \pi/2$.

Intersections between a horizontal line at height $P$ and the curve give values of $\theta$ representing unattenuated waves. We see that for the case which we have considered, in which $\theta_0 < \pi/2$ and $\theta_0 \cot \theta_0 > 1$, there are unattenuated waves if

$$P > -\tan\theta_0/\theta_0 \qquad (14.29)$$

For $P = -\infty$ (no slot depth and no wall reactance) the system for $\theta_0 < \pi/2$ constitutes a wave guide operated below cutoff frequency for the type of wave we have considered. If we increase $P$ ($|P|$ decreasing; the inductive reactance of the walls increasing) this finally results in the propagation of a wave. There are two intersections, at $\theta = \pm\theta_1$, representing propagation to the right and propagation to the left. The variation of $\theta_1$ with $P$ is such that as $P$ is increased (made less negative) $\theta_1$ is increased; that is, the greater is $P$ (the smaller $|P|$), the more slowly the wave travels.

There is another set of waves for which $\theta$ is imaginary; these represent passive modes which do not transmit energy but merely decay with distance. In investigating these modes we will let

$$\theta = j\Phi \tag{14.30}$$

so that the waves vary with $z$ as

$$e^{(\Phi/d)z} \tag{14.31}$$

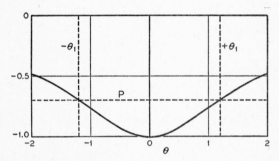

Fig. 14.3—The structure of Fig. 14.1 is first analyzed in the absence of an electron stream. Here a quantity proportional to $H_x/E_z$ at the susceptance sheet is plotted vs $\theta = \beta d$, a quantity proportional to the phase constant $\beta$. The solid curve is for the inner open space; the dashed line is for the susceptance sheet. The two intersections at $\pm\theta_1$ correspond to transmission of a forward and a backward wave.

Now (14.28) becomes

$$P = -\tan (\Phi^2 + \theta_0^2)^{1/2}/(\Phi^2 + \theta_0^2)^{1/2} \tag{14.32}$$

In Fig. 14.4 the right-hand side of (14.28) has been plotted vs $\Phi$, again for $\theta_0 = 1/10$.

Here there will be a number of intersections with any horizontal line representing a particular value of $P$ (a particular value of wall susceptance), and these will occur at paired values of $\Phi$ which we shall call $\pm\Phi_n$. The corresponding waves vary with distance as $\exp (\pm \Phi_n z/d)$.

Suppose we increase $P$. As $P$ passes the point $-(\tan \theta_0)/\theta_0$, $\Phi^n$ for a pair of these passive waves goes to zero; then for $P$ just greater than $-(\tan \theta_0)/\theta_0$ we have two active unattenuated waves, as may be seen by comparing Figs. 14.4 and 14.3.

## 14.3 Waves in the Presence of Electrons

In this section we deal with the equations

$$P = \frac{-(\epsilon_1/\epsilon)^{1/2} \tanh\left[(\epsilon_1/\epsilon)^{1/2}(\theta^2 - \theta_0^2)^{1/2}\right]}{(\theta^2 - \theta_0^2)^{1/2}} \tag{14.25}$$

and

$$\epsilon_1/\epsilon = 1 - \frac{A}{(\theta_e - \theta)^2} \tag{14.15}$$

We consider cases in which the electron velocity is much less than the velocity of light; hence

$$\theta_e \gg \theta_0 \tag{14.33}$$

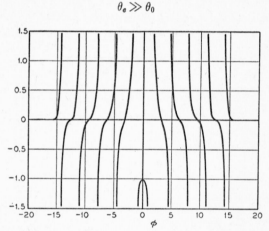

Fig. 14.4—If a quantity proportional to $H_x/E_z$ at the edge of the central region is plotted vs $\Phi = -j\theta$, this curve is obtained. There are an infinite number of intersections with a horizontal line representing the susceptance of the finned structure. These correspond to passive modes, for which the field decays exponentially with distance away from the point of excitation.

In Fig. 14.5, the right-hand side of (14.25) has been plotted vs. $\theta$ for $\theta_e = 10\,\theta_0$, corresponding to an electron velocity 1/10 the speed of light. Values of $\theta = 1/10$ and $A = 1/100$ have been chosen merely for convenience.* The curve has not been shown in the region from $\theta = .9$ to $\theta = 1.1$, where $\epsilon_1/\epsilon$ is negative, and this region will be discussed later.

For a larger value of $P(|\,P\,|$ small), $P_1$ in Fig. 14.5, there are 4 intersections corresponding to 4 unattenuated waves. The two outer intersections obviously correspond to the "circuit" waves we would have in the absence of electrons. The other two intersections near $\theta = .9\theta_e$ and $\theta = 1.1\theta_e$ we call electronic or space-charge waves.

* At a beam voltage $V_0 = 1,000$ and for $d = 0.1$ cm, $A = 1/100$ means a current density of about 330 ma/cm², which is a current density in the range encountered in practice.

For instance, increasing $P$ to values larger than $P_1$ changes $\theta$ for the circuit waves a great deal but scarcely alters the two "electronic wave" values of $\theta$, near $\theta = \theta_e(1 \pm 0.1)$. On the other hand, for large values of $P$ the values of $\theta$ for the electronic waves are approximately

$$\theta = \theta_e \pm \sqrt{A} \tag{14.34}$$

Thus, changing $A$ alters these values, but changing $A$ has little effect on the values of $\theta$ for the circuit waves.

Now, the larger the $P$ the slower the circuit wave travels; and, hence, for large values of $P$ the electrons travel faster than the circuit wave. Our narrow-beam analysis also indicated two circuit waves and two unattenuated electronic waves for cases in which the electron speed is much larger than the speed of the increasing wave. It also showed, however, that, as the difference between the electron speed and the speed of the unperturbed

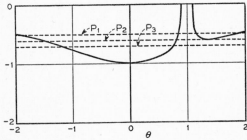

Fig. 14.5—When electrons are present in the open space of the circuit of Fig. 14.1, the curves of Fig. 14.3 are modified as shown here. The nature of the waves depends on the relative magnitude of the susceptance of the finned structure, which is represented by the dashed horizontal lines. For $P_1$, there are four unattenuated waves, for $P_3$, two unattenuated waves and an increasing wave and a decreasing wave. Line $P_2$ represents a transition between the two cases.

wave was made less, a pair of waves appeared, one increasing and one decreasing. This is also the case in the broad beam case.

In Fig. 14.5, when $P$ is given the value indicated by $P_2$, an "electronic" wave and a "circuit" wave coalesce; this corresponds to $y_1$ and $y_2$ running together at $b = (3/2)(2)^{1/3}$ in Fig. 8.1. For a somewhat smaller value of $P$, such as $P_3$, there will be a pair of complex values of $\theta$ corresponding to an increasing wave and a decreasing wave. We may expect the rate of increase at first to rise and then to fall as $P$ is gradually decreased from the value $P_2$, corresponding to the rise and fall of $x_1$ as $b$ is decreased from $(3/2)(2)^{1/3}$ in Fig. 8.1.

It is interesting to know whether or not these increasing waves persist down to $P = -\infty$ (no inductance in the walls). When $P = -\infty$, the only way (14.25) can be satisfied is by

$$\coth\left((\epsilon_1/\epsilon)^{1/2}(\theta^2 - \theta_0^2)^{1/2}\right) = 0 \tag{14.35}$$

This  will  occur  only  if

$$(\epsilon_1/\epsilon)^{1/2}(\theta^2 - \theta_0^2)^{1/2} = j\left(n\pi + \frac{\pi}{2}\right)$$

$$(\epsilon_1/\epsilon)(\theta^2 - \theta_0^2) = -\left(n\pi + \frac{\pi}{2}\right)^2$$

(14.36)

Let

$$\theta = u + jw \qquad (14.37)$$

From  (14.37),  (14.36)  and  (14.15)

$$\left[1 - \frac{A}{((\theta_e - u) + jw)^2}\right]((u + jw)^2 - \theta_0^2) = -\left(n\pi + \frac{\pi}{2}\right)^2 \qquad (14.38)$$

If  we  separate  the  real  and  imaginary  parts,  we  obtain

$$[(A - 1)(\theta_e - u)^2 - (A + 1)w^2](u^2 - w^2 - \theta_0^2)$$

$$- 4Auw^2(\theta_e - u) = [(\theta_e - u)^2 + w^2]\left(n\pi + \frac{\pi}{2}\right)^2 \qquad (14.39)$$

$$w(u[(\theta_e - u)^2 + w^2] - A[(\theta_e - u)^2 - w^2] + (\theta_e - u)(u^2 - w^2 - \theta_0^2)) = 0$$

(14.40)

The  right-hand  side  of  (14.39)  is  always  positive.  Because  always  $A < 1$, the  first  term  on  the  left  of  (14.39)  is  always  negative  if  $u^2 > (w^2 + \theta_0^2)$, which  will  be  true  for  slow  rates  of  increase.  Thus,  for  very  small  values of  $w$,  (14.39)  cannot  be  satisfied.  Thus,  it  seems  that  there  are  no  waves such  as  we  are  looking  for,  that  is,  slow  waves  $(u \ll c)$.  It  appears  that the  increasing  waves  must  disappear  or  be  greatly  modified  when  $P$  approaches  $-\infty$.

So  far  we  have  considered  only  four  of  the  waves  which  exist  in  the presence  of  electrons.  A  whole  series  of  unattenuated  electron  waves  exist in  the  range

$$\theta_e - \sqrt{A} < \theta < \theta_e + \sqrt{A}$$

In  this  range  $(\epsilon_1/\epsilon)^{1/2}$  is  imaginary,  and  it  is  convenient  to  rewrite  (14.25) as

$$P = \frac{(-\epsilon_1/\epsilon)^{1/2} \tan\left[(-\epsilon_1/\epsilon)^{1/2}(\theta^2 - \theta_0^2)^{1/2}\right]}{(\theta^2 - \theta_0^2)^{1/2}} \qquad (14.41)$$

The  chief  variation  in  this  expression  over  the  range  considered  is  that  due to  variation  in  $(-\epsilon_1/\epsilon)^{1/2}$.  For  all  practical  purposes  we  may  write

$$P = \frac{(-\epsilon_1/\epsilon)^{1/2} \tan\left[(-\epsilon_1/\epsilon)^{1/2}(\theta_e^2 - \theta_0)^{1/2}\right]}{(\theta_e^2 - \theta_0^2)^{1/2}} \qquad (14.42)$$

Near $\theta = \theta_e$, the tangent varies with infinite rapidity, making an infinite number of crossings of the axis.

In Fig. 14.6, the right-hand side of (14.41) has been plotted for a part of the range $\theta = 0.90\,\theta_e$ to $\theta = 1.10\,\theta_e$. The waves corresponding to the intersections of the rapidly fluctuating curve with a horizontal line representing $P$ are unattenuated space-charge waves. The nearer $\theta$ is to $\theta_e$, the larger $(-\epsilon_1/\epsilon)$ is. The amplitude of the electric field varies with $y$ as

$$\cosh\left(j(-\epsilon_1/\epsilon)^{1/2}(\beta^2 - \beta_0^2)^{1/2}y\right) = \cos\left((-\epsilon_1/\epsilon)^{1/2}(\beta^2 - \beta_0^2)^{1/2}y\right) \quad (14.45)$$

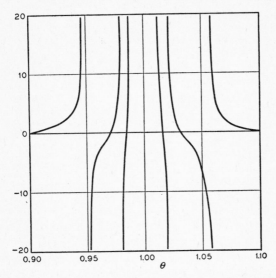

Fig. 14.6—The curve for the central region is not shown completely in Fig. 14.5. A part of the detail around $\theta = 1$, which means a phase velocity equal to the electron velocity, is shown in Fig. 14.6. The curve crosses the axis, and any other horizontal line, an infinite number of times (only some of the branches are shown). Thus, there is a large number of unattenuated "space charge" waves. For these, the amplitude varies sinusoidally in the $y$ direction. Some of these have no physical reality, because the wavelength in the $y$ direction is short compared with the space between electrons.

For small values of $|\theta - \theta_e|$ the field fluctuates very rapidly in the $y$ direction, passing through many cycles between $y = 0$ and $y = d$. For very small values of $|\theta - \theta_e|$ the solution does not correspond to any actual physical problem: spreads in velocity in any electron stream, and ultimately the discrete nature of electron flow, preclude the variations indicated by (14.45).

The writer cannot state definitely that there are not increasing waves for which the real part of $\theta$ lies between $\theta_e - \sqrt{A}$ and $\theta_e + \sqrt{A}$, but he sees no reason to believe that there are.

There are, however, other waves which exhibit both attenuation and propagation. The roots of (14.32) are modified by the introduction of the electrons. To show this effect, let $\Phi_n$ be a solution of (14.32), and $j(\Phi_n + \delta)$ be a solution of (14.25). The waves considered will thus vary with distance as

$$e^{[(\Phi_n + \delta)/d]z} \tag{14.43}$$

We see that we must have

$$(\epsilon_1/\epsilon)^{1/2} (\Phi_n^2 + \theta_0^2)^{1/2} \cot (\Phi_n^2 + \theta_0^2)^{1/2}$$
$$= ((\Phi_n + \delta)^2 + \theta_0^2)^{1/2} \cot [(\epsilon_1/\epsilon)^{1/2}((\Phi_n + \delta)^2 + \theta_0^2)^{1/2}] \tag{14.44}$$

$$(\epsilon_1/\epsilon)^{1/2} = \left(1 - \frac{A}{(\theta_e - j\Phi_n + \delta)^2}\right)^{1/2} \tag{14.15a}$$

As $A \ll 1$, it seems safe to neglect $\delta$ in (14.15a) and to expand, writing

$$(\epsilon_1/\epsilon)^{1/2} = 1 - \alpha \tag{14.46}$$

$$\alpha = \frac{A}{2(\theta_e - j\Phi_n)^2} = \frac{A[(\theta_e^2 - \Phi_n^2) + 2j\theta_e\Phi_n]}{2(\theta_e^2 + \Phi_n^2)^2} \tag{14.47}$$

If $|\delta| \ll \Phi_n$, we may also write

$$((\Phi_n + \delta)^2 + \theta_0^2)^{1/2} = \frac{\Phi_n \delta}{(\Phi_n^2 + \theta_0^2)^{1/2}} + (\Phi_n^2 + \theta_0^2)^{1/2} \tag{14.48}$$

We thus obtain, if we neglect products of $\delta$ and $\alpha$

$$(1 - \alpha) \cot (\Phi_n^2 + \theta_0^2)^{1/2} = \left[1 + \frac{\Phi_n \delta}{(\Phi_n^2 + \theta_0^2)^{1/2}}\right] \cot (\Phi_n^2 + \theta_0^2)^{1/2}$$
$$- \left(\frac{\Phi_n \delta}{(\Phi_n^2 + \theta_0^2)^{1/2}} - \alpha\right) \csc^2 (\Phi_n^2 + \theta_0^2)^{1/2} \tag{14.49}$$

Solving this for $\delta$, we obtain

$$\delta = -\frac{(\Phi_n^2 + \theta_0^2)^{1/2}}{\Phi_n} \left[\frac{\cos (\Phi_n^2 + \theta_0^2)^{1/2} + \csc (\Phi_n^2 + \theta_0^2)^{1/2}}{\cos (\Phi_n^2 + \theta_0^2)^{1/2} - \csc (\Phi_n^2 + \theta_0^2)^{1/2}}\right] \alpha \tag{14.50}$$

$$\delta = \left[\frac{(\theta_e^2 - \Phi_n^2)}{\Phi_n(\theta_e^2 + \Phi_n^2)^2} + j \frac{2\theta_e}{(\theta_e^2 + \Phi_n^2)^2}\right]$$
$$\cdot \left[\frac{\csc^2 (\Phi_n^2 + \theta_0^2)^{1/2} + \cos (\Phi_n^2 + \theta_0^2)^{1/2}}{\csc (\Phi_n^2 + \theta_0^2)^{1/2} - \cos (\Phi_n^2 + \theta_0^2)^{1/2}}\right] \frac{A(\theta_0^2 + \Phi_n^2)^{1/2}}{2} \tag{14.51}$$

As the waves vary with distance as $\exp [(\pm \Phi_n + \delta)z/d]$, this means that all modified waves travel in the $-z$ direction, and very fast, for the imaginary part of $\delta$, which is inversely proportional to the phase velocity, will be small.

These backward-traveling waves cannot give gain in the $+z$ direction, and could give gain in the $-z$ direction only under conditions similar to those discussed in Chapter XI.

## 14.4 A SPECIAL TYPE OF SOLUTION

Consider (14.25) in a case in which

$$\theta_0 \ll \theta_e \tag{14.52}$$

$$\theta_e \ll 1 \tag{14.53}$$

In this case in the range

$$\theta < \theta_e - \sqrt{A} \quad \text{and} \quad \theta > \theta_e + \sqrt{A} \tag{14.54}$$

we can replace the hyperbolic tangent by its argument, giving

$$P = -(\epsilon_1/\epsilon) = \frac{A}{(\theta_e - \theta)^2} - 1. \tag{14.55}$$

This can be solved for $\theta$, giving

$$\theta = \theta_e \mp \sqrt{A/(P + 1)} \tag{14.56}$$

If

$$P < -1$$

Then $\theta$ will be complex and there will be a pair of waves, one increasing and one decreasing. We note that, under these circumstances, there is no circuit wave, either with or without electrons.

What we have is in essence an electron stream passing through a series of inductively detuned resonators, as in a multi-resonator klystron. Thus, the structure is in essence a distributed multi-resonator klystron, with lossless resonators. If the resonators have loss, we can let

$$P = (-jG + B)/\theta_0 \sqrt{\epsilon/\mu} \tag{14.57}$$

where $G$ is the resonant conductance of the slots. In this case, (14.56) becomes

$$\theta = \theta_e \pm \left( \frac{A\theta \sqrt{\epsilon/\mu}}{-jG + (B + \theta_0 \sqrt{\epsilon/\mu})} \right)^{1/2} \tag{14.58}$$

Near resonance we can assume $G$ is a constant and that $B$ varies linearly with frequency. Accordingly, we can show the form of the gain of the increasing wave by plotting vs. frequency the quantity $g$

$$g = \text{Im}(-j + \omega/\omega_0)^{-1/2} \tag{14.59}$$

In Fig. 14.7, $g$ is plotted vs. $\omega/\omega_0$.

## 14.5 COMPARISON WITH PREVIOUS THEORY

We will compare our field solution with the theory presented earlier by comparing separately circuit effects and electronic effects.

### 14.6a *Comparison of Circuit Equations*

According to Chapter VI the field induced in an active mode by the current $i$ should be

$$E_z = \frac{\Gamma^2 \Gamma_1 (E^2/\beta^2 P)}{2(\Gamma_1^2 - \Gamma^2)} \, i$$

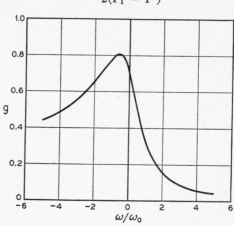

Fig. 14.7—In a plot such as that of Fig. 14.5, the horizontal line for the fins may not intersect the solid line for the central space at all. Particularly, this will be true as the central space is made very narrow. There will still be an increasing and a decreasing wave, however. Suppose, now, that the finned structure is lossy. We find that the gain in db of the increasing wave will vary with frequency as shown. Here $\omega_0$ is the resonant frequency of the slots in the finned structure.

whence

$$E_z = \frac{j\theta^2 R}{(\theta_1^2 - \theta^2)} \, i \tag{14.60}$$

where $R$ is a positive constant proportional to $(E^2/\beta^2 P)$.

Suppose that in Fig. 14.2 we have at $y = d$ not only the current $jBE_z$ flowing in the wall admittance, but an additional current $i$ given by (14.60) as well. Then instead of (14.28) we have

$$\frac{1}{\theta_0 (\sqrt{\epsilon/\mu})} \frac{i}{jE_z} + P = -\frac{\tanh (\theta^2 - \theta_0^2)^{1/2}}{(\theta^2 - \theta_0^2)^{1/2}} \tag{14.61}$$

For simplicity, let $\theta_0 \ll \theta$. Then we obtain from (14.61)

$$i = j\theta_0 \sqrt{\epsilon/\mu} \left( -P - \frac{\tanh \theta}{\theta} \right) E_z \tag{14.62}$$

We must identify this with (14.60). Thus, over the range considered, we must have approximately

$$(\theta_1^2/\theta^2 - 1)/R = \theta_0\sqrt{\epsilon/\mu}(P + (\tanh\theta)/\theta) \qquad (14.63)$$

At $\theta = \theta_1$, we must have both sides zero, so that

$$P = -(\tanh\theta_1)/\theta_1 \qquad \text{and} \qquad (14.64)$$

$$(1 - (\theta_1/\theta)^2)/R = \sqrt{\epsilon/\mu}((\tanh\theta_1)/\theta_1 - (\tanh\theta)/\theta) \qquad (14.65)$$

Taking the derivative with respect to $\theta$

$$\frac{2\theta_1^2}{\theta^3 R} = \theta_0\sqrt{\epsilon/\mu}\left(-\frac{\operatorname{sech}^2\theta}{\theta} + \frac{\tanh\theta}{\theta^2}\right) \qquad (14.66)$$

These must be equal at $\theta = \theta_1$, so that

$$1/R = (1/2)(\theta_0\sqrt{\epsilon/\mu})\left(\frac{\tanh\theta_1}{\theta_1} - \operatorname{sech}^2\theta_1\right) \qquad (14.67)$$

Thus, according to the methods of Chapter VI, our circuit equation should be

$$\left(\frac{1}{\theta_0\sqrt{\epsilon/\mu}}\right)\frac{i}{jE_z} = (1/2)\left(\frac{\tanh\theta_1}{\theta_1} - \operatorname{sech}^2\theta_1\right)(1 - (\theta_1/\theta)^2) \qquad (14.68)$$

Using (14.64), the correct equation (14.62) becomes

$$\left(\frac{1}{\theta_0\sqrt{\epsilon/\mu}}\right)\frac{i}{jE_z} = \frac{\tanh\theta_1}{\theta_1} - \frac{\tanh\theta}{\theta} \qquad (14.69)$$

In a typical traveling-wave tube, we might have

$$\theta_1 = 2.5$$

In Fig. 14.8, the right-hand side of (14.69) is plotted as a solid line and the right-hand side of (14.68) is plotted as a dashed line for $\theta_1 = 2.5$.

### 14.5b Electronic Comparison

Consider (14.25), which is the equation with electrons. For simplicity, let $\theta_0 \ll \theta$, so that

$$\frac{B}{\sqrt{\epsilon/\mu}\,\theta_0} = P = -\frac{(\epsilon_1/\epsilon)^2 \tanh[(\epsilon_1/\epsilon)^{1/2}\theta]}{\theta} \qquad (14.70)$$

For no electrons we would have

$$\frac{B}{\theta_0\sqrt{\epsilon/\mu}} = P = -\frac{\tanh\theta}{\theta} \qquad (14.71)$$

Thus, if we wish we may write (14.70) in the form

$$P_e = -\frac{\tanh \theta}{\theta} - P \tag{14.72}$$

where

$$P_e = (1/\theta)[(\epsilon_1/\epsilon)^{1/2} \tanh [(\epsilon_1/\epsilon)^{1/2} \theta - \tanh \theta] \tag{14.73}$$

The quantities on the right of (14.72) refer to the circuit in the absence of electrons; if there are no electrons $P_e = 0$ and (14.72) yields the circuit

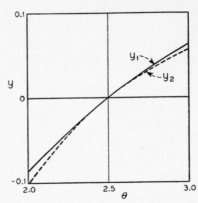

Fig. 14.8—Suppose we compare the circuit admittance for the structure of Fig. 14.1 with that used in earlier calculations. Here the solid curve is proportional to the difference of the $H_z$'s for the finned structure and for the central space (the impressed current) divided by $E_z$. The dashed curve is the simple expression (6.1) used earlier fitted in magnitude and slope.

waves. Thus, $P_e$ may be regarded as the equivalent of an added current $i$ at the wall, such that

$$\frac{i}{jE_z} = \theta \sqrt{\epsilon/\mu} P_e \tag{14.74}$$

Now, the root giving the increasing wave, the one we are most interested in, occurs a little way from the pole, where $(\epsilon_1/\epsilon)^{1/2}$ may be reasonably large if $\theta$ is large. It would seem that one of the best comparisons which could be made would be that between the approximate analysis and a very broad beam case, for which $\theta$ is very large. In this case, we may take approximately, away from $\theta = \theta_e$

$$\tanh [(\epsilon_1/\epsilon)^{1/2} \theta] = \tanh \theta = 1 \tag{14.75}$$

$$P_e = (1/\theta)[(\epsilon_1/\epsilon)^{1/2} - 1$$

$$P_e = (1/\theta)\left[\left(1 - \frac{A}{(\theta_e - \theta)^2}\right)^{1/2} - 1\right] \tag{14.76}$$

Let us expand in terms of the quantity $A/(\theta_e - \theta)^2$, assuming this to be small compared with unity. We obtain

$$P_e = \frac{A}{2\theta(\theta_e - \theta)^2}\left[1 + \frac{A}{4(\theta_e - \theta)^2} + \cdots\right] \qquad (14.77)$$

The theory of Chapter VII is developed by assuming that all electrons are acted on by the same a-c field. When this is not so, it is applied approximately by using an "effective current" or "effective field" as in Chapter IV; either of these concepts leads to the same averaging over the electron flow. An effective current can be obtained by averaging over the flow the current density times the square of the field, evaluated in the absence of electrons, and dividing by the square of the field at the reference position. This is equivalent to the method used in evaluating the effective field in Chapter III.

In the device of Fig. 14.2, if we take as a reference position $y = \pm d$, the effective current $I_0$ per unit depth

$$I_0 = \frac{J_0 \int_0^d \cosh^2 (\gamma y) \, dy}{\cosh^2 \gamma d} \qquad (14.78)$$

$$I_0 = (Jd/2)\left(\frac{\tanh \gamma d}{\gamma d} + \mathrm{sech}^2 \gamma d\right) \qquad (14.79)$$

This is the effective current associated with the half of the flow from $y = 0$ to $y = d$. Here $\gamma$ is the value for no electrons. For $\theta \ll \beta$, $\gamma = \beta$. For large values of $\theta$, then

$$I_0 = J_0 d/2\theta \qquad (14.80)$$

Now, the corresponding a-c convection current per unit depth will be:

$$i = -j\frac{I_0\beta_e}{2V_0(\beta_e - \beta)^2} E \qquad (14.81)$$

Here $E$ is the total field acting on the electrons in the $z$-direction. From (7.1) we see that we assumed this to be the field due to the circuit (the first term in the brackets) plus a quantity which we can write

$$E_{z1} = \frac{j\beta^2}{\omega C_1} i \qquad (14.82)$$

Accordingly

$$E = E_z + E_{z1} \qquad (14.83)$$

and we can write $i$

$$i = -j \frac{I_0 \beta_e}{2V_0(\beta_e - \beta)^2}\left(E_z + \frac{j\beta^2}{\omega C_1} i\right) \tag{14.84}$$

$$i = \frac{jI_0 \theta_e \, dE_z}{2V_0[K - (\theta_e - \theta)^2]} \tag{14.85}$$

Here $K$ is a parameter specifying the value of $\beta^2/\omega C_1$. As (14.85) need hold over only a rather small range of $\beta$, and $C$ is not independent of $\beta$, we will regard $K$ as a constant.

The parameter $P_e$ corresponding to (14.85) is

$$P_e = \frac{I_0 \, d(\theta_e/\theta_0)}{2\sqrt{\epsilon/\mu} \, V_0}[K - (\theta_e - \theta)^2]^{-1} \tag{14.86}$$

Now, from (14.80), for large values of $\theta$

$$\frac{I_0 \, d(\theta_e/\theta_0)}{2\sqrt{\epsilon/\mu} \, V_0} = \frac{J_0 \, d^2(\theta_e/\theta_0)}{4\sqrt{\epsilon/\mu} \, \theta V_0} \tag{14.87}$$

As

$$\sqrt{\epsilon/\mu} = \epsilon/\sqrt{\mu\epsilon} = \epsilon c,$$

$$\theta_e/\theta_0 = c/u_0,$$

and

$$A = \frac{J_0 \, d^2}{2\epsilon u_0 V_0} \tag{14.12}$$

$$P_e = \frac{A}{2\theta[K - (\theta_e - \theta)^2]} \tag{14.88}$$

Let us now expand (14.88) assuming $K$ to be very small

$$P_e = \frac{A}{2\theta(\theta_e - \theta)^2}\left[1 + \frac{K}{(\theta_e - \theta)^2} + \cdots\right] \tag{14.89}$$

If we let

$$K = A/4 \tag{14.90}$$

we see that these first two terms agree with the expansion of the broad-beam expression, (14.77). The leading term was not adjusted; the space-charge parameter $K$ was, since there is no other way of evaluating the parameter in this case.

In Fig. 14.9, the value of $\theta P_e$ as obtained, actually, from (14.73) rather than (14.76), is plotted as a solid line and the value corresponding to the earlier theory, from (14.86) with $K$ adjusted according to (14.88), is plotted as a dashed line, for

$$A = 0.01$$

$$\theta_e = 8$$

We see that (14.88), which involves the approximations made in our earlier calculations concerning traveling-wave tubes, is a remarkably good fit to the broad-beam expression derived from field theory up very close to the points $(\theta_e - \theta) = A$, which are the boundaries between real and imaginary arguments of the hyperbolic tangent and correspond to the points where the ordinate is zero in Fig. 14.5.

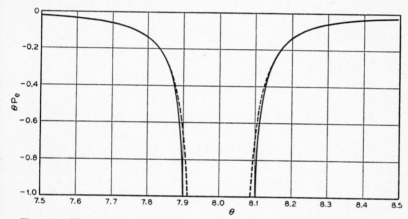

Fig. 14.9—These curves compare an exact electronic susceptance for the broad beam case (solid curve) with the approximate expression used earlier (dashed curve). In the approximate expression, the "effective current" was evaluated, not fitted; the space-charge parameter was chosen to give a fit.

Over the range in which the argument of the hyperbolic tangent in the correct expression is imaginary, the approximate expression of course exhibits none of the complex behavior characteristics of the correct expression and illustrated by Fig. 14.6. From (14.88) we see that the multiple excursions of the true curve from $-\infty$ to $+\infty$ are replaced in the approximate curve by a single dip down toward 0 and back up again. R. C. Fletcher has used a method similar to that explained above in computing the effective helix impedance and the effective space-charge parameter $Q$ for a solid beam inside of a helically conducting sheet. His work, which is valuable in calculating the gain of traveling-wave tubes, is reproduced in Appendix VI.

### 14.5c The Complex Roots

The propagation constants represent intersections of a circuit curve such as that shown in Fig. 14.8 and an electronic curve such as that shown in Fig.

14.9. The propagation constants obtained in Chapters II and VIII represent such intersections of approximate circuit and electronic curves, such as the dotted lines of Fig. 14.8 and 14.9. Propagation constants obtained by field solutions represent intersections of the more nearly exact circuit and electronic curves such as the solid curves of Figs. 14.8 and 14.9.

If we plot a circuit curve giving

$$(1/\theta_0 \sqrt{\epsilon/\mu})(i/jE_z)$$

as given by (14.65) (the right-hand side of 14.75) and an electronic curve giving

$$(1/\theta_0 \sqrt{\epsilon/\mu})(i/jE_z) = P_e$$

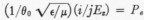

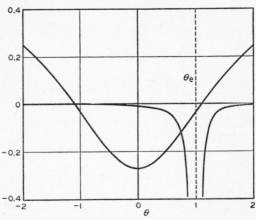

Fig. 14.10—The curves of Fig. 14.5 may be replaced by those of Fig. 14.6. Here the curve which is concave upward represents the circuit susceptance and the other curve represents the electronic susceptance (as in Fig. 14.9).

as given by (14.73) (the left-hand side of (14.72)), the plot, which is shown in Fig. 14.10, contains the same information as the plot of Fig. 14.5 for which $\theta_0$, $\theta_e$ and $A$ are the same. In Fig. 14.10, however, one curve represents the circuit without electrons and the other represents the added effect of the electrons.

We have seen that the approximate expressions of Chapter VII fit the broad-beam curves well for real propagation constants (real values of $\theta$) (Fig. 14.8 and 14.9). Hence, we expect that complex roots corresponding to the increasing waves which are obtained using the approximate expressions will be quite accurate when the circuit curve is not too far from the electronic curve for real values of $\theta$; that is, when the parameters (electron velocity, for instance) do not differ too much from those values for which the circuit curve is tangent to the electronic curve.

Unfortunately, the behavior of a function for values of the variables far from those represented by its intersection with the real plane may be very sensitive to the shape of the intersection with the real plane. Thus, we would scarcely be justified by the good fit of the approximations represented in Figs. 14.8 and 14.9 in assuming that the complex roots obtained using the approximations will be good except when they correspond to a near approach of the electronic and circuit curves, as in Fig. 14.10.

In fact, using the approximate curves, we find that the increasing wave vanishes for electron velocities less than a certain lower limiting velocity. This corresponds to cutting by the circuit curve of the dip down from $+\infty$ of the approximate electronic curve (the dip is not shown in Fig. 14.9). This is not characteristic of the true solution. An analysis shows, however,

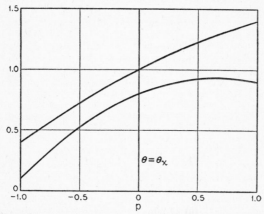

Fig. 14.11—Complex roots are obtained when curves such as those of Fig. 14.10 do not have the number of intersections required (by the degree of the equation) for real values of the abscissa and ordinate. In this figure, two parabolas narrowly miss intersect:ng. Suppose these represent circuit and electronic susceptance curves. We find that the gain of the increasing wave will increase with the square root of the separation at the abscissa of equal slopes, and inversely as the square root of the difference in second derivatives.

that there will be a limiting electron velocity below which there is no increasing wave if there is a charge-free region between the electron flow and the circuit.

## 14.6 SOME REMARKS ABOUT COMPLEX ROOTS

If we examine our generalized circuit expression (14.60) we see that the circuit impedance parameter $(E^2/\beta^2 P)$ is inversely proportional to the slope of the circuit curve at the point where it crosses the horizontal axis. Thus, low-impedance circuits cut the axis steeply and high-impedance circuits cut the axis at a small slope.

We cannot go directly from this information to an evaluation of gain in terms of impedance; the best course in this respect is to use the methods of

Chapter VIII. We can, however, show a relation between gain and the properties of the circuit and electronic curves for cases in which the curves almost touch (an electron velocity just a little lower than that for which gain appears). Suppose the curves nearly touch at $\theta = \theta_x$, as indicated in Fig. 14.11. Let

$$\theta = \theta_x + p \tag{14.91}$$

Let us represent the curves for small values of $p$ by the first three terms of a Taylor's series. Let the ordinate $y$ of the circuit curve be given by

$$y = a_1 + b_1 p + c_1 p^2 \tag{14.92}$$

and let the ordinate of the electronic curve be given by

$$y = a_2 + b_2 p + c_2 p^2 \tag{14.93}$$

Then, at the intersection

$$(c_1 - c_2)p^2 + (b_1 - b_2)p + (a_1 - a_2) = 0$$

$$p = -(1/2)\frac{b_1 - b_2}{c_1 - c_2} \pm j \sqrt{\frac{(a_1 - a_2)}{(c_1 - c_2)} - \frac{(b_1 - b_2)^2}{4(c_1 - c_2)^2}} \tag{14.94}$$

If we choose $\theta_x$ as the point at which the slopes are the same

$$b_1 - b_2 = 0 \tag{14.95}$$

$$p = \pm j \sqrt{\frac{(a_1 - a_2)}{(c_1 - c_2)}} \tag{14.96}$$

and we see that the imaginary part of $p$ increases with the square root of the separation, and at a rate inversely proportional to the difference in second derivatives. This is exemplified by the behavior of $x_1$ and $x_2$ for $b$ a little small than $(3/2)(2)^{1/3}$ in Fig. 8.1.

Now, referring to Fig. 14.10, we see that a circuit curve which cuts the axis at a shallow angle (a high-impedance circuit curve) will approach or be tangent to the electronic curve at a point where the second derivative is small, while a steep (low impedance) circuit curve will approach the electronic curve at a point where the second derivative is high. This fits in with the idea that a high impedance should give a high gain and a low impedance should give a low gain.

## Problems

1. Set up the equations appropriate to a cylindrical electron stream filling a circuit such as that of Fig. 4.8.

2. For the conditions of Problem 1, sketch the admittance looking into the stream as a function of $\beta$ for real values of $\beta$.

3. Write the equations holding inside the electron stream similar to those in Section 1 but assuming that the electrons are free to move transversely.

4. In the case considered in Problem 3, what is to be done about the fact that electron motion in the $y$ direction causes the boundary of the flow to be scalloped?

5. Including the effect of the scalloped boundary, how will the impedance looking into the beam vary with $\beta$?

# CHAPTER XV

## MAGNETRON AMPLIFIER

Synopsis of Chapter

THE HIGH EFFICIENCY of the magnetron oscillator is attributed to motion of the electrons toward the anode (toward a region of higher d-c potential) at high r-f levels. Thus, an electron's loss of energy to the r-f field is made up, not by a slowing-down of its motion in the direction of wave propagation, but by abstraction of energy from the d-c field.[1]

Warnecke and Guenard[2] have published pictures of magnetron amplifiers and Brossart and Doehler have discussed the theory of such devices.[3]

No attempt will be made here to analyze the large-signal behavior of a magnetron amplifier or even to treat the small-signal theory extensively. However, as the device is very closely related to conventional traveling-wave tubes, it seems of some interest to illustrate its operation by a simple small-signal analysis.

The case analyzed is indicated in Fig. 15.1. A narrow beam of electrons flows in the $+z$ direction, constituting a current $I_0$. There is a magnetic field of strength $B$ normal to the plane of the paper (in the $x$ direction), and a d-c electric field in the $y$ direction. The beam flows near to a circuit which propagates a slow wave. Fig. 15.3, which shows a finned structure opposed to a conducting plane and held positive with respect to it, gives an idea of a physical realization of such a device. The electron stream could come from a cathode held at some potential intermediate between that of the finned structure and that of the plane. In any event, in the analysis the electrons are assumed to have such an initial d-c velocity and direction as to make them travel in a straight line, the magnetic and electric forces just cancelling.

The circuit equation developed in Chapter XIII in connection with transverse motions of electrons is used. Together with an appropriate ballistical equation, this leads to a fifth degree equation for $\Gamma$.

---

[1] For an understanding of the high-level behavior of magnetrons the reader is referred to: J. B. Fisk, H. D. Hagstrum and P. L. Hartman, "The Magnetron as a Generator of Centimeter Waves," *Bell System Technical Journal*, Vol. XXV, April 1946. "Microwave Magnetrons" edited by George B. Collins, McGraw-Hill, 1948.

[2] R. Warnecke and P. Guenard, "Sur L'Aide Que Peuvent Apporter en Television Quelques Recentes Conceptions Concernant Les Tubes Electroniques Pour Ultra-Hautes Frequences," *Annales de Radioelectricite*, Vol. III, pp. 259–280, October 1948.

[3] J. Brossart and O. Doehler, "Sur les Proprietes des Tubes a Champ Magnetique Constant: les Tubes a Propagation D'Onde a Champ Magnetique,"[*Annales de Radioelectricite*, Vol. III, pp. 328–338, October 1948.

The nature of this equation indicates that gain may be possible in two ranges of parameters. One is that in which the electron velocity is near to or equal to (as, (15.25)) the circuit phase velocity. In this case there is gain provided that the transverse component of a-c electric field is not zero, and provided that it is related to the longitudinal component as it is for the circuit of Fig. 15.3. It seems likely that this corresponds most nearly to usual magnetron operation.

The other interesting range of parameters is that near

$$\beta_e/\beta_1 = 1 - \beta_m/\beta_1 \tag{15.31}$$

Here $\beta_e$ refers to the electrons, $\beta_1$ to the circuit and $\beta_m$ is the cyclotron frequency divided by the electron velocity. When (15.31) holds, there is gain whenever the parameter $\alpha$, which specifies the ratio of the transverse to the longitudinal fields, is not $+1$. For the circuit of Fig. 15.3, $\alpha$ approaccs $+1$ near the fins if the separation between the fins and the plane is great enough in terms of the wavelength. However, $\alpha$ can be made negative near the fins

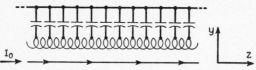

Fig. 15.1—In a magnetron amplifier a narrow electron stream travels in crossed electric and magnetic fields close to a wave transmission circuit.

if the potential of the fins is made negative compared with that of the plane, and the electrons are made to move in the opposite direction.

In either range of parameters, the gain of the increasing wave in db per wavelength is proportional to the square root of the current rather than to the cube root of the current. This means a lower gain than for an ordinary traveling-wave tube with the same circuit and current.

Increasing and decreasing waves with a negative phase velocity are possible when the magnetic field is great enough.

## 15.1 Circuit Equation

The circuit equation will be the same as that used in Chapter XIII, that is,

$$V = \frac{-j\omega\Gamma_1 K(\Phi\rho - (I_0/u_0)\Phi'y)}{(\Gamma^2 - \Gamma_1^2)} \tag{13.10}$$

It will be assumed that the voltage is given by

$$\Phi = (Ae^{-j\Gamma y} + Be^{j\Gamma y}) \tag{15.1}$$

so that

$$\Phi'V = -jV(Ae^{-j\Gamma y} - Be^{j\Gamma y}) \tag{15.2}$$

At any $y$ — position we can write

$$\Phi'V = -j\Gamma\alpha\Phi V \qquad (15.3)$$

$$\alpha = \frac{Ae^{-j\Gamma y} - Be^{j\Gamma y}}{Ae^{-j\Gamma y} + Be^{j\Gamma y}} \qquad (15.4)$$

If $\Gamma$ is purely imaginary, $\alpha$ is purely real, and as $\Gamma$ will have only a small real component, $\alpha$ will be considered as a real number. We see that $\alpha$ can range from $+\infty$ to $-\infty$. For instance, consider a circuit consisting of opposed two-dimensional slotted members as shown in Fig. 15.2. For a field with a cosh distribution in the $y$ direction, $\alpha$ is positive above the axis, zero on the axis and negative below the axis. For a field having a sinh distribution in the $y$

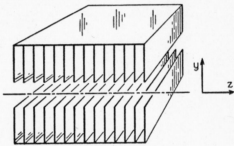

Fig. 15.2—If the circuit is as shown, the ratio between longitudinal and transverse field will be different in sign above and below the axis. This can have an important effect on the operation of the amplifier.

direction, $\alpha$ is infinite on the axis, positive above the axis and negative below the axis.

We find then, that, (13.10) becomes

$$V = \frac{-j\omega\Gamma_1\Phi K(\rho + j\alpha(I_0/u_0)\Gamma y)}{\Gamma^2 - \Gamma_1^2} \qquad (15.5)$$

## 15.2 Ballistic Equations

The d-c electric field in the $y$ direction will be taken as $-E_0$. Thus

$$\frac{d\dot{y}}{dt} = \eta\left[E_0 + \frac{\partial(\Phi V)}{\partial y} - B(\dot{z} + u_0)\right] \qquad (15.6)$$

In order to maintain a rectilinear unperturbed path

$$E_0 = Bu_0 \qquad (15.7)$$

so that (15.6) becomes

$$\frac{d\dot{y}}{dt} = \eta\,\frac{\partial(\Phi V)}{\partial y} - \eta B\dot{z} \qquad (15.8)$$

Following the usual procedure, we obtain

$$\dot{y} = \frac{-j\eta\Gamma\alpha\Phi V - \eta Bz}{u_0(j\beta_e - \Gamma)} \tag{15.9}$$

We have also

$$\frac{d\dot{z}}{dt} = \eta\,\frac{\partial\Phi V}{\partial x} + \eta B\dot{y}$$

$$\dot{z} = \frac{-\eta\Gamma\Phi V + \eta B\dot{y}}{u_0(j\beta_e - \Gamma)} \tag{15.10}$$

From (15.9) and (15.10) we obtain

$$z = \frac{-\eta\Gamma\Phi V[(j\beta_e - \Gamma) + j\alpha\beta_m]}{u_0[(j\beta_e - \Gamma)^2 + \beta_m^2]} \tag{15.11}$$

where

$$\beta_m = \omega_m/u_0 \tag{15.12}$$

$$\omega_m = \eta B \tag{15.13}$$

Here $\omega_m$ is the cyclotron radian frequency.

As before, we have

$$\rho = \frac{\Gamma\rho_0\dot{z}}{u_0(j\beta_e - \Gamma)} \tag{15.14}$$

whence

$$\rho = \frac{\Gamma^2\eta I_0\Phi V[(j\beta_e - \Gamma) + j\alpha\beta_m]}{u_0^3(j\beta_e - \Gamma)[(j\beta_e - \Gamma)^2 + \beta_m^2]} \tag{15.15}$$

We can also solve (15.9) and (15.10) for $\dot{y}$

$$\dot{y} = \frac{-j\eta\Gamma\Phi V[\alpha(j\beta_e - \Gamma) + j\beta_m]}{u_0[(j\beta_e - \Gamma)^2 + \beta_m^2]}. \tag{15.16}$$

Now, to the first order

$$\dot{y} = \frac{\partial y}{\partial t} + u_0\,\frac{\partial y}{\partial z}$$

$$y = \frac{\dot{y}}{u_0(j\beta_e - \Gamma)} \tag{15.17}$$

and from (15.16) and (15.17)

$$y = \frac{-j\eta\Gamma\Phi V[\alpha(j\beta_e - \Gamma) + j\beta_m]}{u_0^2(j\beta_e - \Gamma)[(j\beta_e - \Gamma)^2 + \beta_m^2]}. \tag{15.18}$$

If we use (15.15) and (15.18) in connection with (15.5) we obtain

$$\Gamma^2 - \Gamma_1^2 = \frac{-j\beta_e \Gamma_1 \Gamma^2[(j\beta_e - \Gamma) + 2j[\alpha/(1 + \alpha^2)]\beta_m]H^2}{(j\beta_e - \Gamma)[(j\beta_e - \Gamma)^2 + \beta_m^2]} \quad (15.19)$$

$$H^2 = \frac{(1 + \alpha^2)\Phi^2 KI_0}{2V_0}. \quad (15.20)$$

Now let

$$-\Gamma_1 = -j\beta_1 \quad (15.21)$$

$$-\Gamma = -j\beta_1(1 + p) \quad (15.22)$$

If we assume

$$p \ll 1 \quad (15.23)$$

and neglect $p$ in sums in comparison with unity, we obtain

$$p(\beta_e/\beta_1 - 1 - p)[(\beta_e/\beta_1 - 1 - p)^2 - (\beta_m/\beta_1)^2]$$
$$= -\frac{\beta_e}{2\beta_1}\left[(\beta_e/\beta_1 - 1 - p) + \frac{2\alpha\beta_m}{(1 + \alpha^2)\beta_1}\right]H^2. \quad (15.24)$$

We are particularly interested in conditions which lead to an imaginary value of $p$ which is as large as possible. We will obtain such large values of $p$ when one of the factors multiplying $p$ on the left-hand side of (15.24) is small. There are two possibilities. One is that the first factor is small. We explore this by assuming

$$\beta_e/\beta_1 - 1 = 0 \quad (15.25)$$

$$p^2\left(p^2 - \frac{\beta_m^2}{\beta_1^2}\right) = (1/2)\left(-p + \frac{2\alpha\beta_m}{(1 + \alpha^2)\beta_1}\right)H^2, \quad (15.26)$$

If $p$ is very small, we can write approximately

$$-p^2\frac{\beta_m^2}{\beta_1^2} = \frac{\alpha}{(1 + \alpha^2)}\frac{\beta_m}{\beta_1}H^2$$
$$p = \pm j[\alpha/(1 + \alpha^2)]^{1/2}(\beta_1/\beta_m)^{1/2}H \quad (15.27)$$

We see that $p$ goes to zero if $\alpha = 0$ and is real if $\alpha$ is negative. If we consider what this means circuit-wise, we see that there will be gain with the d-c voltage applied between a circuit and a conducting plane as shown in Fig. 15.3.

Another possible condition in the neighborhood of which $p$ is relatively large is

$$\beta_e/\beta_1 - 1 = \pm \beta_m/\beta_1 \quad (15.28)$$

In this case

$$p(\pm\beta_m/\beta_1 - p)(\mp 2(\beta_m/\beta_1)p + p^2)$$

$$= -\left(1 \pm \frac{\beta_m}{\beta_1}\right)\left[(\pm\beta_m/\beta_1 - p) + \frac{2\alpha\beta_m}{(1 + \alpha^2)\beta_1}\right]H^2. \qquad (15.29)$$

As $p$ is small, we write approximately

$$p^2 = \pm\frac{1}{4}\frac{(1 \pm \alpha)^2}{1 + \alpha^2}\left(\frac{\beta_1}{\beta_m} \pm 1\right)H^2. \qquad (15.30)$$

We see that we obtain an imaginary value of $p$ only for the $-$ sign in (15.28) that is, if

$$\beta_e/\beta_1 = 1 - \beta_m/\beta_1 \qquad (15.31)$$

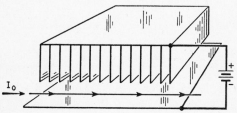

Fig. 15.3—The usual arrangement is to have the finned structure positive and opposed to a conducting plane.

In this case

$$p = \pm j\frac{1}{2}[(1 - \alpha)/(1 + \alpha)^{1/2}](\beta_e/\beta_m)^{1/2}H. \qquad (15.32)$$

In this case we obtain gain for any value of $\alpha$ smaller than unity. We note that $\alpha = 1$ is the value $\alpha$ assumes far from the axis in a two-dimensional system of the sort illustrated in Fig. 15.2, for either a cosh or a sinh distribution in the $+y$ direction.

The assumption of $-\Gamma = -j\beta_1(1 + p)$ in (15.22) will give forward ($+z$) traveling-waves only. In order to investigate backward traveling-waves, we must assume

$$-\Gamma = +j\beta_1(1 + p) \qquad (15.33)$$

where again $p$ is considered a small number. If we use this in (15.19), we obtain

$$p\left(\frac{\beta_e}{\beta_1} + 1 + p\right)\left[\left(\frac{\beta_e}{\beta_1} + 1 + p\right)^2 - \frac{\beta_m^2}{\beta_1^2}\right]$$

$$= -\frac{1}{2}\frac{\beta_e}{\beta_1}\left[\left(\frac{\beta_e}{\beta_1} + 1 + p\right) + \frac{2\alpha\beta_m}{(1 + \alpha^2)\beta_1}\right]H^2. \qquad (15.34)$$

As before we look for solutions for $p$ where the terms multiplying $p$ on the left are small. The only vanishing consistent with positive values of $\beta_e$ and $\beta_1$ is obtained for

$$\frac{\beta_e}{\beta_1} + 1 = +\frac{\beta_m}{\beta_1}.$$  (15.35)

Under this condition (15.34) yields for $p$

$$p = \pm j \frac{1}{2} \frac{(1 + \alpha)}{(1 + \alpha^2)^{1/2}} \left(\frac{\beta_e}{\beta_m}\right)^{1/2} H.$$  (15.36)

Thus we can obtain backward-increasing backward-traveling waves for all values of $\alpha$ except $\alpha = -1$. For the situation shown in Fig. 15.3, with a backward wave, $\alpha$ is always negative, approaching $-1$ at large distances from the plane electrode, so that the gain is identical with that given by (15.32).

We note that (15.27), (15.32) and (15.36) show that $p$ is proportional to the product of current times impedance divided by voltage to the $\frac{1}{2}$ power, while, in the case of the usual traveling-wave tube, this small quantity occurs to the $\frac{1}{3}$ power. The $\frac{1}{3}$ power of a small quantity is larger than the $\frac{1}{2}$ power; and, hence for a given circuit impedance, current and voltage, the gain of the magnetron amplifier will be somewhat less than the gain of a conventional traveling-wave tube.

PROBLEMS

1. Draw vectors showing the phase relations of the field components, charge density velocities and displacement $y$ for the increasing waves.

2. Where does the energy transferred to the fields of the circuit come from?

3. Fit the boundary conditions for an initially unmodulated electron stream and find an initial loss parameter corresponding to $A$.

# CHAPTER XVI

# DOUBLE-STREAM AMPLIFIERS

SYNOPSIS OF CHAPTER

IN TRAVELING-WAVE TUBES, it is desirable to have the electrons flow very close to the metal circuit elements, where the radio-frequency field of the circuit is strong, in order to obtain satisfactory amplification. It is, however, difficult to confine the electron flow close to metal circuit elements without an interception of electrons, which entails both loss of efficiency and heating of the circuit elements. This latter may be extremely objectionable at very short wavelengths for which circuit elements are small and fragile.

In the double-stream amplifier the gain is not obtained through the interaction of electrons with the field of electromagnetic resonators, helices or other circuits. Instead, an electron flow consisting of two streams of electrons having different average velocities is used. When the currents or charge densities of the two streams are sufficient, the streams interact so as to give an increasing wave.[1,2,3,4] Electromagnetic circuits may be used to impress a signal on the electron flow, or to produce an electromagnetic output by means of the amplified signal present in the electron flow. The amplification, however, takes place in the electron flow itself, and is the result of what may be termed an electromechanical interaction.[5]

While small magnetic fields are necessarily present because of the motions of the electrons, these do not play an important part in the amplification. The important factors in the interaction are the electric field, which stores energy and acts on the electrons, and the electrons themselves. The charge of the electrons produces the electric field; the mass of the electrons, and their kinetic energy, serve much as do inductance and magnetic stored energy in electromagnetic propagation.

[1] J. R. Pierce and W. B. Hebenstreit, "A New Type of High-Frequency Amplifier," *B.S.T.J.*, Vol. 28, pp. 33–51, January 1949.
[2] A. V. Hollenberg, "Experimental Observation of Amplification by Interaction between Two Electron Streams," *B.S.T.J.*, Vol. 28, pp. 52–58, January 1949.
[3] A. V. Haeff, "The Electron-Wave Tube—A Novel Method of Generation and Amplification of Microwave Energy," *Proc. IRE*, Vol. 37, pp. 4–10, January 1949.
[4] L. S. Nergaard, "Analysis of a Simple Model of a Two-Beam Growing-Wave Tube," *R.C.A. Review*, Vol. 9, pp. 585–601, December 1948.
[5] Some similar electromechanical waves are described in papers by J. R. Pierce, "Possible Fluctuations in Electron Streams Due to Ions," *Jour. App. Phys.*, Vol. 19, pp. 231–236, March 1948, and "Increasing Space-Charge Waves," *Jour. App. Phys.*, Vol. 20, pp. 1060–1066, Nov. 1949.

By this sort of interaction, a traveling wave which increases as it travels, i.e., a traveling wave of negative attenuation, may be produced. To start such a wave, the electron flow may be made to pass through a resonator or a short length of helix excited by the input signal. Once initiated, the wave grows exponentially in amplitude until the electron flow is terminated or until non-linearities limit the amplitude. An amplified output can be obtained by allowing the electron flow to act on a resonantor, helix or other output circuit at a point far enough removed from the input circuit to give the desired gain.

In general, for a given geometry there is a limiting value of current below which there is no increasing wave. For completely intermingled electron streams, the gain rises toward an asymptotic limit as the current is increased beyond this value. The ordinate of Fig. 16.3 is proportional to gain and the abscissa to current.

When the electron streams are separated, the gain first rises and then falls as the current is increased. This effect, and also the magnitude of the increasing wave set up by velocity modulating the electron streams, have been discussed in the literature.[6]

Double-stream amplifiers have several advantages. Because the electrons interact with one another, the electron flow need not pass extremely close to complicated circuit elements. This is particularly advantageous at very short wavelengths. Further, if we make the distance of electron flow between the input and output circuits long enough, amplification can be obtained even though the input and output circuits have very low impedance or poor coupling to the electron flow. Even though the region of amplification is long, there is no need to maintain a close synchronism between an electron velocity and a circuit wave velocity, as there is in the usual traveling-wave tube.

## 16.1 Simple Theory of Double-Stream Amplifiers

For simplicity we will assume that the flow consists of coincident streams of electrons of d-c velocities $u_1$ and $u_2$ in the $z$ direction. It will be assumed that there is no electron motion normal to the $z$ direction. M.K.S. units will be used.

It turns out to be convenient to express variation in the $z$ direction as

$$\exp -j\beta z$$

rather than as

$$\exp -\Gamma z$$

[6] J. R. Pierce, "Double-Stream Amplifiers," *Proc. I.R.E.*, Vol. 37, pp. 980–985, Sept. 1949.

as we have done previously. This merely means letting

$$\Gamma = j\beta \tag{16.1}$$

The following nomenclature will be used

$J_1$, $J_2$  d-c current densities
$u_1$, $u_2$  d-c velocities
$\rho_{01}$, $\rho_{02}$  d-c charge densities

$$\rho_{01} = -J_1/u_1, \; \rho_{02} = -J_2/u_2$$

$\rho_1$, $\rho_2$  a-c charge densities
$v_1$, $v_2$  a-c velocities
$V_1$, $V_2$  d-c voltages with respect to the cathodes
$V$      a-c potential
$\beta_1 = \omega/u_1, \; \beta_2 = \omega/u_2$

From (2.22) and (2.18) we obtain

$$\rho_1 = \frac{\eta J_1 \beta^2 V}{u_1^3 (\beta_1 - \beta)^2} \tag{16.2}$$

and

$$\rho_2 = \frac{\eta J_2 \beta^2 V}{u_2^3 (\beta_2 - \beta)^2}. \tag{16.3}$$

It will be convenient to call the fractional velocity separation $b$, so that

$$b = \frac{2(u_1 - u_2)}{u_1 + u_2}. \tag{16.4}$$

It will also be convenient to define a sort of mean velocity $u_0$

$$u_0 = \frac{2u_1 u_2}{u_1 + u_2}. \tag{16.5}$$

We may also let $V_0$ be the potential drop specifying a velocity $u_0$, so that

$$u_0 = \sqrt{2\eta V_0} \tag{16.6}$$

It is further convenient to define a phase constant based on $u_0$

$$\beta_e = \frac{\omega}{u_0}. \tag{16.7}$$

We see from (16.4), (16.5) and (16.6) that

$$\beta_1 = \beta_e(1 - b/2) \tag{16.8}$$

$$\beta_2 = \beta_e(1 + b/2) \tag{16.9}$$

We shall treat only a special case, that in which

$$\frac{J_1}{u_1^3} = \frac{J_2}{u_2^3} = \frac{J_0}{u_0^3}. \tag{16.10}$$

Here $J_0$ is a sort of mean current which, together with $u_0$, specifies the ratios $J_1/u_1^3$ and $J_2/u_2^3$, which appear in (4) and (5).

In terms of these new quantities, the expression for the total a-c charge density $\rho$ is, from (16.2) and (16.3) and (16.6)

$$\rho = \rho_1 + \rho_2 = \frac{J_0 \beta^2}{2u_0 V_0}$$

$$\cdot \left[ \frac{1}{\left[ \beta_e \left( 1 - \dfrac{b}{2} \right) - \beta \right]^2} + \frac{1}{\left[ \beta_e \left( 1 + \dfrac{b}{2} \right) - \beta \right]^2} \right] V. \tag{16.11}$$

Equation (16.11) is a *ballistic* equation telling what charge density $\rho$ is produced when the flow is bunched by a voltage $V$. To solve our problem, that is, to solve for the phase constant $\beta$, we must associate (16.11) with a *circuit* equation which tells us what voltage $V$ the charge density produces. We assume that the electron flow takes place in a tube too narrow to propagate a wave of the frequency considered. Further, we assume that the wave velocity is much smaller than the velocity of light. Under these circumstances the circuit problem is essentially an electrostatic problem. The a-c voltage will be of the same sign as, and in phase with the a-c charge density $\rho$. In other words the "circuit effect" is purely capacitive.

Let us assume at first that the electron stream is very narrow compared with the tube through which it flows, so that $V$ may be assumed to be constant over its cross section. We can easily obtain the relation between $V$ and $\rho$ in two extreme cases. If the wavelength in the stream is very short ($\beta$ large), so that transverse a-c fields are negligible, then, from Poisson's equation, we have

$$\rho = -\epsilon \frac{\partial^2 V}{\partial z^2} \tag{16.12}$$

$$\rho = \epsilon \beta^2 V$$

If, on the other hand, the wavelength is long compared with the tube radius ($\beta$ small) so that the fields are chiefly transverse, the lines of force running from the beam outward to the surrounding tube, we may write

$$\rho = CV \tag{16.13}$$

Here $C$ is a constant expressing the capacitance per unit length between the region occupied by the electron flow and the tube wall.

We see from (16.12) and (16.13) that, if we plot $\rho/V$ vs. $\beta/\beta_e$ for real values of $\beta$, $\rho/V$ will be constant for small values of $\beta$ and will rise as $\beta^2$ for large values of $\beta$, approximately as shown in Fig. 16.1.

Now, we have assumed that the charge is produced by the action of the voltage, according to the ballistical equation (16.11). This relation is plotted in Fig. 2, for a relatively large value of $J_0/u_0V_0$ (curve 1) and for a smaller value of $J_0/u_0V_0$ (curve 2). There are poles at $\beta/\beta_e = 1 \pm \dfrac{b}{2}$, and a minimum between the poles. The height of the minimum increases as $J_0/u_0V_0$ is increased.

A circuit curve similar to that of Fig. 16.1 is also plotted on Fig. 16.2. We see that for the small-current case (curve 2) there are four intersections, giving *four real* values of $\beta$ and hence *four unattenuated* waves. However, for

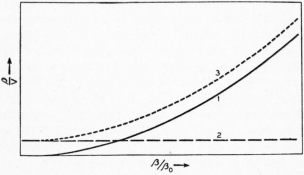

Fig. 16.1—Circuit curves, in which the ordinate is proportional to the ratio of the charge per unit length to the voltage which it produces. Curve 1 is for an infinitely broad beam; curve 2 is for a narrow beam in a narrow tube. Curve 3 is the sum of 1 and 2, and approximates an actual curve.

the larger current (curve 1) there are only two intersections and hence two unattenuated waves. The two additional values of $\beta$ satisfying both the circuit equation and the ballistical equation are complex conjugates, and represent waves traveling at the same speed, but with equal positive negative attenuations.

Thus we deduce that, as the current densities in the electron streams are raised, a wave with negative attenuation appears for current densities above a certain critical value.

We can learn a little more about these waves by assuming an approximate expression for the circuit curve of Fig. 1. Let us merely assume that over the range of interest (near $\beta/\beta_e = 1$) we can use

$$\rho = \alpha^2 \epsilon \beta^2 V \qquad (16.14)$$

Here $\alpha^2$ is a factor greater than unity, which merely expresses the fact that the charge density corresponding to a given voltage is somewhat greater than if there were field in the $z$ direction only for which equation (16.12) is valid. Combining (16.14) with (16.11) we obtain

$$\frac{1}{\left(\beta_e\left(1 - \dfrac{b}{2}\right) - \beta\right)^2} + \frac{1}{\left(\beta_e\left(1 + \dfrac{b}{2}\right) - \beta\right)^2} = \frac{1}{\beta_e^2 U^2} \qquad (16.15)$$

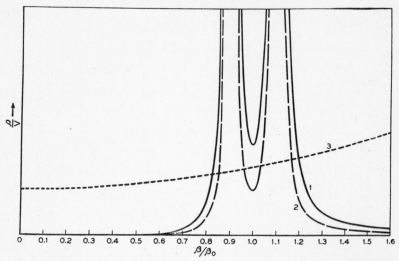

Fig. 16.2—This shows a circuit curve, 3, and two electronic curves which give the sum of the charge densities of the two streams divided by the voltage which bunches them. With curve 2, there will be four unattenuated waves. With curve 1, which is for a higher current density than curve 2, there are two unattenuated waves, an increasing wave and a decreasing wave.

where

$$U^2 = \frac{J_0}{2\alpha^2 \epsilon \beta_e^2 u_0 V_0}. \qquad (16.16)$$

In solving (16.15) it is most convenient to represent $\beta$ in terms of $\beta_e$ and a new variable $h$

$$\beta = \beta_e(1 + h) \qquad (16.17)$$

Thus, (16.15) becomes

$$\frac{1}{\left(h - \dfrac{b}{2}\right)^2} + \frac{1}{\left(h + \dfrac{b}{2}\right)^2} = \frac{1}{U^2}. \qquad (16.18)$$

Solving for $h$, we obtain

$$h = \pm\left(\frac{b}{2}\right)\left[\left(\frac{2U}{b}\right)^2 + 1 \pm \left(\frac{2U}{b}\right)\sqrt{\left(\frac{2U}{b}\right)^2 + 4}\right]^{1/2}. \quad (16.19)$$

The positive sign inside of the brackets always gives a real value of $h$ and hence unattenuated waves. The negative sign inside the brackets gives unattenuated waves for small values of $U/b$. However, when

$$\left(\frac{U}{b}\right)^2 > \frac{1}{8} \quad (16.20)$$

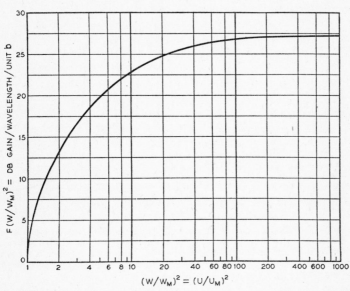

Fig. 16.3—The abscissa is proportional to d-c current. As the current is increased, the gain in db per wavelength approaches 27.3b, where $b$ is the fractional separation in velocity. If the two electron streams are separated physically, the gain is lower and first rises and then falls as the current is increased.

there are two waves with a phase constant $\beta_e$ and with equal and opposite attenuation constants.

Suppose we let $U_M$ be the minimum value of $U$ for which there is gain. From (16.20)

$$U_M^2 = b^2/8 \quad (16.21)$$

From (16.19) we have, for the increasing wave,

$$h = jb\left[\frac{U}{\sqrt{2}\,U_M}\sqrt{2\left(\frac{U}{U_M}\right)^2 + 1} - \left(\frac{U}{U_M}\right)^2 - 1\right]^{1/2}. \quad (16.22)$$

The gain in db/wavelength is

$$\text{db/wavelength} = 20(2\pi)\log_{10}e^{|h|}$$

$$= 54.6 \, | \, h \, | \qquad (16.23)$$

We see that, by means of (16.22) and (16.23), we can plot db/wavelength per unit $b$ vs. $(U/U_M)^2$. This is plotted in Fig. 16.3. Because $U^2$ is proportional to current, the variable $(U/U_M)^2$ is the ratio of the actual current to the current which will just give an increasing wave. If we know this ratio, we can obtain the gain in db/wavelength by multiplying the corresponding ordinate from Fig. 16.3 by $b$.

We see that, as the current is increased, the gain per wavelength at first rises rapidly and then rises more slowly, approaching a value $27.3b$ db/wavelength for very large values of $(U/U_M)^2$.

We now have some idea of the variation of gain per wavelength with velocity separation $b$ and with current $(U/U_M)^2$. A more complete theory requires the evaluation of the lower limiting current for gain (or of $U_M^2$) in terms of physical dimensions and an investigation of the boundary conditions to show how strong an increasing wave is set up by a given input signal.[1, 6]

## 16.2 FURTHER CONSIDERATIONS

There are a number of points to be brought out concerning double-stream amplifiers. Analysis shows[6] that any physical separation of the electron streams has a very serious effect in reducing gain. Thus, it is desirable to intermingle the streams thoroughly if possible.

If the electron streams have a fractional velocity spread due to space charge which is comparable with the deliberately imposed spread $b$, we may expect a reduction in gain.

Haeff[3] describes a single-stream tube and attributes its gain to the space-charge spread in velocities. In his analysis of this tube he divides the beam into a high and a low velocity portion, and assigns the mean velocity to each. This is not a valid approximation.

Analysis indicates that a multiply-peaked distribution of current with velocity is necessary for the existent increasing waves, and gain in a "single stream" of electrons is still something of a mystery.

## PROBLEMS

1. Use a field analysis to find the lower limiting current density for an increasing wave in case of electron flow of constant current density completely filling a conducting tube of radius $a$, assuming (16.10) to hold.

2. Assume a very thin sheet of electron flow a distance $y$ away from a conducting plane, where $\beta_e y \ll 1$. What simple form does the limiting current per unit beam width (width measured normal to $y$ and $z$) take?

3. For a circuit curve as shown in 3 of Fig. 16.1, are there increasing waves of the two electron streams move in opposite directions?

# CHAPTER XVII

# CONCLUSION

ALTHOUGH THIS BOOK contains some descriptive material concerning high-level behavior, it is primarily a treatment of the linearized or low-level behavior of traveling-wave tubes and of some related devices. In the case of traveling-wave tubes with longitudinal motion of electrons only, the treatment is fairly extended. In the discussions of transverse fields, magnetron amplifiers and double-stream amplifiers, it amounts to little more than an introduction.

One problem to which the material presented lends itself is the calculation of gain of longitudinal-field traveling-wave tubes. To this end, a summary of gain calculation is included as Appendix VII.

Further design information can be worked out as, for instance, exact gain curves at low gain with lumped or distributed loss, perhaps taking the space-charge parameter $QC$ into account, or, a more extended analysis concerning noise figure.

The material in the book may be regarded from another point of view as an introduction, through the treatment of what are really very simple cases, to the high-frequency electronics of electron streams. That is, the reader may use the book merely to learn how to tackle new problems. There are many of these.

One serious problem is that of extending the non-linear theory of the traveling-wave tube. For one thing, it would be desirable to include the effects of loss and space charge. Certainly, a matter worthy of careful investigation is the possibility of increasing efficiency by the use of a circuit in which the phase velocity decreases near the output end. Nordsieck's work can be a guide in such endeavors.

Even linear theory excluding the effects of thermal velocities could profitably be extended, especially to disclose the comparative behavior of narrow electron beams and of broad beams, both those confined by a magnetic field, in which transverse d-c velocities are negligible and in which space charge causes a lowering of axial velocity toward the center of the beam, and also those in which transverse a-c velocities are allowed, especially the Brillouin-type flow, in which the d-c axial velocity is constant across the beam, but electrons have an angular velocity proportional to radius.

Further problems include the extension of the theory of magnetron amplifiers and of double-stream amplifiers to a scope comparable with that of the theory of conventional traveling-wave tubes. The question of velocity distribution across the beam is particularly important in double-stream amplifiers, whose very operation depends on such a distribution, and it is important that the properties of various kinds of distribution be investigated.

Finally, there is no reason to suspect that the simple tubes described do not have undiscovered relatives of considerable value. Perhaps diligent work will uncover them.

# APPENDIX I

# MISCELLANEOUS INFORMATION

This appendix presents an assortment of material which may be useful to the reader.

## CONSTANTS

Electronic charge-to-mass ratio:
$\eta = e/m = 1.759 \times 10^{11}$ Coulomb/kilogram

Electronic charge: $e = 1.602 \times 10^{-19}$ Coulomb

Dielectric constant of vacuum: $\epsilon = 8.854 \times 10^{-12}$ Farad/meter

Permitivity of vacuum: $\mu = 1.257 \times 10^{-6}$ Henry/meter

Boltzman's constant: $k = 1.380 \times 10^{-23}$ Joule/degree

## CROSS PRODUCTS

$$(A' \times A'')_x = A'_y A''_z - A'_z A''_y$$
$$(A' \times A'')_y = A'_z A''_x - A'_x A''_z$$
$$(A' \times A'')_z = A'_x A''_y - A'_y A''_x$$

## MAXWELL'S EQUATIONS: RECTANGULAR COORDINATES

$$\frac{\partial E_z}{\partial y} - \frac{\partial E_y}{\partial z} = -j\omega\mu H_x \qquad \frac{\partial H_z}{\partial y} - \frac{\partial H_y}{\partial z} = j\omega\epsilon E_x + J_x$$

$$\frac{\partial E_x}{\partial z} - \frac{\partial E_z}{\partial x} = -j\omega\mu H_y \qquad \frac{\partial H_x}{\partial z} - \frac{\partial H_z}{\partial x} = j\omega\epsilon E_y + J_y$$

$$\frac{\partial E_y}{\partial x} - \frac{\partial E_x}{\partial y} = -j\omega\mu H_z \qquad \frac{\partial H_y}{\partial x} - \frac{\partial H_x}{\partial y} = j\omega\epsilon E_z + J_z$$

## MAXWELL'S EQUATIONS: AXIALLY SYMMETRICAL

$$\frac{\partial E_\varphi}{\partial z} = +j\omega\mu H_\rho \qquad\qquad \frac{\partial H_\varphi}{\partial z} = -(j\omega\epsilon E_\rho + J_\rho)$$

$$\frac{\partial E\rho}{\partial z} - \frac{\partial E_z}{\partial \rho} = -j\omega\mu H_\varphi \qquad \frac{\partial H_\rho}{\partial z} - \frac{\partial H_z}{\partial \rho} = j\omega\epsilon E_\varphi + J_\varphi$$

$$\frac{\partial}{\partial \rho}(\rho E_\varphi) = -j\omega\mu\rho H_z \qquad \frac{\partial}{\partial \rho}(\rho H_\varphi) = \rho(j\omega\epsilon E_z + J_z)$$

### Miscellaneous Formulae Involving $I_n(x)$ and $K_n(x)$

1. $I_{\nu-1}(Z) - I_{\nu+1}(Z) = \dfrac{2\nu}{Z} I_\nu(Z),$      $K_{\nu-1}(Z) - K_{\nu+1}(Z) = -\dfrac{2\nu}{Z} K_\nu(Z)$

2. $I_{\nu-1}(Z) + I_{\nu+1}(Z) = 2I_\nu'(Z),$      $K_{\nu-1}(Z) + K_{\nu+1}(Z) = -2K_\nu'(Z)$

3. $ZI_\nu'(Z) + \nu I_\nu(Z) = ZI_{\nu-1}(Z),$      $ZK_\nu'(Z) + \nu K_\nu(Z) = -ZK_{\nu-1}(Z)$

4. $ZI_\nu'(Z) - \nu I_\nu(Z) = ZI_{\nu+1}(Z),$      $ZK_\nu'(Z) - \nu K_\nu(Z) = -ZK_{\nu+1}(Z)$

5. $\left(\dfrac{d}{ZdZ}\right)^m \{Z^\nu I_\nu(Z)\} = Z^{\nu-m} I_{\nu-m}(Z),$   $\left(\dfrac{d}{ZdZ}\right)^m \{Z^\nu K_\nu(Z)\}$

$$= (-)^m Z^{\nu-m} K_{\nu-m}(Z)$$

6. $\left(\dfrac{d}{ZdZ}\right)^m \left\{\dfrac{I_\nu(Z)}{Z^\nu}\right\} = \dfrac{I_{\nu+m}(Z)}{Z^{\nu+m}},$    $\left(\dfrac{d}{ZdZ}\right)^m \left\{\dfrac{K_\nu(Z)}{Z^\nu}\right\} = (-)^m \dfrac{K_{\nu+m}(Z)}{Z^{\nu+m}}$

7. $I_0'(Z) = I_1(Z),$      $K_0'(Z) = -K_1(Z)$

8. $I_{-\nu}(Z) = I_\nu(Z),$      $K_{-\nu}(Z) = K_\nu(Z)$

9. $K_{1/2}(Z) = \left(\dfrac{\pi}{2Z}\right)^{1/2} e^{-z}$

10. $I_\nu(Ze^{m\pi i}) = e^{m\nu\pi i} I_\nu(Z)$

11. $K_\nu(Ze^{m\pi i}) = e^{-m\nu\pi i} K_\nu(Z) - i\, \dfrac{\sin m\nu\pi}{\sin \nu\pi}\, I_\nu(Z)$

12. $I_\nu(Z) K_{\nu+1}(Z) + I_{\nu+1}(Z) K_\nu(Z) = 1/Z$

For small values of $X$:

13. $I_0(X) = 1 + .25\, X^2 + .015625\, X^4 + \cdots$

14. $I_1(X) = .5X + .0625\, X^3 + .002604\, X^5 + \cdots$

15. $K_0(X) = -\left\{\gamma + \ln\left(\dfrac{X}{2}\right)\right\} I_0(X) + \dfrac{1}{4} X^2 + \dfrac{3}{128} X^4 + \cdots\right\}$

16. $K_1(X) = \left\{\gamma + \ln\left(\dfrac{X}{2}\right)\right\} I_1(X) + \dfrac{1}{X} - \dfrac{1}{4} X - \dfrac{5}{64} X^3 + \cdots\right\}$

$$\gamma = .5772 \ldots \text{ (Euler's constant)}$$

For large values of $X$:

17. $I_0(X) \sim \dfrac{e^X}{(2\pi X)^{1/2}} \left\{1 + \dfrac{.125}{X} + \dfrac{.0703125}{X^2} + \dfrac{.073242}{X^3} + \cdots\right\}$

18. $I_1(X) \sim \dfrac{e^x}{(2\pi X)^{1/2}}\left\{1 - \dfrac{.375}{X} - \dfrac{.1171875}{X^2} - \dfrac{.102539}{X^3} - \cdots\right\}$

19. $K_0(X) \sim \left(\dfrac{\pi}{2X}\right)^{1/2} e^{-x}\left\{1 - \dfrac{.125}{X} + \dfrac{.0703125}{X^2} - \dfrac{.073242}{X^3} + \cdots\right\}$

20. $K_1(X) \sim \left(\dfrac{\pi}{2X}\right)^{1/2} e^{-x}\left\{1 + \dfrac{.375}{X} - \dfrac{.1171875}{X^2} + \dfrac{.102539}{X^3} - \cdots\right\}.$

Fig. A1.1 shows $I_0(X)$ (solid line) and the first two terms of 13 and the first term of 17 (dashed lines).

Fig. A1.2 shows $I_1(X)$ (solid line) and the first term of 14 and the first term of 18 (dashed lines).

Fig. A1.3 shows $K_0(X)$ (solid line) and $-\left\{\gamma + \ln\left(\dfrac{X}{2}\right)\right\} I_0(X)$ and the first term of 19 (dashed lines).

Fig. A1.4 shows $K_1(X)$ (solid line) and $\left\{\gamma + \ln\left(\dfrac{X}{2}\right)\right\} I_1(X) + 1/X$ and the first term of 20 (dashed lines).

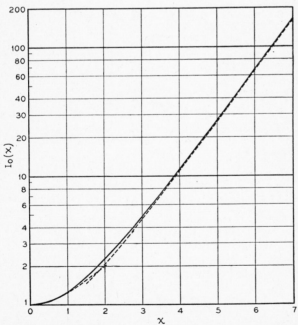

Fig. A1.1—The correct value of $I_0(X)$ (solid line), the first two terms of the series expansion 13 (dashed line from origin), and the first term of the asymptotic series 17 (dashed line to right).

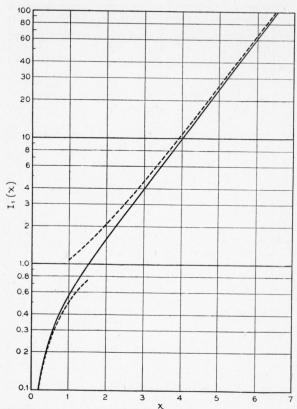

Fig. A1.2—The correct value of $I_1(X)$ (solid line), the first term of the series expansion 14 (lower dashed line), and the first term of the asymptotic series 18 (upper dashed line).

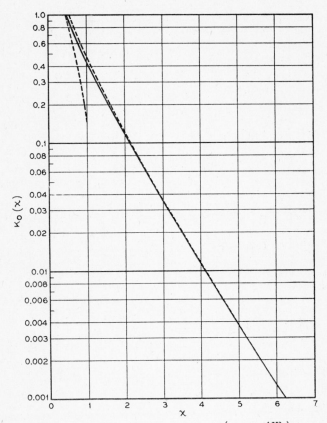

Fig. A1.3—The correct value of $K_0(X)$ (solid line), $-\left\{\gamma + \ln\left(\dfrac{X}{2}\right)\right\} I_0(X)$ from the series expansion 15 (left dashed line), and the first term of the asymptotic series 19 (right dashed line).

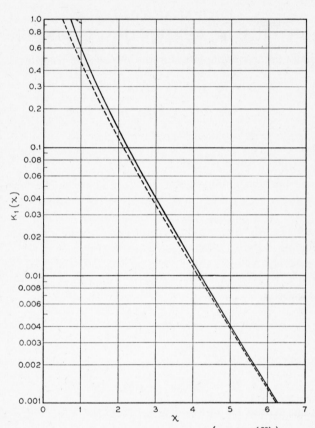

Fig. A1.4—The correct value of $K_1(X)$ (solid line), $\left\{\gamma + \ln\left(\dfrac{X}{2}\right)\right\}$ $I_1(X)$ from the series expansion 16 (upper dashed line), and the first term of the asymptotic series 20 (lower dashed line).

# APPENDIX II

# PROPAGATION ON A
# HELICALLY CONDUCTING CYLINDER

The circuit parameter important in the operation of traveling-wave tubes is:

$$(E_z^2/\beta^2 P)^{1/3} \tag{1}$$

$$\beta = \omega/v. \tag{2}$$

Here $E_z$ is the peak electric field in the direction of propagation, $P$ is the power flow along the helix, and $v$ is the phase velocity of the wave. The quantity $E_z^2/\beta^2 P$ has the dimensions of impedance.

While the problem of propagation along a helix has not been solved, what appears to be a very good approximation has been obtained by replacing the helix with a cylinder of the same mean radius $\alpha$ which is conducting only in a helical direction making an angle $\Psi$ with the circumference, and nonconducting in the helical direction normal to this.

An appropriate solution of the wave equation in cylindrical co-ordinates for a plane wave having circular symmetry and propagating in the $z$ direction with velocity

$$v = \frac{\omega}{\beta}, \tag{3}$$

less than the speed of light $c$, is

$$E_z = [AI_0(\gamma r) + BK_0(\gamma r)]e^{j(\omega t - \beta_z)} \tag{4}$$

where $I_0$ and $K_0$ are the modified Bessel functions, and

$$\gamma^2 = \beta^2 - \left(\frac{\omega}{c}\right)^2 = \beta^2 - \beta_0^2. \tag{5}$$

The form of the $z$ (longitudinal) components of an electromagnetic field varying as $e^{j(\omega t - \beta z)}$ and remaining everywhere finite might therefore be

$$H_{z1} = B_1 I_0(\gamma r)e^{j(\omega t - \beta z)} \tag{6}$$

$$E_{z3} = B_3 I_0(\gamma r)e^{j(\omega t - \beta z)} \tag{7}$$

inside radius $a$, and

$$H_{z2} = B_2 K_0(\gamma r)e^{j(\omega t - \beta z)} \tag{8}$$

229

$$E_{z4} = B_4 K_0(\gamma r) e^{j(\omega t - \beta z)} \tag{9}$$

outside radius $a$. Omitting the factor $e^{j(\omega t - \beta z)}$ the radial and circumferential components associated with these, obtained by applying the curl equation, are, inside radius $a$,

$$H_{\phi 3} = B_3 \frac{j\omega\epsilon}{\gamma} I_1(\gamma r) \tag{10}$$

$$H_{r1} = B_1 \frac{j\beta}{\gamma} I_1(\gamma r) \tag{11}$$

$$E_{\phi 1} = -B_1 \frac{j\omega\mu}{\gamma} I_1(\gamma r) \tag{12}$$

$$E_{r3} = B_3 \frac{j\beta}{\gamma} I_1(\gamma r) \tag{13}$$

and outside radius $a$

$$H_{\phi 4} = -B_4 \frac{j\omega\epsilon}{\gamma} K_1(\gamma r) \tag{14}$$

$$H_{r2} = -B_2 \frac{j\beta}{\gamma} K_1(\gamma r) \tag{15}$$

$$E_{\phi 3} = B_2 \frac{j\omega\mu}{\gamma} K_1(\gamma r) \tag{16}$$

$$E_{r4} = -B_4 \frac{j\beta}{\gamma} K_1(\gamma r). \tag{17}$$

The boundary conditions which must be satisfied at the cylinder of radius $a$ are that the tangential electric field must be perpendicular to the helix direction

$$E_{z3} \sin \Psi + E_{\phi 1} \cos \Psi = 0 \tag{18}$$

$$E_{z4} \sin \Psi + E_{\phi 2} \cos \Psi = 0, \tag{19}$$

the tangential electric field must be continuous across the cylinder

$$E_{z3} = E_{z4} \text{ (and } E_{\phi 1} = E_{\phi 2}), \tag{20}$$

and the tangential component of magnetic field parallel to the helix direction must be continuous across the cylinder, since there can be no current in the surface perpendicular to this direction.

$$H_{z1} \sin \Psi + H_{\phi 3} \cos \Psi = H_{z2} \sin \Psi$$
$$+ H_{\phi 4} \cos \Psi. \tag{21}$$

These equations serve to determine the ratios of the $B$'s and to determine $\gamma$ through

$$(\gamma a)^2 \frac{I_0(\gamma a) K_0(\gamma a)}{I_1(\gamma a) K_1(\gamma a)} = (\beta_0 \, a \cot \Psi)^2. \tag{22}$$

We can easily express the various field components listed in (6) through (17) in terms of a common amplitude factor. As such expressions are useful in understanding the nature of the field, it seems desirable to list them in an orderly fashion.

INSIDE THE HELIX:

$$E_z = B I_0(\gamma r) e^{j(\omega t - \beta z)} \tag{23}$$

$$E_r = j B \frac{\beta}{\gamma} I_1(\gamma r) e^{j(\omega t - \beta z)} \tag{24}$$

$$E_\Phi = -B \frac{I_0(\gamma a)}{I_1(\gamma a)} \frac{1}{\cot \psi} I_1(\gamma r) e^{j(\omega t - \beta z)} \tag{25}$$

$$H_z = -j \frac{B}{k} \frac{\gamma}{\beta_0} \frac{I_0(\gamma a)}{I_1(\gamma a)} \frac{1}{\cot \psi} I_0(\gamma r) e^{j(\omega t - \beta z)} \tag{26}$$

$$H_r = \frac{B}{k} \frac{\beta}{\beta_0} \frac{I_0(\gamma a)}{I_1(\gamma a)} \frac{1}{\cot \psi} I_1(\gamma r) e^{j(\omega t - \beta z)} \tag{27}$$

$$H_\Phi = j \frac{B}{k} \frac{\beta_0}{\gamma} I_1(\gamma r) e^{j(\omega t - \beta z)}. \tag{28}$$

OUTSIDE THE HELIX:

$$E_z = B \frac{I_0(\gamma a)}{K_0(\gamma a)} K_0(\gamma r) e^{j(\omega t - \beta z)} \tag{29}$$

$$E_r = -j B \frac{\beta}{\gamma} \frac{I_0(\gamma a)}{K_0(\gamma a)} K_1(\gamma r) e^{j(\omega t - \beta z)} \tag{30}$$

$$E_\Phi = -B \frac{I_0(\gamma a)}{K_1(\gamma a)} \frac{1}{\cot \psi} K_1(\gamma r) e^{j(\omega t - \beta z)} \tag{31}$$

$$H_z = j \frac{B}{k} \frac{\gamma}{\beta_0} \frac{I_0(\gamma a)}{K_1(\gamma a)} \frac{1}{\cot \psi} K_0(\gamma r) e^{j(\omega t - \beta z)} \tag{32}$$

$$H_r = \frac{B}{k} \frac{I_0(\gamma a)}{K_1(\gamma a)} \frac{1}{\cot \psi} K_1(\gamma r) e^{j(\omega t - \beta z)} \tag{33}$$

$$H_\Phi = -j \frac{B}{k} \frac{\beta_0}{\gamma} \frac{I_0(\gamma a)}{K_0(\gamma a)} K_1(\gamma r) e^{j(\omega t - \beta z)} \tag{34}$$

Here

$$k = \sqrt{\mu/\epsilon} = 120 \, \pi \text{ ohms} \tag{35}$$

The power associated with the propagation is given by

$$P = \tfrac{1}{2} \operatorname{Re} \int E \times H^* \, d\tau \tag{36}$$

taken over a plane normal to the axis of propagation. This is

$$P = \pi \operatorname{Re} \left[ \int_0^a (E_r H_\Phi^* - E_\Phi H_r^*) r \, dr + \int_a^\infty (E_r H_\Phi^* - E_\Phi H_r^*) r \, dr \right] \tag{37}$$

or, where the I's and K's are of argument $\gamma a$ unless otherwise specified,

$$
\begin{aligned}
P = \pi E_z^2(0) \frac{\beta \beta_0^2}{\gamma^2 \omega \mu} &\left[ \left( 1 + \frac{I_0 K_1}{I_1 K_0} \right) \int_0^a I_1^2(\gamma r) r \, dr \right. \\
&\left. + \left( \frac{I_0}{K_0} \right)^2 \left( 1 + \frac{I_1 K_0}{I_0 K_1} \right) \int_a^\infty K_1^2(\gamma r) r \, dr \right] \\
= E_z^2(0) \frac{\pi}{2k} \frac{\beta \beta_0 a^2}{\gamma^2} &\left[ \left( 1 + \frac{I_0 K_1}{I_1 K_0} \right) (I_1^2 - I_0 I_2) \right. \\
&\left. + \left( \frac{I_0}{K_0} \right)^2 \left( 1 + \frac{I_1 K_0}{I_0 K_1} \right) (K_0 K_2 - K_1^2) \right].
\end{aligned}
\tag{38}
$$

where $k = 120 \, \pi$ ohms.
Let us now write

$$(E_z^2 / \beta^2 P)^{1/3} = (\beta / \beta_0)^{1/3} (\gamma / \beta)^{4/3} F(\gamma a) \tag{39}$$

where

$$
\begin{aligned}
F(\gamma a) = \left\{ \left( \frac{(\gamma a)^2}{240} \right) \left[ (I_1^2 - I_0 I_2) \left( 1 + \frac{I_0 K_1}{I_1 K_0} \right) \right. \right. \\
\left. \left. + \left( \frac{I_0}{K_0} \right)^2 (K_0 K_2 - K_1^2) \left( 1 + \frac{I_1 K_0}{K_1 I_0} \right) \right] \right\}^{-1/3}.
\end{aligned}
\tag{40}
$$

We can rewrite the expression for $F(\gamma a)$ by using relation, 12, appendix I:

$$F(\gamma a) = \left( \frac{\gamma a}{240} \frac{I_0}{K_0} \left[ \left( \frac{I_1}{I_0} - \frac{I_0}{I_1} \right) + \left( \frac{K_0}{K_1} - \frac{K_1}{K_0} \right) + \frac{4}{\gamma \alpha} \right] \right)^{-1/3}. \tag{41}$$

# APPENDIX III

# STORED ENERGIES OF
# CIRCUIT STRUCTURES

## A3.1 FORCED SINUSOIDAL FIELD

If $v \ll c$, the field can be very nearly represented inside the cylinder of radius $a$ by

$$V = V_0 \frac{I_0(\beta r)}{I_0(\beta a)} e^{-j\beta z} = \frac{E}{j\beta} \frac{I_0(\beta r)}{I_0(\beta a)} e^{-j\beta z} \tag{1}$$

and outside by

$$V = V_0 \frac{K_0(\gamma r)}{K(\gamma a)} e^{-j\beta z} \tag{2}$$

Inside

$$\frac{\partial V}{\partial r} = \beta \frac{I_1(\beta r)}{I_0(\beta a)} e^{-j\beta z} V_0 \tag{3}$$

$$\frac{\partial V}{\partial z} = -j\beta \frac{I_0(\beta r)}{I_0(\beta a)} e^{-j\beta z} V_0 \tag{4}$$

Outside

$$\frac{\partial V}{\partial r} = -\beta \frac{K_1(\beta r)}{K_0(\beta a)} e^{-j\beta z} V_0 \tag{5}$$

$$\frac{\partial V}{\partial z} = -j\beta \frac{K_0(\beta r)}{K_0(\beta a)} e^{-j\beta z} V_0 \tag{6}$$

Because there is a sinusoidal variation in the $z$ direction, the average stored electric energy per unit length will be

$$W_E = \left(\frac{1}{2}\right)\left(\frac{\epsilon}{2}\right) \int_{r=0}^{\infty} [(E_{r\,\max})^2 + (E_{z\,\max})^2](2\pi r \, dr) \tag{7}$$

Here $E_{r\,\max}$ and $E_{z\,\max}$ are maximum values at $r = a$. The total electric plus magnetic stored energy will be twice this. This gives

233

$$W = \frac{\pi\epsilon(\gamma a)^2}{2\gamma^2}\left[\frac{I_0^2 - I_0 I_2}{I_0^2} + \frac{K_0 K_2 - K_0^2}{K_0^2}\right]E^2$$

$$W = \frac{\pi\epsilon\gamma a}{\gamma^2}\left[\frac{I_1}{I_0} + \frac{K_1}{K_0}\right]E^2 \tag{8}$$

$$(E^2/\beta^2 P)^{1/3} = (c/v)^{1/3}(v/v_g)^{1/3}\left[\frac{120}{\beta a\left(\frac{I_1}{I_0} + \frac{K_1}{K_0}\right)}\right]^{1/3} \tag{9}$$

## A3.2 PILL-BOX RESONATORS

Schelkunoff gives on page 268 of Electromagnetic Waves an expression for the peak electric energy stored in a pill-box resonator, which may be written as

$$.135\ \pi\ \epsilon\ a^2 h E^2$$

Here $a$ is the radius of the resonator and $h$ is the axial length. For a series of such resonators, the peak stored electric energy per unit length, which is also the average electric plus magnetic energy per unit length, is

$$W = .135\ \pi\ \epsilon\ a^2 E^2 \tag{10}$$

For resonance

$$a = 1.2\lambda_0/\pi \tag{11}$$

Whence

$$W = .0618\ \epsilon\lambda_0^2 E^2 \tag{12}$$

And

$$(E^2/\beta^2 P)^{1/3} = 5.36\ (v/v_g)^{1/3}\ (v/c)^{1/3} \tag{13}$$

The case of square resonators is easily worked out.

## A3.3 PARALLEL WIRES

Let us consider very fine very closely spaced half-wave parallel wires with perpendicular end plates.

If $z$ is measured along the wires, and $y$ perpendicular to $z$ and to the direction of propagation, the field is assumed to be

$$E_z = E \cos \beta x e^{\pm\beta y} \cos \frac{2\pi}{\lambda_0} z$$

$$E_y = E \sin \beta x e^{\pm\beta y} \cos \frac{2\pi}{\lambda_0} z \tag{14}$$

Here the $+$ sign applies for $y < 0$ and the $-$ sign for $y > 0$. We will then find that

$$W = 2W_E = \frac{\epsilon E^2 \lambda_0}{2} \int_0^\infty e^{-2\beta y} \, dy$$

$$W = \frac{\epsilon \lambda_0}{4\beta} E^2 \tag{15}$$

and

$$(E^2/\beta^2 P)^{1/3} = 6.20 \, (v/v_g)^{1/3} \tag{16}$$

The surface charge density $\sigma$ on one side of the array of wires (say, $y > 0$) is given by the $y$ component of field at $y = 0$.

$$\sigma = \epsilon E_y = \epsilon E \sin \beta x \cos \frac{2\pi}{\lambda_0} z \tag{17}$$

This is related to the current $I$ (flowing in the $z$ direction) per unit distance in the $x$ direction by

$$\frac{\partial I}{\partial z} = -\frac{\partial \sigma}{\partial t} \tag{18}$$

From (18) and (17) we obtain for the current on one side of the array

$$I = -\frac{j\omega \lambda_0 \epsilon}{2\pi} E \sin \beta x \sin \frac{2\pi}{\lambda_0} z \tag{19}$$

If we use the fact that $\omega \lambda_0 / 2\pi = c$ and $c \epsilon = 1/\sqrt{\mu/\epsilon}$, we obtain

$$I = \frac{-jE}{\sqrt{\mu/\epsilon}} \sin \beta x \sin \frac{2\pi}{\lambda_0} z \tag{20}$$

If $R$ is the surface resistivity of either side ($y > 0$, $y < 0$) of the wires, when the wires act as a resonator (a standing wave) the average power lost per unit length for both sides is

$$P = \tfrac{1}{8} R \lambda_0 E^2 / (\mu/\epsilon) \tag{21}$$

In this case the stored electric energy is half the value given by (15), and we find

$$Q = (\sqrt{\mu/\epsilon}/R) \, (v/c) \tag{22}$$

# APPENDIX IV

# EVALUATION OF SPACE—CHARGE PARAMETER $Q$

Consider the system consisting of a conducting cylinder of radius $a$ and an internal cylinder of current of radius $a_1$ with a current

$$ie^{j\omega t}e^{-\Gamma z}. \tag{1}$$

Let subscript 1 refer to inside and 2 to outside. We will assume magnetic fields of the form

$$H_{\varphi 1} = AI_1(\gamma r) \tag{2}$$

$$H_{\varphi 2} = BI_1(\gamma r) + CK_1(\gamma r) \tag{3}$$

From Maxwell's equations we have,

$$\frac{\partial}{\partial r}(rH_\varphi) = j\omega \epsilon rE_z + rJ_z \tag{4}$$

Now

$$\frac{\partial}{\partial z}(zI_1(z)) = zI_0(z) \tag{5}$$

$$\frac{\partial}{\partial z}(zK_1(z)) = -zK_0(z) \tag{6}$$

Hence

$$E_{z1} = \frac{-j\gamma}{\omega\epsilon} AI_0(\gamma r) \tag{7}$$

$$E_{z2} = \frac{-j\gamma}{\omega\epsilon}(BI_0(\gamma r) - CK_0(\gamma r)) \tag{8}$$

at $r = a$, $E_{z2} = 0$

$$C = B\frac{I_0(\gamma a)}{K_0(\gamma a)} \tag{9}$$

at $r = a_1$, $E_{z1} = E_{z2}$

$$AI_0(\gamma a_1) = B\left(I_0(\gamma a_1) - \frac{I_0(\gamma a)}{K_0(\gamma a)}K_0(\gamma a_1)\right)$$

$$A = B\left(1 - \frac{I_0(\gamma a)}{K_0(\gamma a)}\frac{K_0(\gamma a_1)}{I_0(\gamma a_1)}\right) \tag{10}$$

236

In going across boundary, we integrate (4) over the infinitesimal radial distance which the current is assumed to occupy

$$rdH_\varphi = rJdr$$

$$2\pi rJdr = i \tag{11}$$

$$rjdr = \frac{i}{2\pi}$$

Thus

$$dH_\varphi = \frac{i}{2\pi r} = \frac{i}{2\pi a_1} = (H_{\varphi 2} - H_{\varphi 1})_{a_1} \tag{12}$$

$$B\left[ I_1(\gamma a_1) + \frac{I_0(\gamma a)}{K_0(\gamma a)} K_1(\gamma a_1) - I_1(\gamma a_1)\left(1 - \frac{I_0(\gamma a)K_0(\gamma a_1)}{K_0(\gamma a)I_0(\gamma a_1)}\right)\right] = \frac{i}{2\pi a_1}$$

$$B = \frac{i}{2\pi a_1}\left[\frac{I_0(\gamma a)}{K_0(\gamma a)} K_1(\gamma a_1) + \frac{I_0(\gamma a)}{K_0(\gamma a)} \frac{K_0(\gamma a_1)}{I_0(\gamma a_1)} I_1(\gamma a_1)\right]^{-1}$$

$$B = \frac{i}{2\pi a_1} \frac{K_0(\gamma a)}{I_0(\gamma a)I_1(\gamma a_1)}\left[\frac{K_1(\gamma a_1)}{I_1(\gamma a_1)} + \frac{K_0(\gamma a_1)}{I_0(\gamma a_1)}\right]^{-1} \tag{13}$$

at $r = a_1$

$$E_{z1} = E_{z2} = \left(\frac{-j\gamma}{\omega\epsilon}\right)\left(\frac{i}{2\pi a_1}\right)\frac{K_0(\gamma a)}{I_0(\gamma a)}\frac{I_0(\gamma a_1)}{I_1(\gamma a_1)}$$

$$\left(1 - \frac{I_0(\gamma a)}{K_0(\gamma a)}\frac{K_0(\gamma a_1)}{I_0(\gamma a_1)}\right)\left[\frac{K_1(\gamma a_1)}{I_1(\gamma a_1)} + \frac{K_0(\gamma a_1)}{I_0(\gamma a_1)}\right]^{-1} \tag{14}$$

Now

$$\frac{1}{\omega\epsilon} = \frac{\sqrt{\mu/\epsilon}}{\beta_0} = \frac{377}{\beta_0} \tag{15}$$

Hence

$$i\beta V = E_z = j\frac{\gamma^2}{\beta_0} I_0^2(\gamma a_1)G(\gamma a, \gamma a_1)i$$

$$V = \left(\frac{\gamma}{\beta_0}\right)\left(\frac{\gamma}{\beta}\right) I_0^2(\gamma a_1)G(\gamma a, \gamma a_1)q \tag{16}$$

$$G(\gamma a, \gamma a_1) = 60\left[\frac{K_0(\gamma a_1)}{I_0(\gamma a_1)} - \frac{K_0(\gamma a)}{I_0(\lambda a)}\right] \tag{17}$$

In obtaining this form, use was made of the fact that

$$K_1(z)I_0(z) + K_0(z)I_1(z) = \frac{1}{z}$$

Now

$$Q = \frac{\beta}{\omega C_1(E^2/\beta^2 P)} \tag{18}$$

where $(E^2/\beta^2 P)$ is the value of this quantity at $r = a_1$ . In order to evaluate $Q$ we note that

$$V = -\frac{j\Gamma}{\omega C_1} i = \frac{-j(j\beta)}{\omega C_1} i$$

$$V = \frac{\beta}{\omega C_1} i$$

$$\frac{\beta}{\omega C_1} = \frac{V}{i} = \left(\frac{\gamma}{\beta_0}\right)\left(\frac{\gamma}{\beta}\right) I_0^2(\gamma a_1)G(\gamma a, \gamma a_1) \tag{20}$$

$$\frac{\beta}{\omega C_1} = \left(\frac{\beta}{\beta_0}\right)\left(\frac{\gamma}{\beta}\right)^2 I_0^2(\gamma a_1)G(\gamma a, \gamma a_1)$$

On the axis, $(E^2/\beta^2 P)$ has a value $(E^2/\beta^2 P)_0$

$$(E^2/\beta^2 P)_0 = \left(\frac{\beta}{\beta_0}\right)\left(\frac{\gamma}{\beta}\right)^4 F^3(a) \tag{21}$$

At a radius $a_1$

$$(E^2/\beta^2 P) = \left(\frac{\beta}{\beta_0}\right)\left(\frac{\gamma}{\beta}\right)^4 F^3(\gamma a)I_0^2(\gamma a_1) \tag{22}$$

Hence

$$Q(\gamma/\beta)^2 = \frac{G(\gamma a, \gamma a_1)}{F^3(\gamma a)} \tag{23}$$

# DIODE EQUATIONS

## FROM LLEWELLYN AND PETERSON

These apply to electrons injected into a space between two planes $a$ and $b$ normal to the $x$ direction. Plan $b$ is in the $+x$ direction from plane $a$. Current density $I$ and convection current $q$ are positive in the $-x$ direction. The d-c velocities $u_a$, $u_b$ and the a-c velocities $v_a$, $v_b$ are in the $+x$ direction. $T$ is the transit time. The notation in this appendix should not be confused with that used in other parts of this book. It was felt that it would be confusing to change the notation in Llewellyn's and Peterson's[1] well-known equations.

TABLE I

ELECTRONICS EQUATIONS

Numerics Employed:

$$\eta = 10^7 \frac{e}{m} = 1.77 \times 10^{15}, \qquad \epsilon = 1/(36\pi \times 10^{11}) \frac{\eta}{\epsilon} \doteq 2 \times 10^{28}$$

Direct-Current Equations:

Potential-velocity: $\eta V_D = (1/2)u^2$ (1)

Space-charge-factor definition: $\zeta = 3(1 - T_0/T)$

Distance: $x = (1 - \zeta/3)(u_a + u_a)T/2$  (2)

Current density: $(\eta/\epsilon)I_D = (u_a + u_b)2\zeta/T^2$

Space-charge ratio: $I_D/I_m = (9/4)\zeta(1 - \zeta/3)^2$ (3)

Limiting-current density:

$$I_m = \frac{2.33}{10^6} \frac{(\sqrt{V_{Da}} + \sqrt{V_{Db}})^2}{x^2}$$ (4)

Alternating-Current Equations:

Symbols employed:

$$\beta = i\theta, \qquad \theta = \omega T, \qquad i = \sqrt{-1}$$

[1] F. B. Llewellyn and L. C. Peterson "Vacuum Tube Networks," *Proc. I.R.E.*, vol. 32, pp. 144–166, March, 1944.

$$P = 1 - e^{-\beta} - \beta e^{-\beta} \doteq \frac{\beta^2}{2} - \frac{\beta^3}{3} + \frac{\beta^4}{8} \cdots$$

$$Q = 1 - e^{-\beta} \doteq \beta - \frac{\beta^2}{2} + \frac{\beta^3}{6} - \frac{\beta^4}{24} \cdots$$

$$S = 2 - 2e^{-\beta} - \beta - \beta e^{-\beta} \doteq - \frac{\beta^3}{6} + \frac{\beta^4}{12} - \frac{\beta^5}{40} + \frac{\beta^6}{180}$$

General equations for alternating current
$q$ = alternating conduction-current density
$v$ = alternating velocity

$$\left. \begin{array}{l} V_b - V_a = A^*I + B^*q_a + C^*v_a \\ q_b = D^*I + E^*q_a + F^*v_a \\ v_b = G^*I + H^*q_a + I^*v_a \end{array} \right\} \tag{5}$$

## TABLE II

### VALUES OF ALTERNATING-CURRENT COEFFICIENTS

$$A^* = \frac{1}{\epsilon} u_a + u_b \frac{T^2}{2} \frac{1}{\beta} \qquad\qquad E^* = \frac{1}{u_b} [u_b - \zeta(u_a + u_b)]e^{-\beta}$$

$$\left[ 1 - \frac{\zeta}{3}\left(1 - \frac{12S}{\beta^3}\right)\right] \quad F^* = \frac{\epsilon}{\eta} \frac{2\zeta}{T^2} \frac{(u_a + u_b)}{u_b} \beta e^{-\beta}$$

$$B^* = \frac{1}{\epsilon} \frac{T^2}{\beta^3} [u_a(P - \beta Q) - u_b P \qquad G^* = - \frac{\eta}{\epsilon} \frac{T^2}{\beta^3} \frac{1}{u_b} [u_b(P - \beta Q)$$

$$+ \zeta(u_a + u_b)P] \qquad\qquad\quad - u_a P + \zeta(u_a + u_b)P]$$

$$C^* = - \frac{1}{\eta} 2\zeta(u_a + u_b) \frac{P}{\beta^2} \qquad\qquad H^* = - \frac{\eta}{\epsilon} \frac{T^2}{2} \frac{(u_a + u_b)}{u_b}$$

$$D^* = 2\zeta \frac{(u_a + u_b)}{u_b} \frac{P}{\beta^2} \qquad\qquad\qquad\qquad (1 - \zeta)\frac{e^{-\beta}}{\beta}$$

$$I^* = \frac{1}{u_b}[u_a - \zeta(u_a + u_b)]e^{-\beta}$$

Complete space-charge, $\zeta = 1$.

$$A^* = \frac{1}{\epsilon}(u_a + u_b)\frac{T^2}{3\beta}\left(1 + \frac{6S}{\beta^3}\right)$$

$$B^* = \frac{1}{\epsilon}\frac{T^2}{\beta^3}u_a(2P - \beta Q)$$

$$C^* = -\frac{2}{\eta}\,(u_a + u_b)\,\frac{P}{\beta^2}$$

$$D^* = 2\,\frac{(u_a + u_b)}{(u_b)}\,\frac{P}{\beta^2}$$

$$E^* = -\frac{u_a}{u_b}\,e^{-\beta}$$

$$F^* = \frac{\epsilon}{\eta}\,\frac{2}{T^2}\,\frac{(u_a + u_b)}{(u_b)}\,\beta e^{-\beta}$$

$$G^* = -\frac{\eta}{\epsilon}\,\frac{T^2}{\beta^3}\,(2P - \beta Q)$$

$$H^* = 0$$

$$I^* = -e^{-\beta}$$

# EVALUATION OF IMPEDANCE AND $Q$ FOR THIN AND SOLID BEAMS[1]

Let us first consider a thin beam whose breadth is small enough so that the field acting on the electrons is essentially constant. The normal mode solutions obtained in Chapters VI and VII apply only to this case. The more practical situation of a thick beam will be considered later. The normal mode method consists of simultaneously solving two equations, one relating the r-f field produced on the circuit by an impressed r-f current from the electron stream and the other relating r-f current produced in the electron stream by an impressed r-f field from the circuit.

We have the circuit equation

$$E = -\left[ \frac{\Gamma^2 \Gamma_0 K}{\Gamma^2 - \Gamma_0^2} + \frac{2jQK\Gamma^2}{\beta_e} \right] i \qquad (1)$$

and the electronic equation

$$i = \frac{j\beta_e}{(j\beta_e - \Gamma)^2} \frac{I_0}{2V_0} E. \qquad (2)$$

The solution of these two equations gives $\Gamma$ in terms of $\Gamma_0$, $K$, and $Q$, which must be evaluated separately for the particular circuit being considered.

The field solution is obtained by solving the field equations in various regions and appropriately matching at the boundaries. For a hollow beam of electrons of radius $b$ traveling in the $z$ direction inside a helix of radius $a$ and pitch angle $\psi$, the matching consists of finding the admittances $\left( \dfrac{H_\varphi}{E_z} \right)$ inside and outside the beam and setting the difference equal to the admittance of the beam. Thus the admittance just outside the beam for an idealized helix will be[2]

$$Y_0 = \frac{H_{\varphi 0}}{E_{z0}} = j \frac{\omega\epsilon}{\gamma} \frac{I_1(\gamma b) - \delta K_1(\gamma b)}{I_0(\gamma b) + \delta K_0(\gamma b)}, \qquad (3)$$

[1] This appendix is taken from R. C. Fletcher, "Helix Parameters in Traveling-Wave Tube Theory," *Proc. I.R.E.*, Vol. 38, pp. 413–417 (1950).

[2] L. J. Chu and J. D. Jackson, "Field Theory of Traveling-Wave Tubes," *I.R.E., Proc.*, Vol. 36, pp. 853–863, July, 1948.

O. E. H. Rydbeck, "Theory of the Traveling-Wave Tube," *Ericsson Technics*, No. 46 pp. 3–18, 1948.

where

$$\delta = \frac{1}{K_0^2(\gamma a)} \left( \left( \frac{\beta_0 a \cot \Psi}{\gamma a} \right)^2 I_1(\gamma a) K_1(\gamma a) - I_0(\gamma a) K_0(\gamma a) \right),$$

$$\beta_0^2 = \omega^2 \mu \epsilon,$$

and

$$\gamma^2 = -\Gamma^2 - \beta_0^2.$$

(The $I$'s and $K$'s are modified Bessel functions). The admittance inside the beam is

$$Y_i = \frac{H_{\varphi i}}{E_{zi}} = \frac{j\omega \epsilon}{\gamma} \frac{I_1(\gamma b)}{I_0(\gamma b)}. \tag{4}$$

Boundary conditions require that $E_{z0} = E_{zi} = E_z$ and $H_{z0} - H_{zi} = \dfrac{i}{2\pi b}$. Combining the boundary conditions, we see that

$$Y_0 - Y_i = \frac{1}{2\pi b} \frac{i}{E_z}, \tag{5}$$

where the ratio of $\dfrac{i}{E_z}$ is given by (2). Thus the field method gives two equations which are equivalent to the circuit and electronic equations of the normal mode method.

## A6.1 NORMAL MODE PARAMETERS FOR THIN BEAM

The constants appearing in eq. (1) can be evaluated by equating the circuit equation (1) to the circuit equation (5). Thus if $Y_c = Y_0 - Y_i$,

$$-\frac{\Gamma^2 \Gamma_0 K}{\Gamma^2 - \Gamma_0^2} - \frac{2jQK\Gamma^2}{\beta_e} = +\frac{1}{2\pi b Y_c}. \tag{6}$$

The constants can be obtained by expanding each side of eq. (6) in terms of the zero and pole occurring in the vicinity of $\Gamma_0$. Thus if $\gamma_0$ and $\gamma_p$ are the zero and pole of $Y_c$, respectively,

$$Y_c \simeq -(\gamma_p - \gamma_0) \left( \frac{\partial Y_c}{\partial \gamma} \right)_{\gamma = \gamma_0} \left( \frac{\gamma - \gamma_0}{\gamma - \gamma_p} \right), \tag{7}$$

and the two sides of eq. (6) will be equivalent if

$$\Gamma_0^2 = -\gamma_0^2 - \beta_0^2, \tag{8}$$

$$\frac{2Q}{\beta_e} = \left( 1 + \frac{\beta_0^2}{\gamma_0^2} \right)^{-1/2} \frac{\gamma_0}{\gamma_p^2 - \gamma_0^2}, \tag{9}$$

and

$$\frac{1}{K} = -j\pi b\gamma_0^2\left(1 + \frac{\beta_0^2}{\gamma_0^2}\right)^{3/2}\left(\frac{\partial Y_e}{\partial Y}\right)_{\gamma=\gamma_0}. \tag{10}$$

$\gamma_0$ and $\gamma_p$ can be obtained from eqs. (3) and (4) through the implicit equations

$$(\beta a \cot \Psi)^2 = (\gamma_0 a)^2 \frac{I_0(\gamma_0 a)K_0(\gamma_0 a)}{I_1(\gamma_0 a)K_1(\gamma_0 a)}, \tag{11}$$

$$\frac{I_0(\gamma_p b)}{K_0(\gamma_p b)} = -\frac{1}{K_0^2(\gamma_p a)}$$

$$\cdot \left[\left(\frac{\beta_0 a \cot \Psi}{\gamma_p a}\right)^2 I_1(\gamma_p a)K_1(\gamma_p a) - I_0(\gamma_p a)K_0(\gamma_p a)\right], \tag{12}$$

and $1/K$ is found to be

$$\frac{1}{K} = \pi \sqrt{\frac{\epsilon}{\mu}}\left(1 + \frac{\beta_0^2}{\gamma_0^2}\right)^{3/2}\frac{\beta_0^2}{I_0^2(\gamma_0 b)}\frac{I_0(\gamma_0 a)}{K_0(\gamma_0 a)}\left[\frac{I_1(\gamma_0 a)}{I_0(\gamma_0 a)} - \frac{I_0(\gamma_0 a)}{I_1(\gamma_0 a)}\right.$$

$$\left. + \frac{K_0(\gamma_0 a)}{K_1(\gamma_0 a)} - \frac{K_1(\gamma_0 a)}{K_0(\gamma_0 a)} + \frac{4}{\gamma_0 a}\right]. \tag{13}$$

The equations for $\gamma_0$ and $K$ are the same as those given by Appendix II, evaluated by solving the field equations for the helix without electrons present. The evaluation of $\gamma_p$, and thus $Q$, represents a new contribution. Values of $Q\frac{\gamma_0}{\beta_e}\left(1 + \frac{\beta_0^2}{\gamma_0^2}\right)^{-1/2}$ are plotted in Fig. A6.1 as a function of $\gamma_0 a$ for various ratios of $b/a$. (It should be noted that for most practical applications the factor $\frac{\gamma_0}{\beta_e}\left(1 + \frac{\beta_0^2}{\gamma_0^2}\right)^{-1/2}$ is very close to unity, so that the ordinate is practically the value of $Q$ itself.)

Appendix IV gives a method for estimating $Q$ based on the solution of the field equations for a conductor replacing the helix and considering the resultant field to be $-\frac{2jKQ\Gamma^2}{\beta_e} i$. This estimate of $Q$ is plotted as the dashed lines of Fig. A6.1.

A6.2 THICK BEAM CASE

For an electron beam which entirely fills the space out to the radius $b$, the electronic equations of both the normal mode method and the field method are altered in such a way as to considerably complicate the solution. In order to find a solution for this case some simplifying assumptions must be made. A convenient type of assumption is to replace the thick beam by an "equivalent" thin beam, for which the solutions have already been worked out.

Two beams will be equivalent if the value of $\dfrac{H_\varphi}{E_z}$ is the same outside the beams, since the matching to the circuit depends only on this admittance.

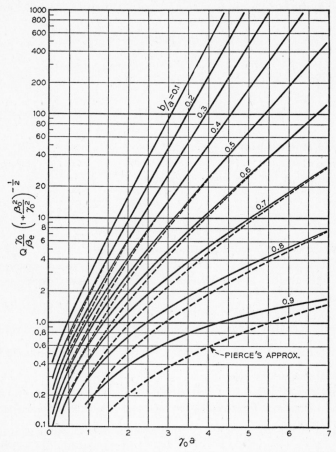

Fig. A6.1—Passive mode parameter $Q$ for a hollow beam of electrons of radius $b$ inside a helix of radius $a$ and natural propagation constant $\gamma_0$. The solid line was obtained by equating the circuit equation of the normal mode method, which defines $Q$, with a corresponding circuit equation found from the field theory method. The dashed line was obtained in Appendix IV from a solution of the field equations for a conductor replacing the helix.

The problem, then, of making a thin beam the equivalent of a thick beam is the problem of arranging the position and current of a thin beam to give the same admittance at the radius $b$ of the thick beam. This is of course impossible for all values of $\gamma$. It is desirable therefore that the admittances be the same close to the complex values of $\gamma$ which will eventually solve the equations.

The solution of the field equations for the solid beam yields the value for $\dfrac{H_\varphi^{(1)}}{E_z}$ at the radius $b$ as

$$\frac{H_\varphi}{E_z} = \frac{j\omega\epsilon}{\gamma}\, \frac{nI_1(n\gamma b)}{I_0(n\gamma b)}, \tag{14}$$

where

$$n^2 = 1 + \frac{1}{\beta_0}\sqrt{\frac{\mu}{\epsilon}}\, \frac{\beta_e I_0}{2\pi b^2 V_0}\, \frac{1}{(j\beta_e - \Gamma)^2}. \tag{15}$$

Thus the electronic equation for the solid beam which must be solved simultaneously with the circuit equation (given above by either the normal mode approximation or the field solution) must be

$$Y_e = \frac{H_\varphi}{E_z} - Y_i = \frac{j\omega\epsilon b}{\gamma b}\left[\frac{nI_1(n\gamma b)}{I_0(n\gamma b)} - \frac{I_1(\gamma b)}{I_0(\gamma b)}\right]. \tag{16}$$

Complex roots for $\gamma$ will be expected in the vicinity of real values of $\gamma$ for which $Y_e \approx Y_c$ and $\dfrac{dY_e}{d\gamma} \approx \dfrac{dY_c}{d\gamma}$. By plotting $Y_e$ and $Y_c$ vs. real values of $\gamma$, it is found that the two curves become tangent close to the value of $\gamma$ for which $n = 0$, using typical operating conditions (Fig. A6.2). Our procedure for choosing a hollow beam equivalent of the solid beam, then, will be to equate the values of $Y_e$ and $\dfrac{dY_e}{d\gamma}$ at $n = 0$. This will give us two equations from which to solve for the electron beam diameter and d-c current for the equivalent hollow beam.

If the hollow beam is placed at the radius $sb$ with a current of $tI_0$, the value of $\dfrac{H_\varphi}{E_z}$ at the radius $b$ gives the value for $Y_{eH}$ as

$$Y_{eH} = \left(\frac{H_\varphi}{E_z}\right)_b - Y_i = -j\omega\epsilon b\,\frac{t}{2}\,(1 - n^2)\,\frac{I_0^2(s\gamma b)}{I_0^2(\gamma b)}$$

$$\cdot \left(1 - \gamma^2 b^2 I_0^2(s\gamma b)\,\frac{t}{2}\,(1 - n^2)\left[\frac{K_0(s\gamma b)}{I_0(s\gamma b)} - \frac{K_0(\gamma b)}{I_0(\gamma b)}\right]\right)^{-1}. \tag{17}$$

Equating this with eq. (16) at $n = 0$ yields the equation

$$\frac{1}{t} = \frac{1}{2}\,\theta^2 I_0^2(s\theta)\left[\frac{K_0(s\theta)}{I_0(s\theta)} + \frac{K_1(\theta)}{I_1(\theta)}\right], \tag{18}$$

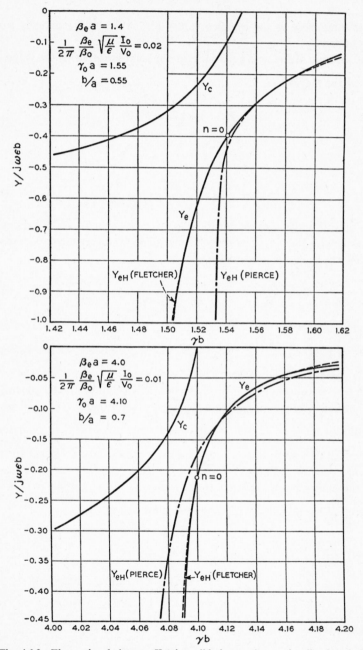

Fig. A6.2—Electronic admittance $Y_e$ of a solid electron beam of radius $b$ and circuit admittance $Y_c$ of a helix of radius $a$ plotted vs. real values of the propagation constant $\gamma$ in the vicinity of where $\dfrac{dY_e}{d\gamma} = \dfrac{dY_c}{d\gamma}$ where complex solutions for $\gamma$ are expected, for two typical sets of operating conditions. Plotted on the same graph is the electron admittance $Y_{eH}$ for two equivalent hollow electron beams: the dashed curve (Fletcher) is matched to $Y_e$ at $n = 0$, while the dot-dashed curve (Pierce, Appendix IV) is matched at $n = 1$ (off the graph).

where $\theta = \gamma_e b$ and $\gamma_e$ is the value of $\gamma$ at $n = 0$; i.e. for $\gamma_e \gg \beta_0$

$$\gamma_e = \beta_e + \sqrt{\frac{1}{\beta_0}} \sqrt{\frac{\mu}{\epsilon}} \frac{\beta_e I_0}{2\pi b^2 V_0} \approx \beta_e. \tag{19}$$

In the vicinity of $n = 0$, $n$ varies very rapidly with $\gamma$, and hence matching $\left(\dfrac{\partial Y_e}{\partial n}\right)_\gamma$ is practically the same as matching $\dfrac{dY_e}{d\gamma}$. With this approximation eqs. (16) and (17) can be differentiated with respect to $n$ and set equal at

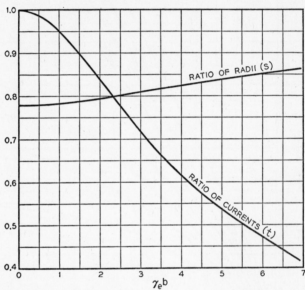

Fig. A6.3—Parameters of the hollow electron beam which is matched to the solid electron beam of radius $b$ and current $I_0$ at $\gamma = \gamma_e \simeq \beta_e$, where $n = 0$. $sb$ is the radius and $tI_0$ is the current of the equivalent hollow beam.

$n = 0$ to yield the second relation

$$\frac{1}{t} = \theta^2 I_0^2(\theta) I_0^2(s\theta) \left[ \frac{K_0(s\theta)}{I_0(s\theta)} + \frac{K_1(\theta)}{I_1(\theta)} \right]^2 \tag{20}$$

Equations (18) and (20) can then be solved to give the implicit equation for $s$ as

$$\frac{K_0(s\theta)}{I_0(s\theta)} = -\frac{K_1(\theta)}{I_1(\theta)} + \frac{1}{2I_1^2(\theta)} \tag{21}$$

and the simpler equation for $t$

$$t = \frac{4}{\theta^2} \frac{I_1^2(\theta)}{I_0^2(s\theta)}. \tag{22}$$

$s$ and $t$ are plotted as a function of $\theta$ in Fig. A6.3. The value of $Y_{eH}$ using these values of $s$ and $t$ is compared in Fig. A6.2 with $Y_e$ in the vicinity of where $Y_c$ is almost tangent to $Y_e$ for two typical sets of operating conditions.

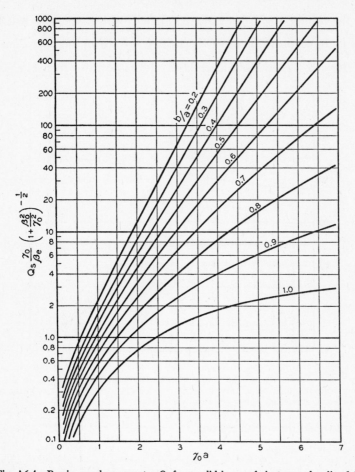

Fig. A6.4—Passive mode parameter $Q_s$ for a solid beam of electrons of radius $b$ inside a helix of radius $a$ and natural propagation constant $\gamma_0$, obtained from the equivalent hollow beam parameters of Fig. 3 taken at $\gamma_e = \gamma_0$. All the normal mode solutions which have been found[2], [3] for a hollow beam will be approximately valid for a solid beam if $Q$ is replaced by $Q_s$ and $K$ is replaced by $K_s$ (Fig. 5).

It is of course possible to pick other criteria for determining an "equivalent" hollow beam. In Chapter XIV, in essence, $Y_e$ and $Y_{eH}$ were expanded in terms of $(1 - n^2)$ and the coefficients of the first two terms were equated. This has been done for the cylindrical beams, and the values of $s$ and $t$ found by this method determine values of $Y_{eH}$ shown in Fig. A6.2. The greater departure from the true curve of $Y_e$ would indicate that this approximation is not as good as that described above.

It is now possible to find the values of $Q_s$ and $K_s$ appropriate to the solid

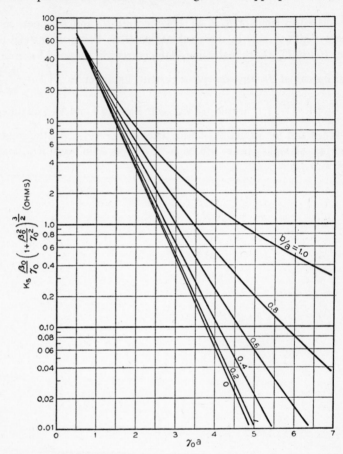

Fig. A6.5—Circuit impedance $K_s$ for a solid beam of electrons of radius $b$ inside a helix of radius $a$ and natural propagation constant $\gamma_0$, obtained from the equivalent hollow beam parameters of Fig. 3 taken at $\gamma_e = \gamma_0$. $K_s$ should replace $K = \dfrac{E^2}{2\beta^2}$ [2], [3] in order for the normal mode solutions for a hollow beam to be applicable to a solid beam.

beam. Thus if $Q\left(\gamma_0 a, \dfrac{b}{a}\right)$ and $K\left(\gamma_0 a, \dfrac{b}{a}\right)$ are the values for the hollow beam calculated from eqs. (9), (12) and (13),

$$Q_s = Q\left(\gamma_0 a, s\,\dfrac{b}{a}\right), \tag{23}$$

and

$$K_s = tK\left(\gamma_0 a,\ s\,\frac{b}{a}\right). \tag{24}$$

The $t$ is placed in front of $K$ in eq. (24) because $tI_0$ and $K$ appear in the thin beam solutions only in the combination $tI_0K$. Using $tK$ instead of $K$ allows us to use $I_0$, the actual value of the current in the solid beam in the solutions instead of $tI_0$, the equivalent current. Values of $Q_s\dfrac{\gamma_0}{\beta_s}\left(1+\dfrac{\beta_0{}^2}{\gamma_0{}^2}\right)^{-1/2}$ and $K_s\dfrac{\beta_0}{\gamma_0}\cdot\left(1+\dfrac{\beta_0{}^2}{\gamma_0{}^2}\right)^{+3/2}$ are plotted vs. $\gamma_0a$ in Figs. A6.4 and A6.5 for different values of $b/a$ and for values of $t$ and $s$ taken at $\gamma_s = \gamma_0$. All the solutions obtained for the hollow beam will be valid for the solid beam if $Q_s$ and $K_s$ are substituted for $Q$ and $K$.

# HOW TO CALCULATE THE GAIN OF A TRAVELING-WAVE TUBE

The gain calculation presented here neglects the effect at the output of all waves except the increasing wave. Thus, it can be expected to be accurate only for tubes with a considerable net gain. The gain is expressed in db as

$$G = A + BCN \tag{1}$$

Here $A$ represents an initial loss in setting up the increasing wave and $BCN$ represents the gain of the increasing wave.

We will modify (1) to take into account approximately the effect of the cold loss of $L$ db in reducing the gain of the increasing wave by writing

$$G = A + [BCN - \alpha L] \tag{2}$$

Here $\alpha$ is the fraction of the cold loss which should be subtracted from the gain of the increasing wave. This expression should hold even for moderately non-uniform loss (see Fig. 9.5).

Thus, what we need to know to calculate the gain are the quantities

$$A, B, C, N, \alpha, L$$

## A7.1 Cold Loss $L$ db

The best way to get the cold loss $L$ is to measure it. One must be sure that the loss measured is the loss of a wave traveling in the circuit and not loss at the input and output couplings.

## A7.2 Length of Circuit in Wavelengths, $N$

We can arrive at this in several ways. The ratio of the speed of light $c$ to the speed of an electron $u_0$ is

$$\frac{c}{u_0} = \frac{505}{\sqrt{V_0}} \tag{3}$$

where $V_0$ is the accelerating voltage. Thus, if $\ell$ is the length of the circuit and $\lambda$ is the free-space wavelength and $\lambda_g$ is the wavelength along the axis of the helix

$$\lambda_g = \lambda \, \frac{u_0}{c} \tag{4}$$

$$N = \frac{\ell}{\lambda_g} = \frac{\ell}{\gamma} \frac{c}{u_0} \tag{5}$$

Also, if $\mathcal{L}_w$ is the total length of wire in the helix, approximately

$$N = \frac{L_w}{\lambda} \tag{6}$$

## A7.3 THE GAIN PARAMETER $C$

The gain parameter can be expressed

$$C = \left( \frac{E^2}{\beta^2 P} \frac{I_0}{8V_0} \right)^{1/3} = \left( \frac{KI_0}{4V_0} \right)^{1/3} \tag{7}$$

Here $K$ is the helix impedance properly defined. $I_0$ is the beam current in amperes and $V_0$ is the beam voltage.

## A7.4 HELIX IMPEDANCE $K$

In Fig. 5 of Appendix VI, $K \left( \dfrac{\beta_0}{\gamma_0} \right) \left( 1 + \left( \dfrac{\beta_0}{\gamma_0} \right)^2 \right)^{3/2}$ is plotted vs. $\gamma_0 a$ for values of $b/a$. $K_s$ is the effective value of $K$ for a solid beam of radius $b$, and $a$ is the radius of the helix. $\gamma_0$ is to be identified with $\gamma$ for present purposes, and is given by

$$\gamma_0 = \frac{2\pi}{\lambda_g} \left[ 1 - \left( \frac{\gamma_g}{\lambda} \right)^2 \right]^{1/2} \tag{8}$$

where $\lambda_g$ is given in terms of $\lambda$ by (4). We see that in most cases (for voltages up to several thousand)

$$(\lambda_g/\lambda)^2 \ll 1 \tag{9}$$

and we may usually use as a valid approximation

$$\gamma_0 = \frac{2\pi}{\lambda_g} \tag{10}$$

and

$$\gamma_0 a = \frac{2\pi a}{\lambda_g} \tag{11}$$

As $\beta_0 = 2\pi/\lambda$, this approximation gives

$$1 + \left( \frac{\beta_0}{\gamma_0} \right)^2 = 1 + \left( \frac{\lambda_g}{\lambda} \right)^2$$

and we may assume

$$\left(1 + \left(\frac{\beta_0}{\gamma_0}\right)^2\right)^{3/2} = 1 \tag{12}$$

Thus, we may take $K_s$ as the ordinate of Fig. 5 multiplied by $c/u_0$, from (3), for instance.

The true impedance may be somewhat less than the impedance for a helically conducting sheet. If the ratio of the circuit impedance to that of a helically conducting sheet is known (see Sections 3 and 4.1 of Chapter III, and Fig. 3.13, for instance), the value of $K_s$ from Fig. 5 can be multiplied by this ratio.

## A7.5   THE SPACE-CHARGE PARAMETER $Q$

The ordinate of Fig. 4 of Appendix VI shows $Q_s \dfrac{\gamma_0}{\beta_e} \left(1 + \left(\dfrac{\beta_0}{\gamma_0}\right)^2\right)^{-1/2}$ vs. $\gamma a$ for several values of $b/a$. Here $Q_s$ is the effective value of $Q$ for a solid beam of radius $b$. As before, for beam voltages of a few thousand or lower, we may take

$$\left(1 + \left(\frac{\beta_0}{\gamma_0}\right)^2\right)^{-1/2} = 1$$

The quantity $\beta_e$ is just

$$\beta_e = \frac{2\pi a}{\lambda_g} \tag{13}$$

and from (8) we see that for low beam voltages we can take

$$\beta_e = \gamma = \gamma_0$$

so that the ordinate in Fig. 4 can usually be taken as simply $Q_s$.

## A7.6   THE INCREASING WAVE PARAMETER $B$

In Fig. 8.10, $B$ is plotted vs. $QC$. $C$ can be obtained by means of Sections 3 and 4, and $Q$ by means of Section 5. Hence we can obtain $B$.

## A7.7   THE GAIN REDUCTION PARAMETER $\alpha$

From (2) we see that we should subtract from the gain of the increasing wave in db $\alpha$ times the cold loss $L$ in db. In Fig. 8.13 a quantity $\partial x_1/\partial d$, which we can identity as $\alpha$, is plotted vs. $QC$.

## A7.8   THE LOSS PARAMETER $d$

The loss parameter $d$ can be expressed in terms of the cold loss, $L$ in db, the length of the circuit in wavelengths, $N$, and $C$

$$d = \left(\frac{2.3L}{20}\right)\left(\frac{1}{2\pi NC}\right) \tag{14}$$

$$d = 0.0183 \frac{L}{NC} \tag{15}$$

## A7.9 THE INITIAL LOSS $A$

The quantity $A$ of (2) is plotted vs. $d$ in Fig. 9.3. This plot assumes $QC = 0$, and may be somewhat in error. Perhaps Fig. 9.4 can be used in estimating a correction; it looks as if the initial loss should be less with $QC \neq 0$ even when $d \neq 0$. In any event, an error in $A$ means only a few db, and is likely to make less error in the computed gain than does an error in $B$, for instance.

# BIBLIOGRAPHY

## 1946

Barton, M. A. Traveling wave tubes, *Radio*, v. 30, pp. 11–13, 30–32, Aug., 1946.
Blanc-Lapierre, A. and Lapostolle, P. Contribution à l'étude des amplificateurs à ondes progressives, *Ann. des Telecomm.*, v. 1, pp. 283–302, Dec., 1946.
Kompfner, R. Traveling wave valve—new amplifier for centimetric wavelengths. *Wireless World*, v. 52, pp. 369–372, Nov., 1946.
Pierce, J. R. Beam traveling-wave tube, *Bell Lab. Record*, v. 24, pp. 439–442, Dec., 1946.

## 1947

Bernier, J. Essai de théorie du tube électronique à propagation d'onde, *Ann. de Radioélec.*, v. 2, pp. 87–101, Jan., 1947. *Onde Élec.*, v. 27, pp. 231–243, June, 1947.
Blanc-Lapierre, A., Lapostolle, P., Voge, J. P., and Wallauschek, R. Sur la théorie des amplificateurs à ondes progressives, *Onde Élec.*, v. 27, pp. 194–202, May, 1947.
Kompfner, R. Traveling-wave tuge as amplifier at microwaves, *I.R.E., Proc.*, v. 35, pp. 124–127, Feb., 1947.
Kompfner, R. Traveling-wave tube—centimetre-wave amplifier, *Wireless Engr.*, v. 24, pp. 255–266, Sept., 1947.
Pierce, J. R. Theory of the beam-type traveling-wave tube, *I.R.E., Proc.*, v. 35, pp. 111–123, Feb., 1947.
Pierce, J. R. and Field, L. M. Traveling-wave tubes, *I.R.E., Proc.*, v. 35, pp. 108–111, Feb., 1947.
Roubine, E. Sur le circuit à hélice utilisé dans le tube à ondes progressives, *Onde Élec.*, v. 27, pp. 203–208, May, 1947.
Shulman, C. and Heagy, M. S. Small-signal analysis of traveling-wave tube, *R.C.A. Rev.*, v. 8, pp. 585–611, Dec., 1947.

## 1948

Brillouin, L. Wave and electrons traveling together—a comparison between traveling wave tubes and linear accelerators, *Phys. Rev.*, v. 74, pp. 90–92, July 1, 1948.
Brossart, J. and Doehler, O. Sur les propriétés des tubes à champ magnétique constant. Les tubes à propagation d'onde à champ magnétique, *Ann. de Radioélec.*, v. 3, pp. 328–338, Oct., 1948.
Cutler, C. C. Experimental determination of helical-wave properties, *I.R.E., Proc.*, v. 36, pp. 230–233, Feb., 1948.
Chu, L. J. and Jackson, J. D. Field theory of traveling-wave tubes, *I.R.E., Proc.*, v. 36, pp. 853–863, July, 1948.
Döehler, O. and Kleen, W. Phénomènes non lineaires dans les tubes à propagation d'onde. *Ann. de Radioélec.*, v. 3, pp. 124–143, Apr., 1948.
Döehler, O. and Kleen, W. Sur l'influence de la charge d'espace dans le tube à propagation d'onde, *Ann. de Radioélec.*, v. 3, pp. 184–188, July, 1948.
Blanc-Lapierre, A., Kuhner, M., Lapostolle, P., Jessel, M. and Wallauschek, R. Étude et réalisation d'amplificateurs à hélice. *Ann. des Telecomm.*, v. 3, pp. 257–308, Aug.–Sept., 1948.
Blanc-Lapierre, A. and Kuhner, M. Réalisation d'amplificateurs à onde progressive à hélice. Résultats généraux, pp. 259–264.
Lapostolle, P. Les phénomènes d'interaction dans le tube à onde progressive, Théorie et vérifications expérimentales, pp. 265–291.
Jessel, M. and Wallauschek, R. Étude expérimentale de la propagation de long d'une ligne à retard en forme d'hélice, pp. 291–299.
Wallauschek, R. Détermination expérimentale des caractéristiques d'amplificateurs à onde progressive, Résultats obtenus, pp. 300–308.
Lapostolle, P. Étude des diverses ondes susceptibles de se propager dans une ligne en interaction avec un faisceau électronique. Application à la théorie de l'amplificateur à onde progressive, *Ann. des Telecomm.*, v. 3, pp. 57–71, Feb., pp. 85–104, Mar., 1948.

Pierce, J. R. Effect of passive modes in traveling wave tubes, *I.R.E., Proc.*, v. 36, pp. 993–997, Aug., 1948.

Pierce, J. R. Transverse fields in traveling-wave tubes, *Bell Sys. Tech. Jl.*, v. 27, pp. 732–746, Oct., 1948.

Rydbeck, O. E. H. Theory of the traveling-wave tube, *Ericsson Technics*, no. 46, pp. 3–18, 1948.

Tomner, J. S. A. Experimental development of traveling-wave tubes, Acta Polytech., *Elec. Engg.*, v. 1, no. 6, pp. 1–21, 1948.

Nergaard, L. S. Analysis of a simple model of a two-beam growing-wave tube, RCA Rev. vol. 9, pp. 585–601, Dec. 1948.

*1949*

Doehler, O. and Kleen, W. Influence du vecteur électrique transversal dans la ligne à retard du tube à propagation d'onde, *Ann. de Radioélec.*, v. 4, pp. 76–84, Jan., 1949.

Bruck, L. Comparison des valeurs mesurees pour le gain lineaine du tube à propagation d'onde avec les valeurs indiquées par diverses theories. *Annales de Radioélectricete*, v. IV, pp. 222–232, July, 1949.

Döehler, O. and Kleen, W. Sur le rendement du tube à propagation d'onde. *Annales de Radioélectricete*, v. IV, pp. 216–221, July, 1949.

Döehler, O., Kleen, W. and Palluel, P. Les tubes à propagation d'onde comme oscillateurs à large bande d'accord électronique. *Ann. de Radioélec.*, v. 4, pp. 68–75, Jan., 1949.

Döhler, O. and Kleen, W. Über die Wirkungsweise der "Traveling-Wave" Röhre. *Arch. Elektr. Übertragung*, v. 3, pp. 54–63, Feb., 1949.

Field, L. M. Some slow-wave structures for traveling-wave tubes. *I.R.E., Proc.*, v. 37, pp. 34–40, Jan., 1949.

Guenard, P., Berterattiere, R. and Doehler, O. Amplification par interaction electronque dans des tubes sans circuits. *Annales de Radioélectricete*, v. IV, pp. 171–177, July, 1949.

Laplume, J. Théorie du tube à onde progressive. *Onde Élec.*, v. 29, pp. 66–72, Feb., 1949.

Loshakov, L. N. On the propagation of Waves along a coaxial spiral line in the presence of an electron beam. *Zh. Tech. Fiz.*, vol. 19, pp. 578–595, May, 1949.

Dewey, G. C. A periodic-waveguide traveling-wave amplifier for medium powers. *Proc. N.E.C.* (Chicago), v. 4, p. 253, 1948.

Pierce, J. R. and Hebenstreit, W. B. A new type of high-frequency amplifier, Bell System Technical Journal, v. 28, pp. 33–51, January, 1949.

Haeff, A. V. The electron-wave tube—a novel method of generation and amplification of microwave energy, *Proc. I.R.E.*, v. 37, pp. 4–10, January, 1949.

Hollenberg, A. V. The double-stream amplifier, *Bell Laboratories Record*, v. 27, pp. 290–292, August, 1949.

Guenard, P., Berterottiere, R. and Döehler, O. Amplification by direct electronic interaction in valves without circuits, *Ann. Radioelec.*, v. 4, pp. 171–177, July, 1949.

Rogers, D. C. Traveling-wave amplifier for 6 to 8 centimeters, *Elec. Commun.* (London), v. 26, pp. 144–152, June, 1949.

Field, L. M. Some slow wave structures for traveling-wave tubes, *Proc. I.R.E.*, v. 37, pp. 34–40, January, 1949.

Schnitzer, R. and Weber, D. *Frequenz*, v. 3, pp. 189–196, July, 1949.

Pierce, J. R. Circuits for traveling-wave tubes, *Proc. I.R.E.*, v. 37, pp. 510–515, May, 1949.

Pierce, J. R. and Wax, N. A note on filter-type traveling-wave amplifiers, *Proc. I.R.E.*, v. 37, pp. 622–625, June, 1949.

# INDEX